ALLE ZEIT WACH 1842

B. Barbara D. Gignoux C. Vettier

Lectures on Modern Magnetism

With 128 Figures and 22 Tables

Science Press
Beijing

Springer-Verlag
Berlin Heidelberg New York
London Paris Tokyo

B. Barbara, D. Gignoux
Laboratoire Louis Néel of the CNRS, France

C. Vettier
Institut Laue-Langevin, France

Responsible Editor: Li Yifa

Published by Science Press Beijing

Distribution rights throughout the world, excluding The People's Republic of China, granted to
Springer-Verlag Berlin Heidelberg New York London Paris Tokyo

ISBN 3-540-17558-X Springer-Verlag Berlin Heidelberg New York
ISBN 0-387-17558-X Springer-Verlag New York Berlin Heidelberg
ISBN 7-03-000757-3/O·198 Science Press Beijing

Printed in Hong Kong

Printing and Binding: C & C Offset Printing Co., Ltd.
2153/3140-543210

FOREWORD

It gives me great pleasure to see that due to the cooperation and efforts of Chinese and French scientists, a new book dealing with the theory and development of modern magnetism has finally been published. This is indeed an accomplishment of which we can be proud.

Magnetism is an age-old and active branch of learning which has been developing continuously. As early as two thousand years ago, our ancestors had already succeeded in making use of magnetite (Fe_3O_4) in the fabrication of compasses; in the twelfth century, they employed compasses for the first time in navigation, making important contributions to the early development and study of magnetism and magnetic materials.

From the beginning of the twentieth century, French physicists gave a great impetus to the development of work on magnetism. They advanced, one after another, a series of theories in the areas of the diamagnetism and paramagnetism of matter (Langevin, 1905), the molecular field theory of ferromagnetism (Weiss, 1907), antiferromagnetism and ferromagnetism (Néel, 1932 and 1948), as well as discoveries of rare earth iron garnets (Bertaut–Pauthenet, 1956). The Laboratoire Louis Néel in Grenoble has already become one of the most well-known magnetism research centres in the world.

Scientific exchanges between our two countries began at the outset of this century. There are quite a few Chinese physicists of the older generation who studied and worked in France. It is a pleasure to see that in recent years, exchanges and cooperation of this kind have been increased and constantly developed. In the summer of 1979, at the invitation of Academia Sinica, three French physicists, Drs. B. Barbara, D. Gignoux and C. Vettier from the Laboratoire Louis Néel in Grenoble and the Centre National de la Recherche Scientifique came to Beijing to give lectures on fundamental theory and recent developments in modern magnetism. The present book was written on the basis of these notes. I hope that this book will be useful not only to Chinese scientists engaged in magnetism research but also to the scientists of other countries who are working in the same field.

I would like to take this opportunity to express my wish that the scientific and cultural exchanges between our two peoples may grow unceasingly in the interests of the happiness and the advancement of the culture of mankind.

Qian Sanqiang
Vice President of Academia Sinica
Beijing, China.

FOREWORD

Although the properties of magnetite have been drawing the attention of observers for 2500 years, magnetism remains a field of considerable interest. During the last few decades, new discoveries have emerged in this field. Neutron diffraction has revealed unexpected structures, such as those which present sinusoidal modulations; new and powerful techniques, such as the use of the Mössbauer effect or positron annihilation have been employed to further our understanding; phase transitions are now becoming understood and the properties adjacent to critical points have become the subjects of general and satisfactory theories.

But it is probably the rare-earth compounds which, after having provided the best examples of ferrimagnetism in 1956, have offered the most interesting and the most varied new theories and have allowed their verification. Productive results have been connected with this family of elements, as well as with the diversity of compounds that it is possible to obtain by appropriate substitutions of atoms in the crystal lattice. It is in such substances, for example, that we can study new types of interactions among atoms, the carriers of magnetic moment, through the medium of conduction electrons.

Experimental results and applications have kept abreast of new theories. Magnetic bubble memories and the best samarium-cobalt permanent magnets are relatively recent discoveries. We expect amorphous iron to be used to obtain soft magnetic materials in the future. Recently, in centuries-old meteorites, we have discovered the tetrataenite, quadratic superstructure of the alloy iron-nickel (50-50) which is identical to that made artificially twenty years ago in the laboratories at Grenoble. This discovery resulted from a spectacular augmentation of about six orders of magnitude in the speed of diffusion of the atoms produced by neutron irradiation.

The classical treatises on magnetism could now accommodate only with difficulty the rapid evolution of modern knowledge. We are therefore especially grateful to three of our best researchers, uncontested experts in the subjects concerned, for having written a book entitled "Lectures on Modern Magnetism" based on their lectures given in Beijing in 1979. Although it does not claim to be exhaustive, this book emphasises recent developments. Two of the authors, B. Barbara and D. Gignoux, work at the Laboratoire Louis Néel of the CNRS in which the rare-earth garnets were discovered, and which, as a result, has since been distinguished in the study of the structure and magnetic properties of rare-earth compounds. C. Vettier is at the Institut Laue-Langevin, an important centre for highly sophisticated neutron research.

After a brief account of fundamentals, this book examines structures and crystal fields, 4*f* magnetism, ionic and metallic aspects of 3*d* magnetism, the RKKY interactions and many other questions.

This book will be of great use to researchers eager to probe more deeply into those areas of magnetism which still hold a great potential for interesting discoveries.

Louis Néel
Nobel Laureate in Physics
Membre de l'Academie des Sciences de France
Meudon–Bellevue, France.

INTRODUCTION

This book originated from a series of lectures which were given at Beijing University in October 1979. The lectures were intended to give a comprehensive account of some central aspects of basic magnetism in solids; they were accompanied by seminars and discussions on experimental studies of magnetic properties. This was part of a collaboration between the Academia Sinica in Beijing and the Laboratoire Louis Néel in Grenoble.

Modern magnetism has grown to such an extent that the subject cannot be completely covered by a simple series of lectures. Therefore we have decided to focus our attention on the subjects which have been studied experimentally in our laboratory. Here, both bulk magnetization and susceptibility measurements as well as neutron scattering techniques are used to investigate the magnetic properties of solids. In order to account for the general properties of the various magnetic states, phenomenological models can be presented, while more microscopic theories must be used to provide a more detailed description of the magnetically ordered state. We illustrate the interpretation of several experiments using different theoretical models.

The book is organised as follows. Chapters 1 and 2 are introductory; they deal with the quantum theoretical description of atoms, the importance of symmetry and the description of basic experimental methods. The different magnetically ordered states are described in Chapter 3 within the framework of molecular field theory. An approach to the properties of the paramagnetic state is given in Chapter 4. At this stage, a difference is established between localized magnetic moments and itinerant magnetism. Chapter 5 is devoted to the determination of magnetic structures by means of elastic neutron scattering; again the importance of symmetry is emphasised. A natural follow-up is the study of magnetic excitations (crystal field excitations, spin–waves, Stoner models), which are treated in Chapter 6.

Thus, the first part of this book is quite general, dealing with the major aspects of magnetism. From Chapter 7 onwards, more specific topics are discussed.

Chapter 7 is devoted to the magnetism of rare–earth metals. Emphasis is placed on the crystalline electric field and the indirect exchange mechanism. The ionic compounds of the iron group are dealt with in Chapter 8 where the effects of the crystal field are discussed according to the strength of this coupling compared with spin–orbit or Coulomb interactions; a discussion of magnetic interactions is outlined. Metallic $3d$ magnetism is presented in Chapters 9 and 10; Chapter 9 centres on the role of band structure and Chapter 10 deals with the onset of magnetic order.

Some technical aspects of magnetism are treated in Chapter 11 (magnetic bubbles) and Chapter 12 (coercivity). Finally, some more exotic topics which have recently attracted considerable interest are presented. Intermediate valence compounds are dealt with in Chapter 13 and an introduction to phase transition phenomena is given in Chapter 14.

Of course, this presentation is far from exhaustive. However, as mentioned earlier, we did not consciously set out to describe all aspects of modern magnetism. We apologise to the reader for the omissions and simplifications that this decision has entailed, but trust that our somewhat subjective choice of subjects will offer a firm basis for more detailed personal exploration of this fascinating area of solid state physics.

It is our pleasure to express our gratitude to all the Chinese scientists who organized these lectures, in particular Prof. Wang Zhen Xi, Yang Ying Tchang, Zhao Zhung–Xian and Li Bo Zang. Their encouragement in the writing of this book was a tremendous help to us. We are grateful to the Laboratoire L. Néel and also to the Institut Laue–Langevin, where we have learned what we can teach today. Also we would like to thank Professor J. Barbier and Dr. R. Lemaire who organized the collaboration with our Chinese colleagues.

CONTENTS

CHAPTER 1

QUANTUM MECHANICS OF ATOMS

This first chapter is devoted to the introduction of the basic entities of magnetism: the free ions as they may be found in rare earths at high temperatures. It divides into 3 parts: firstly we simply present the most important concepts of the quantum theory, then we emphasise the application of symmetry. Finally, starting from the simplest situation (hydrogen atom), we build up an atom.

1.1 REVIEW OF QUANTUM THEORY

1.1.1 Wave functions and operators

The formalism of quantum mechanics lies in the fact that any state of a quantum system can be described by a function of the generalised coordinates q; actually $\psi(q)$ is a probability amplitude, it is called the wave function of the system under investigation. Once $\psi(q)$ is known, we can calculate, in principle, the value taken by any physical quantity, which is given in terms of the wave functions or probability amplitudes:

$$\iint \psi^*(q')\phi(q, q')\psi(q)\, dq\, dq' \tag{1.1.1}$$

where $\phi(q, q')$ is characteristic of the physical quantity. As an example, $\psi^*(q_0) \cdot \psi(q_0)$ is the probability of different values q_0 of coordinates; in this case we use $\phi(q,q')=\delta(q-q_0)\,\delta(q'-q_0)$. The probability amplitudes are normalised:

$$\int |\psi(q)|^2 dq=1 \tag{1.1.2}$$

The most important property of these wave functions is that they can be superposed (principle of superposition of states). If φ_1 describes a state where the physical quantity f takes on the value f_1, and φ_2 the state which corresponds to f_2, then a state $c_1\varphi_1+c_2\varphi_2$ will describe a state where f will take on either the value f_1 or f_2. In particular, the equations that are satisfied by the $\psi(q)$ functions must be linear in $\psi(q)$. Now that we know how to define the state of a quantum system, let us turn to the mathematical formalism that describes a physical quantity f. For the sake of simplicity, we assume that values taken by f (eigenvalues) form a discrete spectrum f_n with $n=0, 1, 2 \cdots$. The wave functions ψ associated with f_n are called the eigenfunctions: ψ_n describes the states where f takes the values f_n. If the system is in an arbitrary state, measurements of f will give any of the eigenvalues f_n. Thus a wave function which describes an arbitrary state can be expanded in terms of the eigenfunctions of a physical quantity.

$$\psi=\sum a_n\psi_n \tag{1.1.3}$$

$$a_n=\int\psi\psi_n^* dq=\langle\psi_n|\psi\rangle \tag{1.1.4}$$

$|a_n|^2$ is the probability of getting $_n$ as a value for the physical quantity f. The mean value $\bar{f}$ is defined as follows:

$$\bar{f}=\sum_n |a_n|^2 f_n=\int\psi^* \sum_n a_n f_n\psi_n dq \tag{1.1.5}$$

The operator $\hat{f}$ corresponding to $\bar{f}$ is now introduced: $\hat{f}$ acts on the function ψ to give $(\hat{f}\psi)$; the scalar product of ψ and $(\hat{f}\psi)$ should give $\bar{f}$

$$\bar{f}=\int\psi^*(\hat{f}\psi)dq=\langle\psi|\hat{f}|\psi\rangle \tag{1.1.6}$$

It can easily be seen that $\hat{f}$ is a linear operator.

Furthermore, the values taken by a real physical quantity are real; then it can be shown that the linear operators corresponding to real physical quantities must be Hermitian. Thus all the operators that correspond to physical quantities must be Hermitian.

In order to determine the nature of the different operators $\hat{f}$, it is helpful to consider the limiting case of classical mechanics. It can be shown that a quantum system in the limiting case of classical mechanics is described by a wave function of the form:

$$\psi=a\exp i\left(2\pi\frac{S}{h}\right) \tag{1.1.7}$$

where S is the action and h Planck's constant.

1.1.2 Wave equation

Let us try to determine the equation that must be satisfied by the wave function ψ; we already know that this equation should be linear in ψ. The knowledge of ψ at a given time, gives us all the information about the quantum system; it also determines its behaviour at any subsequent time. Mathematically, one can write

$$i\frac{\partial\psi}{\partial t}=\hat{L}\psi \tag{1.1.8}$$

where $\hat{L}$ is a Hermitian linear operator.

If we consider the limiting case of classical mechanics, using (1.1.7), we have

$$\frac{\partial\psi}{\partial t}=\frac{i}{\hbar}\frac{\partial S}{\partial t}\psi, \qquad \hbar=\frac{h}{2\pi} \tag{1.1.9}$$

So the classical equivalent of the operator $\hat{L}$ is the multiplication by $-(1/\hbar)\,\partial S/\partial t$; but $-\partial S/\partial t$ is just the classical Hamiltonian function H. Therefore we can write the wave equation

$$i\hbar\frac{\partial\psi}{\partial t}=\hat{H}\psi \tag{1.1.10}$$

where $\hat{H}$ is called the Hamiltonian of the system; the classical physical quantity that corresponds to $\hat{H}$ is the Hamiltonian function.

Let us consider an operator $\hat{f}$ which corresponds to a physical quantity f.

The time derivative of $\hat{f}$, $\dot{\hat{f}}$, can be defined by using an equation similar to (1.1.6). Using the wave equation (1.1.10), it can be shown that

$$\dot{\hat{f}}=\frac{\partial \hat{f}}{\partial t}+\frac{i}{\hbar}(\hat{H}\hat{f}-\hat{f}\hat{H}) \tag{1.1.11}$$

Thus, if $\hat{f}$ does not depend explicitly on time, $\dot{\hat{f}}$ is proportional to the commutator of $\hat{H}$ and $\hat{f}$. If $\hat{f}$ and $\hat{H}$ commute, $\dot{\hat{f}}=0$ and the values f_n taken by f do not depend on time.

Very important quantum systems are those whose Hamiltonian does not depend on time. In such a case, $\dot{\hat{H}}=0$ and the different values E_n of H are conservative. E_n is a constant which characterises a given state ψ_n; ψ_n is called a stationary state. The wave functions that describe stationary states have the form:

$$\psi_n=\exp\left(\frac{-iE_n t}{\hbar}\right)\varphi_n(q) \tag{1.1.12}$$

where E_n and φ_n are solutions of

$$\hat{H}\varphi=E\varphi \tag{1.1.13}$$

Such stationary states can be degenerate in the sense that, while corresponding to the same energy value E_n, they can be differentiated by other physical quantities.

1.1.3 Schrödinger equation

We know that the Hamiltonian function contains impulsion and interaction potentials. We have to express the quantum operators that correspond to those physical quantities.

At first we assume that the system is made up of free particles. If we displace the system by a small amount $\delta\mathbf{r}$, then $\psi(\mathbf{r}_i)$ transforms as follows:

$$\tilde{\psi}(\mathbf{r}_i)=\psi(\mathbf{r}_i+\delta\mathbf{r})\simeq\psi(\mathbf{r}_i)+\delta\mathbf{r}\cdot\sum_i\nabla_i\psi(\mathbf{r}_i)=[1+\delta\mathbf{r}\cdot\sum_i\nabla_i]\,\psi(\mathbf{r}_i) \tag{1.1.14}$$

But this operation does not modify the Hamiltonian since the space is homogeneous. $\tilde{\psi}$ is also a solution of (1.1.10).

This means that $\sum_i\nabla_i$ commutes with the operator $\hat{H}$ which in turn means that the physical quantity associated with $\sum_i\nabla_i$ is conserved.

In classical mechanics, the physical quantity which is conserved because of space homogeneity is the momentum $\mathbf{p}$. Thus the operator ∇ should be proportional to the operator momentum $\hat{p}$, $\hat{p}=C\nabla$. The proportionality constant is determined by using the wave function (1.1.7) in the limiting case of classical mechanics.

$$\hat{p}\psi=C\frac{i}{\hbar}\nabla S\psi \tag{1.1.15}$$

with $\nabla S=\mathbf{p}$ in classical mechanics. Thus $C=-i\hbar$ and $\mathbf{p}=-i\hbar\nabla$. Since, in the case of a free particle, the classical Hamilton's function is $p^2/2m=p_x^2+p_y^2+p_z^2$, the free particle Hamiltonian $\hat{H}$ is $\hat{H}=\dfrac{\hbar^2}{2m}\hat{\Delta}$ where $\hat{\Delta}$ is the Laplacian operator.

When the particles interact and are placed in an external field, we must add to the kinetic energy a potential energy U. The Hamiltonian $\hat{H}$ is then given by

$$\sum_i \frac{-\hbar^2}{2m_i}\hat{\Delta}_i + U(\mathbf{r}_i) \tag{1.1.16}$$

$U(\mathbf{r}_i)$ is similar to the potential as used in classical mechanics. Then the wave equation (1.1.9) takes the form

$$i\hbar\frac{\partial\psi}{\partial t} = -\frac{\hbar^2}{2m}\hat{\Delta}\psi + U\psi \tag{1.1.17}$$

which is the Schrödinger equation. In the case of stationary states, the equation is simply written as

$$\frac{\hbar^2}{2m}\hat{\Delta}\varphi + (E-U)\varphi = 0 \tag{1.1.18}$$

At this point it is worth noting that if an operator $\hat{f}$ commutes with $\hat{H}$ (i.e., $\hat{H}$ is invariant under the operation of $\hat{f}$), the states corresponding to a definite value E_n are degenerate:

$$\hat{H}|\hat{f}\psi\rangle = \hat{f}|\hat{H}\psi\rangle = E|\hat{f}\psi\rangle \tag{1.1.19}$$

This point is important, as will be seen when we discuss symmetry properties.

So far, we have left out the symmetry operations that play an important role in classical mechanics: the isotropy of space, time reversal and particle identity. First we will discuss the implications of space isotropy.

1.1.4 Angular momentum

We introduce the operator of an infinitely small rotation of real space:

$$1 + \delta\varphi \cdot \sum_a \mathbf{r}_a \times \boldsymbol{\nabla}_a$$

This operator must leave $\hat{H}$ invariant, if space is isotropic. In classical mechanics, we know that from the isotropy of space follows the conservation of the angular momentum $(\mathbf{r}\times\mathbf{p})$. Thus in quantum mechanics, we define the angular momentum $\hat{l}$ operator as:

$$-i\hbar\mathbf{r}\times\boldsymbol{\nabla} = \hbar\hat{l} \tag{1.1.20}$$

Let $\hat{l}_x, \hat{l}_y, \hat{l}_z$ denote the x, y, z components of the angular momentum operator:

$$\hbar\hat{l}_x = y\hat{p}_z - z\hat{p}_y \qquad \hbar\hat{l}_y = z\hat{p}_x - x\hat{p}_z \qquad \hbar\hat{l}_z = x\hat{p}_y - y\hat{p}_x$$

It can be shown that

$$\begin{aligned}[\hat{l}_x, \hat{l}_y] &= \hat{l}_x\hat{l}_y - \hat{l}_y\hat{l}_x = i\hat{l}_z\\ [\hat{l}_y, \hat{l}_z] &= \hat{l}_y\hat{l}_z - \hat{l}_z\hat{l}_y = i\hat{l}_x\\ [\hat{l}_z, \hat{l}_x] &= \hat{l}_z\hat{l}_x - \hat{l}_x\hat{l}_z = i\hat{l}_y\end{aligned} \tag{1.1.21}$$

Thus the three components of $\hat{l}$ do not commute, which shows that this operator is basically different from the position or momentum operators. We introduce the operator $\hat{l}^2 = \hat{l}_x^2 + \hat{l}_y^2 + \hat{l}_z^2$ which measures the "length" of the momentum; we have

$$[\hat{l}^2, \hat{l}_\alpha] = 0 \tag{1.1.22}$$

where α is x, y, z, This means that $\hat{l}^2$ and one of the $\hat{l}_\alpha$ can take a definite value at the same time. It is noteworthy that $\hat{l}^2$ and $\hat{l}$ are conserved when the Hamiltonian $\hat{H}$ has spherical symmetry. On the other hand, if $\hat{H}$ is axially symmetric, only the component of angular momentum along the axis of symmetry is conserved.

It is very useful to write down expressions for $\hat{l}$ in a spherical coordinate system:

$$\hat{l}_z=-i\frac{\partial}{\partial\varphi}$$

$$\hat{l}_\pm=e^{\pm i\varphi}\left(\pm\frac{\partial}{\partial\theta}+i\cot\theta\frac{\partial}{\partial\varphi}\right) \tag{1.1.23}$$

and

$$\hat{l}^2=-\left[\frac{1}{\sin^2\theta}\frac{\partial^2}{\partial\varphi^2}+\frac{1}{\sin\theta}\frac{\partial}{\partial\theta}\left(\sin\theta\frac{\partial}{\partial\theta}\right)\right]$$

which is the angular part of the Laplacian operator.

Let us determine the physical values that the angular momentum projection can take. We have to find the eigenvalues of the corresponding operator. Using a spherical coordinate system, according to (1.1.23) the equation $\hat{l}_z|\psi\rangle=l_z|\psi\rangle$ takes the form:

$$-i\frac{\partial\psi}{\partial\varphi}=l_z\varphi$$

The solution is $\psi=f(r,\theta)e^{il_z\varphi}$. Since ψ must be single valued, it must be periodic in $l_z\varphi$ (period 2π). Then l_z can take on integral values $l_z=m$ with $m=0,\pm1,\pm2,\cdots$ This same result holds for l_x or l_y. But it must be kept in mind, they do not have common eigenfunctions unless the eigenvalues are zero.

Assuming that a particle is in a state ψ_m where $l_z=m$, we can show that $\hat{l}^2$ has a definite value:

$$\hat{l}^2\psi_m=l(l+1)\psi_m$$

where l is the greatest value of m.

Conversely, for a given value of l, m can take all the values $m=l, l-1, \cdots, -l$. This state is degenerate with a $(2l+1)$–fold degeneracy. The state with $l=0$ is non-degenerate and has spherical symmetry.

If the Hamiltonian is invariant under rotation, the angular part of the wave function of a particle can be determined when the values taken by $\hat{l}^2$ and $\hat{l}_z$ are given. The common eigenfunctions $|l,\ m\rangle$ of these two operators can be written as

$$Y_{lm}(\theta,\varphi)=\frac{(-1)^m}{\sqrt{2\pi}}i^l\left[\frac{(l+\frac{1}{2})(l-m)!}{(l+m)!}\right]^{1/2}P_l^m(\cos\theta)e^{im\varphi} \tag{1.1.24}$$

where P_l^m are the associated Legendre Polynomials. The $Y_{lm}(\theta,\varphi)$ are called spherical harmonics. In this standard basis, where both $\hat{l}_z$ and $\hat{l}^2$ are diagonal, the angular momentum operators have the following matrix elements:

$$\begin{aligned}\hat{l}_z|l,m\rangle&=m|l,m\rangle\\ \hat{l}^2|l,m\rangle&=l(l+1)|l,m\rangle\\ \hat{l}_\pm|l,m\rangle&=[l(l+1)-m(m\pm1)]^{1/2}|l,m\pm1\rangle\end{aligned} \tag{1.1.25}$$

Let us consider a system which is made of two subsystems; each subsystem is characterised by its own angular momentum $\hat{l}_a$. The total angular momentum is $\hat{L}=\hat{l}_1+\hat{l}_2$. If the interaction between the two subsystems is weak, then $\hat{l}_1^2$ and $\hat{l}_2^2$ are conserved, they take on the values $l_1(l_1+1)$ and $l_2(l_2+1)$ respectively. What are the possible values of $\hat{L}^2$ and $\hat{L}_z$? We shall see later that $\hat{L}^2$ takes the value $L(L+1)$ with $l_1+l_2>L>|l_1-l_2|$, of course, $\hat{L}_z$ has the value M with $M=+L,\ L-1,\ \cdots,\ -L$. In the case where $\hat{l}_1^2$, $\hat{l}_2^2$, $\hat{L}^2$ have definite values, then $\hat{l}_1\hat{l}_2$, $\hat{L}\hat{l}_1$, $\hat{L}\hat{l}_2$ also have definite values, in particular

$$\hat{l}_1\hat{l}_2=\frac{1}{2}[L(L+1)-l_1(l_1+1)-l_2(l_2+1)] \tag{1.1.26}$$

1.1.5 Spin–Time reversal

Now we consider a system such as an atomic nucleus made of different particles; the total angular momentum is $\hat{L}=\sum_a \hat{l}_a$. When the system is in a state where its internal energy has a definite value corresponding to a given value L of the angular momentum, this state has a $(2L+1)$–fold degeneracy. As a consequence, if we want to describe the nucleus, we must take into account, besides the usual coordinates, an internal discrete variable: the projection of the internal angular momentum. This conclusion is a purely quantum mechanical result. And there is no reason to suppose that this discrete variable is absent when the nucleus reduces to an elementary particle. This internal variable is called spin; the spin of a particle measured in $\hbar$ units is denoted by s. For a given kind of particle, s has a fixed value; $\hbar s$ tends to zero in the classical limiting case ($\hbar\to 0$), whereas $\hbar l$ remains finite if we assume that l becomes infinitely large in classical mechanics.

Spin operators have properties similar to those of angular momentum, but the eigenvalues of $\hat{s}^2$ are not necessary integral; s can take the value 0, 1/2, 1, 3/2$\cdots$, while the projection s_z can take the value $s,\ s-1,\ \cdots,\ -s$. Electrons have a spin of 1/2. The 1/2 spin operator can be represented by using the Pauli matrices. In the standard basis (eigenvectors of $\hat{s}_z$ with $\pm 1/2$ as eigenvalues) we have

$$\hat{s}_x=\frac{1}{2}\begin{pmatrix}0&1\\1&0\end{pmatrix},\quad \hat{s}_y=\frac{1}{2}\begin{pmatrix}0&-i\\i&0\end{pmatrix},\quad \hat{s}_z=\frac{1}{2}\begin{pmatrix}1&0\\0&-1\end{pmatrix} \tag{1.1.27}$$

The total orbital momentum $\hat{j}$ of a particle is $\hat{j}=\hat{l}+\hat{s}$.

Now let us turn to the time reversal problem. When we do not take into account the spin of a particle, the symmetry with respect to the time reversal is expressed by transforming the function ψ into its complex conjugate ψ^* [see (1.1.12)], when the potential energy U does not depend explicitly on the time. In particular, U should not contain any external magnetic field which must be reversed in the case of time reversal.

When spins are present, the wave functions of the system are called spinors whose rank p is twice the sum of the spin s_a of all particles $p=2\sum_a^n s_a$. We apply the time–reversal operations. It can be shown that when n is even, the time–reversal state ψ^{rev} is identical to ψ; whereas in the case of an odd value of n, ψ^{rev} is not identical to ψ; this means that for odd n the state described by

ψ is at least two-fold degenerate. This is Kramers theorem. The degeneracy is removed by applying an external magnetic field.

1.1.6 Perturbation theory

At present we are in a position where we should be able to determine all the properties of a given quantum system. However, the exact solution of Schrödinger's equation can be found only in a few simple cases. But terms of the Hamiltonian may be of different orders of magnitude: the Hamiltonian can be written as

$$\hat{H}=\hat{H}_0+\hat{V} \tag{1.1.28}$$

where $\hat{H}_0$ is rather simple and $\hat{V}$ is a small correction to the unperturbed part $\hat{H}_0$. For the sake of simplicity, we shall not deal with perturbations which depend explicitly on time.

We assume that we know a set of unperturbed functions ψ_n^0, $\psi_{n'}^0$, ... corresponding to the same degenerate eigenvalue E_n^0. We wish to find approximate solutions to the equation

$$(\hat{H}_0+\hat{V})|\psi\rangle=E|\psi\rangle$$

An approximate expression for ψ can be:

$$\psi=\sum_k C_k\psi_k^0 \tag{1.1.29}$$

The C_k coefficients are given by

$$(E-E_k^0)C_k=\sum_m V_{km}C_m \tag{1.1.30}$$

where

$$V_{km}=\langle\psi_k^0|\hat{V}|\psi_m^0\rangle$$

The energy E and the coefficients C_m are expanded in series:

$$E=E_n^0+E^{(1)}+E^{(2)}$$

$$C_n=C_n^{(0)}+C_n^{(1)}$$

where $E^{(i)}$ and $C_m^{(i)}$ are of the i-th order with respect to $\hat{V}$. Limiting ourselves to the first-order perturbation equation (1.1.30) in E, and zero order in C_k, we have

$$C_n=C_n^{(0)},\ C_m=0$$

$$\sum_{n'}(V_{nn'}-E^{(1)}\delta_{nn'})C_{n'}^{(0)}=0 \tag{1.1.31}$$

The $C_n^{(0)}$ are the eigenvectors and the $E^{(1)}$ are the eigenfunctions of this secular equation, which is the fundamental equation of first-order perturbation. In the same way, it can be shown that the second-order perturbation term is given by:

$$C_m^{(1)}=\sum_{n'}\frac{V_{mn'}}{E_n^0-E_m^0}C_{n'}^{(0)}$$

$$\left|\sum_m\frac{V_{nm}V_{mn'}}{E_n^0-E_m^0}-E^{(2)}\delta_{nn'}\right|=0 \tag{1.1.32}$$

It can be noticed that the small perturbation $\hat{V}$ removes the degeneracy of the unperturbed level E^0. This removal may well be partial; this depends on the matrix elements $V_{nn'}$. In consequence, it is important to determine some "selection rules" that can tell us, a priori, if matrix elements between states n

and n' are zero. These selection rules are based on symmetry arguments which will be discussed in another section.

1.1.7 Particle identity

In quantum mechanics, we cannot distinguish between identical particles. This situation results from the fact that if, at a given time, we can determine exactly the position of a particle, we cannot measure its velocity ($\hat{q}_n$ and $\hat{p}_n$ do not commute – uncertainty principle). Thus, in quantum mechanics, identical particles are indistinguishable. This means that we can permute particle coordinates in the wave function of a system.

Let us consider a two-particle system; the two particles appear in the wave function ψ through their coordinates q_1 and q_2 (q represents the usual coordinates and the spin). If we permute the particles 1 and 2, the system is unchanged physically, thus the new wave function differs from the original one by a phase factor:

$$\psi(q_1, q_2)=e^{i\phi}\psi(q_2, q_1)$$

Permuting once more, we get back to the original function, thus $e^{2i\phi}=1$ and we have

$$\psi(q_1, q_2)=\pm\psi(q_2,q_1) \tag{1.1.33}$$

Thus the wave function is either totally symmetric or totally antisymmetric under particle permutation. This can be generalised to multiparticle systems. Bosons (particles with integral spin) have totally symmetric wave functions of the form:

$$\sum\psi_{p_1}(q_1)\psi_{p_2}(q_2)\cdots\psi_{p_N}(q_N) \tag{1.1.34}$$

with all possible permutations of p_1,p_2 (ψ_{p_i} denotes a state of one particle). Fermions (particles with half integral spin) have totally antisymmetric wave functions given by the determinant:

$$\psi=\frac{1}{\sqrt{N!}}\begin{vmatrix} \psi_{p_1}(q_1) & \psi_{p_1}(q_2) & \cdots & \psi_{p_1}(q_N) \\ \psi_{p_2}(q_1) & \psi_{p_2}(q_2) & \cdots & \psi_{p_2}(q_N) \\ \vdots & \vdots & & \vdots \\ \psi_{p_N}(q_1) & \psi_{p_N}(q_2) & \cdots & \psi_{p_N}(q_N) \end{vmatrix} \tag{1.1.35}$$

These properties, which arise from the spin of particles, are very important, in particular, two fermions cannot occupy the same quantum state; if this were the case, then the determinant ψ would be identically zero. This is the Pauli principle. Furthermore, these symmetry properties can affect the energy level scheme, even if the spin is not included in the Schrödinger equation.

As an example, let us consider a two-electron system:the Hamiltonian is given by

$$\hat{H}=\sum_{i=1}^{2}\hat{f}_i+U(\mathbf{r}_1, \mathbf{r}_2)$$

In that case we can write the total wave function as

$$\psi(q_1, q_2)=\varphi(\mathbf{r}_1\ \mathbf{r}_2)\chi(\sigma_1, \sigma_2)$$

here σ_i denotes the spin state of the electron i.

According to (1.1.35)

$$\psi(q_1,q_2)=\frac{1}{2}\Big[\varphi_{p_1}(\mathbf{r}_1)\varphi_{p_2}(\mathbf{r}_2)\pm\varphi_{p_1}(\mathbf{r}_2)\varphi_{p_2}(\mathbf{r}_1)\Big]\Big[\chi_{p_1}(\sigma_1)\chi_{p_2}(\sigma_2)\mp\chi_{p_1}(\sigma_2)\chi_{p_2}(\sigma_1)\Big]$$

Let us concentrate on the spin part first. The antisymmetric form corresponds to a total spin $S=0$ while the symmetric function describes a state with $S=1$. Thus the $S=0$ state has a symmetric orbital wave function

$$\Phi_0=\frac{1}{\sqrt{2}}\left[\varphi_{p_1}(\mathbf{r}_1)\varphi_{p_2}(\mathbf{r}_2)+\varphi_{p_1}(\mathbf{r}_2)\varphi_{p_2}(\mathbf{r}_1)\right]$$

and the $S=1$ state has an antisymmetric orbital wave function

$$\Phi_1=\frac{1}{\sqrt{2}}\left[\varphi_{p_1}(\mathbf{r}_1)\varphi_{p_2}(\mathbf{r}_2)-\varphi_{p_1}(\mathbf{r}_2)\varphi_{p_2}(\mathbf{r}_1)\right]$$

If the interaction U were absent, then these two states would have the same energy. Let us turn on the interaction U; we apply the perturbation theory up to first order. We must calculate the matrix elements of U in the unperturbed basis (Φ_0, Φ_1). It can be shown that

$$U_{0,0}=I+J$$
$$U_{1,1}=I-J \quad U_{0,1}=U_{1,0}=0$$

with

$$I=\iint|\varphi_{p_1}(\mathbf{r}_1)|^2U(\mathbf{r}_1, \mathbf{r}_2)|\varphi_{p_2}(\mathbf{r}_2)|^2d\mathbf{r}_1d\mathbf{r}_2$$
$$J=\iint\varphi_{p_1}(\mathbf{r}_1)\varphi^*_{p_1}(\mathbf{r}_2)U(\mathbf{r}_1, \mathbf{r}_2)\varphi_{p_2}(\mathbf{r}_2)\varphi^*_{p_2}(\mathbf{r}_1)d\mathbf{r}_1d\mathbf{r}_2$$

The two levels $S=0$ and $S=1$ have different energies. This is known as the exchange interaction. The splitting energy $\Delta E=E_{s=0}-E_{s=1}=2J$ can be represented by an exchange spin Hamiltonian:

$$\hat{H}_{ex}=-\frac{1}{2}J(1+4\hat{s}_1\hat{s}_2) \qquad (1.1.36)$$

1.1.8 Symmetry–Selection rules

Let us consider a physical system which is invariant under some symmetry operations; these operations form a group of transformations. So far, we have dealt with space uniformity and isotropy, time reversal, and particle permutation, but there are many other symmetry operations that may be encountered in solid state physics: space symmetry in crystals… .

Since the physical system of interest is invariant under symmetry operations, the Schrödinger equation is also invariant under the same operations. This means that, when applying a symmetry transformation, the wave functions corresponding to a given energy level transform into linear combinations of one another: they give a representation of the group. In other words, if we define a space spanned by the states of the quantum system, the substates associated with one given energy level E_n form an invariant subspace [see (1.1.19)]. This result is a very important one, as can be seen in perturbation theory. Suppose $\hat{H}_0$ is invariant under a group of transformations G_0; usually the perturbation $\hat{V}$, invariant under G, is less symmetric than $\hat{H}_0$. The total Hamiltonian $\hat{H}=\hat{H}_0+\hat{V}$ is then less symmetric than $\hat{H}_0$. This means that a subspace invariant with respect to $\hat{H}_0$, will not be invariant under the operations of G. New invariant subspaces have to be found. The representation Γ_0 of G_0 associated with the unperturbed level E_0 will then decompose into representations of G. Symmetry considerations can tell us how Γ_0 will decompose. This is based on the theory of representations, which will be outlined.

1.2 SYMMETRY PROPERTIES

1.2.1 Theory of group representations

Let us introduce a group G of symmetry operations $(A, B, \cdots)$ whose order is h. By a representation we mean a group of unitary square matrices $\Gamma(A)$ that obey the multiplication operation:

$$\Gamma(A)\Gamma(B)=\Gamma(AB) \tag{1.2.1}$$

The dimension of the square matrices $\Gamma(A)$ is the dimensionality of the representation Γ.

A very simple representation is the identity representation where all the elements of G are replaced by $+1$. It can be noticed that for a given representation we can build "equivalent" representations Γ' by similarity transformations

$$\Gamma'(A)=S^{-1}\Gamma(A)S \tag{1.2.2}$$

where S is a similarity transformation matrix. Suppose that two representations Γ_1 and Γ_2 are known; obviously a new representation can be constructed by combining the matrices of Γ_1 and Γ_2 into larger matrices: for a given element A of G, we have

$$\Gamma(A)=\begin{pmatrix}\Gamma_1(A) & 0\\ 0 & \Gamma_2(A)\end{pmatrix} \tag{1.2.3}$$

The Γ representation is said to be reducible since it is in block form. Of course, a similarity operation as defined in (1.2.2) would destroy such a simple form, but Γ would still be reducible.

A given representation Γ is said to be irreducible if we cannot find a matrix S that transforms all the matrices $\Gamma(A)$ into a block form. As we shall see later, the irreducible representations play a fundamental role: they tell us how functions transform under symmetry operations.

A great orthogonality theorem can be stated as follows: if we consider all the inequivalent irreducible representations $\Gamma(A)$ of a given group, then

$$\sum_{A\in G}\Gamma_i(A)^*_{\mu\nu}\,\Gamma_j(A)_{\alpha\beta}=\frac{h}{l_i}\delta_{\mu\alpha}\delta_{\nu\beta}\delta_{ij} \tag{1.2.4}$$

where the summation runs over all the group elements and l_i is the dimensionality of Γ_i. We have seen that we can find equivalent representations by using similarity transformations. It is then worth using quantities that are invariant under such transformations: sum of diagonal elements. The character of the representation Γ_i is defined as

$$\chi_i(A)=\mathrm{Sp}\{\Gamma_i(A)\}=\sum_{\mu=1}^{l_i}\Gamma'_i(A)_{\mu\mu} \tag{1.2.5}$$

The great orthogonality theorem can be written in terms of the characters:

$$\sum_{A\in G}\chi_i(A)^*\chi_j(A)=h\delta_{ij} \tag{1.2.6}$$

Note that two conjugate elements A and B have the same characters because

$B = XAX^{-1}$, where X is an element of G; then all the elements of a given class have the same character. Then (1.2.6) can be rewritten as:

$$\sum_{\text{class}} \chi_i(A_c)^* \chi_j(A_c) N_c = h\delta_{ij} \tag{1.2.7}$$

Another orthogonality theorem can be stated as follows:

$$\sum_i \chi_i(A_c)^* \chi_i(A_{c^1}) N_c = h\delta_{cc^1} \tag{1.2.8}$$

where the sum is over all irreducible representations and c (c^1) denotes a class. It can be shown that the number of irreducible representations is equal to the number of classes and that

$$\sum_i l_i^2 = h \tag{1.2.9}$$

These theorems and rules allow us to work out the number and dimensionality of irreducible representations as well as the character table of a given group. A reducible representation Γ as in (1.2.3) can be decomposed into irreducible representations Γ_j:

$$\Gamma = \sum_j a_j \Gamma_j \tag{1.2.10}$$

The character χ of Γ is then written

$$\chi(A) = \sum_j a_j \chi_j(A)$$

Using (1.2.6), we have

$$a_j = h^{-1} \sum_A \chi_j(A)^* \chi(A) \tag{1.2.11}$$

This reduction is unique.

Now let us consider a set of n functions f_α which are linearly independent. The f_α are such that if we apply any symmetry operation A of a group G to any f_α it will be transformed into linear combinations of f_β. These f_β functions induce a representation Γ of the group G; they form a basis for the representation Γ. In general Γ is reducible into irreducible representations Γ_i of the group G. It is then important to know which combinations of the f_α transform according to the Γ_i, it is also important to determine some basis functions φ_i^m of the Γ_i.

It can be shown that basis functions belonging to different irreducible representations are orthogonal; the same holds for partner functions of the same unitary irreducible representation.

The identity representation is a special case: functions transforming as Γ_1 are invariant under the operations of G. Such functions can be obtained from partners of Γ_i: the expression $\sum_{m=1}^{l_i} |\varphi_i^m|^2$ is an invariant, l_i is the dimensionality of Γ_i.

On the other hand, linear combinations of f_α which transform as Γ_i can be found by making use of the projection operator:

$$P_{mn}^i = \frac{l_i}{h} \sum_A \Gamma_i(A)_{mn}^* A \tag{1.2.12}$$

where A is an element of G.

When acting on the partner φ_i^n of Γ_i, the projection operator yields another partner φ_i^m. But acting on any combination of f_α, it will yield either zero or the part of this combination which transforms as φ_i^m. Thus applying P_{mn}^i to all linearly independent combinations of f_α will provide basis functions of the Γ_i which are included in the reduction of the Γ. Of course, this procedure requires the knowledge of the $\Gamma_i(A)_{mn}$ matrices and the definition of the operation Af_α.

We can define the direct product of two representations Γ_i and Γ_j of G. Let φ_i^m and φ_j^n be the partners belonging to Γ_i and Γ_j; the functions $\Phi_{ij}^{mn}=\varphi_i^m\cdot\varphi_j^n$ form the basis of a new representation Γ which is called the direct product of Γ_i and Γ_j

$$\Gamma=\Gamma_i\otimes\Gamma_j \tag{1.2.13}$$

The dimensionality l of Γ is given by the product $l=l_i\times l_j$. In general Γ is not irreducible and can be reduced into the irreducible representations Γ_i. The character $\chi^\Gamma(A)$ can be easily obtained:

$$\chi^\Gamma(A)=\sum_{nq}\Gamma_{nq,nq}(A)=\sum_{nq}\Gamma_i(A)_{nn}\Gamma_j(A)_{qq}=\chi_i(A)\chi_j(A) \tag{1.2.14}$$

The character of a direct product is simply the product of the characters. In the case where the two representations Γ_i and Γ_j are the same, we can distinguish between symmetric and antisymmetric squares:

$$\Gamma\otimes\Gamma=[\Gamma]^2{}_S+\{\Gamma\}^2_{AS}$$

The character of these two products can be determined from the relations:

$$[\chi(A)]^2_S=\frac{1}{2}\Big(\chi(A)^2+\chi(A^2)\Big)$$

$$\{\chi(A)\}^2_{AS}=\frac{1}{2}\Big(\chi(A)^2-\chi(A^2)\Big) \tag{1.2.15}$$

1.2.2 Point groups

We will concentrate on symmetry operations that leave a crystal invariant. These operations can be decomposed into three fundamental operations, namely: rotation, mirror reflection, translation. The first two symmetry operations, which leave one point of the solid fixed, are point symmetry operations. The translational symmetry which involves an infinite number of operations applies only to an infinitely large body (crystalline lattice). Let us consider the point symmetry operations first.

A rotation of $2\pi/n$ about a given axis will be denoted by C_n (n-fold axis); a mirror reflection is denoted by σ. A mirror rotation or improper rotation S_n, is the product of C_n and σ: $S_n=C_n\times\sigma=\sigma\times C_n$. Under the inversion operation, i, the crystal is inverted through some origin. These fundamental operations can be added together to form different point groups. In crystals the values taken by n (the order of rotation axis) are restricted to n=1, 2, 3, 4, 6. It turns out that, in this case, there are 32 point groups. They are given in Table 1.2.1. Character tables and basis functions for the irreducible representations of these symmetry groups are given in many text books.

As an example, let us consider the point groups C_3 and C_{3v}. The C_3 group

Table 1.2.1

Notation	Symmetry Elements
Triclinic	
C_1	E
S_2 (C_i)	E i
Monoclinic	
C_2	E C_2
C_{1h} (C_s)	E σ_h
C_{2h}	E C_2 i σ_h
Orthorhombic	
D_2 (V)	E C_2 C_2' C_2'
C_{2v}	E C_2 σ_v σ_v
D_{2h} (V_h)	E C_2 C_2' C_2' i σ_h σ_v σ
Tetragonal	
C_4	E $2C_4$ C_2
S_4	E $2S_4$ C_2
C_{4h}	E $2C_4$ C_2 i $2S_4$ σ_h
D_4	E $2C_4$ C_2 $2C_2'$ $2C_2''$
C_{4v}	E $2C_4$ C_2 $2\sigma_v$ $2\sigma_d$
D_{2d} (V_d)	E C_2 $2C_2'$ $2\sigma_d$ $2S_4$
D_{4h}	E $2C_4$ C_2 $2C_2'$ $2C_2''$ i $2S_4$ σ_h $2\sigma_v$ $2\sigma_d$
Trigonal (Rhombohedral)	
C_3	E $2C_3$
S_6 (C_{3i})	E $2C_3$ i $2S_6$
D_3	E $2C_3$ $3C_2$
C_{3v}	E $2C_3$ $3\sigma_v$
D_{3d}	E $2C_3$ $3C_2$ i $2S_6$ $3\sigma_v$
Hexagonal	
C_6	E $2C_6$ $2C_3$ C_2
C_{3h}	E $2C_3$ σ_h $2S_3$
C_{6h}	E $2C_6$ $2C_3$ C_2 i $2S_3$ $2S_6$ σ_h
D_6	E $2C_6$ $2C_3$ C_2 $3C_2'$ $3C_2''$
C_{6v}	E $2C_6$ $2C_3$ C_2 $3\sigma_v$ $3\sigma_d$
D_{3h}	E $2C_3$ $3C_2$ σ_h $2S_3$ $3\sigma_v$
D_{6h}	E $2C_6$ $2C_3$ C_2 $3C_2'$ $3C_2''$ i $2S_3$ $2S_6$ σ_h $3\sigma_v$ $3\sigma_d$
Cubic	
T	E $8C_3$ $3C_2$
T_h	E $8C_3$ $3C_2$ i $8S_6$ $3\sigma_h$
O	E $8C_3$ $3C_2$ $6C_2$ $6C_4$
T_d	E $8C_3$ $3C_2$ $6\sigma_d$ $6S_4$
O_h	E $8C_3$ $3C_2$ $6C_2$ $6C_4$ i $8S_6$ $3\sigma_h$ $6\sigma_d$ $6S_4$

is Abelian, it contains 3 elements (E, C_3, C_3^2) which form 3 classes. Thus there are 3 irreducible representations Γ_1, Γ_2, Γ_3, which are one dimensional, since the only way to satisfy (1.2.9) is to set $l_i=1$:

$$1^2+1^2+1^2=3$$

This means that acting on the basis functions φ of any irreducible representation of C_3 reduces to a multiplication by a scalar A. Since $C_3^3 \equiv E$, then $A^3=1$ and $A=e^{2\pi ik/3}$; the three values of k, $k=0, 1, 2$, correspond to the three

Table 1.2.2

C_3	E	C_3	C_3^2	
Γ_1	1	1	1	z
Γ_2	1	ε	ε^*	$x+iy$
Γ_3	1	ε^*	ε	$x-iy$

Table 1.2.3

C_{3v}	E	C_3, C_3^2	$3\sigma_v$	
Γ_1	1	1	1	z, x^2+y^2, z^2
Γ_2	1	1	-1	
Γ_3	2	-1	0	x, y

irreducible representations. The characters are given in Table 1.2.2.

The order h of the group C_{3v} is 6, the number of classes is 3, then the dimensionality of each irreducible representation follows from (1.2.9)

$$1^2+1^2+2^2=6$$

We have two one-dimensional and one two-dimensional irreducible representations. Then, the use of (1.2.6) and (1.2.8) completely determines the character table of C_{3v}.

Basis functions for these representations can be found in terms of the usual spatial coordinates. The transformations of $\mathbf{r}$ (x, y, z) under the operations of the group C_{3v} induce a matrix representation Γ of C_{3v}. We use a coordinate system shown in Fig. 1.2.1.

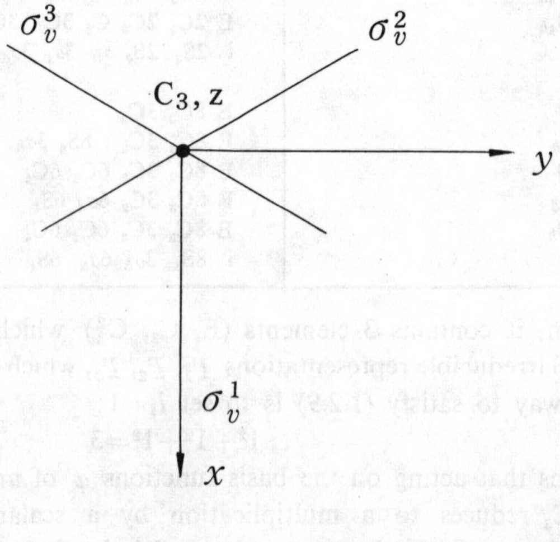

Fig. 1.2.1

The Γ (A) matrices are:

$$\Gamma(\mathrm{E})=\begin{pmatrix}1&0&0\\0&1&0\\0&0&1\end{pmatrix} \qquad \Gamma(\sigma_v^1)=\begin{pmatrix}1&0&0\\0&-1&0\\0&0&1\end{pmatrix}$$

$$\Gamma(\mathrm{C}_3)=\begin{pmatrix}-\frac{1}{2}&\frac{\sqrt{3}}{2}&0\\-\frac{\sqrt{3}}{2}&-\frac{1}{2}&0\\0&0&1\end{pmatrix}$$

The characters χ^{Γ} are given in Table 1.2.4.

Table 1.2.4
Characters of vector representations of C_{3v}

	E	C_3, C_3^2	$3\sigma_v$
Γ	3	0	1

Thus Γ is reducible: $\Gamma=\Gamma_1+\Gamma_3$. It can easily be seen that the z component is invariant under all operations, thus z is a basis function of the identity representation Γ_1. Linear combinations of x and y form the partners belonging to the two-dimensional representation Γ_3. Choosing $\varphi_3^{1,2}=x\pm iy$ as partners, we obtain the following matrices for Γ_3

$$\Gamma_3(\mathrm{E})=\begin{pmatrix}1&0\\0&1\end{pmatrix} \qquad \Gamma_3(\mathrm{C}_3)=\begin{pmatrix}\varepsilon&0\\0&\varepsilon^2\end{pmatrix}$$

$$\Gamma_3(\sigma_v^1)=\begin{pmatrix}0&1\\1&0\end{pmatrix}$$

with

$$\varepsilon=e^{\frac{2i\pi}{3}}$$

Let us determine basis functions which are quadratic in x, y, z. We know that z^2 (basis functions of $[\Gamma_1]_S^2$) transform as Γ_1; functions of the form zx, zy (basis functions of the direct product $\Gamma_1\otimes\Gamma_3$) transform as Γ_3. We can consider the symmetric square $\Gamma=[\Gamma_3]_S^2$. The characters of $[\Gamma_3]_S^2$ are given by (1.2.15)

	E	C_3, C_3^2	$3\sigma_v$
$[\Gamma_3]_S^2$	3	0	1

Thus it can be seen that $[\Gamma_3]_S^2=\Gamma_1+\Gamma_3$. The partner functions of $[\Gamma_3]_S^2$ are $(\varphi_3^1)^2$, $(\varphi_3^2)^2$, $\varphi_3^1\varphi_3^2$. Obviously, $\varphi_3^1\varphi_3^2=(x^2+y^2)$ is an invariant, and transforms as Γ_1; $(\varphi_3^1)^2$, $(\varphi_3^2)^2$ are the basis functions of $[\Gamma_3]_S^2$ that transform as Γ_3 with the same matrices as φ_3^1 and φ_3^2. New basis functions for Γ_3 are $(\varphi_3^1)^2=1/2\ (x^2-y^2)\text{–}ixy$ and $(\varphi_3^2)^2=(x^2-y^2)+ixy$.

So far we have not found any basis function for the Γ_2 irreducible representation of C_{3v}; in order to obtain such a basis, we use the symmetric cube $[\Gamma_3]^3_S$ of Γ_3, the characters are given by the relation:

$$[\chi(A)]^3_S = \frac{1}{3}\chi(A^3) + \frac{1}{2}\chi(A^2)\chi(A) + \frac{1}{6}\chi^3(A)$$

which yields the character table:

	E	C_3, C_3^2	$3\sigma_v$
$[\Gamma_3]^3_S$	4	1	0

The representation $[\Gamma_3]^3_S$ is reducible:

$$[\Gamma_3]^3_S = \Gamma_1 + \Gamma_2 + \Gamma_3$$

We can determine the matrices of transformation of $(\varphi_3^1)^3, (\varphi_3^2)^3, \varphi_3^1(\varphi_3^2)^2, (\varphi_3^1)^2\varphi_3^2$ which form a basis of $[\Gamma_3]^3_S$. By using the projection operator (1.2.12) it can be found that $(\varphi_3^1)^3 + (\varphi_3^2)^3 = \frac{x}{2}(x^2 - 3y^2)$ transforms as Γ_1 and that $(\varphi_3^1)^2 - (\varphi_3^2)^3 = -\frac{iy}{2}(3x^2 - y^2)$ transforms as Γ_2. This procedure can be extended to higher–order terms.

1.2.3 Space groups

So far we have been dealing with point symmetry, which is of importance in studying local properties such as crystal field effects; however, when we discuss long–range magnetic order, the microscopic symmetry of crystals will play an important role. Thus we will discuss briefly the irreducible representations of space groups.

Space group elements are translations, point symmetry operations and combinations of the two; they leave the crystal invariant. Pure translations form an invariant subgroup of the space group G, whose operations define the Bravais lattice of the crystal. There are 14 Bravais lattices belonging to 7 crystal systems or syngonies (Fig. 1.2.2). For each Bravais lattice, we have a set of 3 vectors $\mathbf{a}_1$, $\mathbf{a}_2$, $\mathbf{a}_3$, which define the unit cell and the fundamental translations.

We can associate the 32 point groups with the 14 Bravais lattices, provided that the point group is a subgroup of the syngony of the Bravais lattice, and that no sub ordinate syngony contains the point group. In this manner 73 space groups are obtained, they are called symmorphic space groups: there are no screw axes or glide planes. If we include screw axes and glide planes, we get 157 non–symmorphic space groups. In total, 230 space groups can be obtained. Their elements are denoted by $(A|\mathbf{t})$ where A is a point symmetry operation and $\mathbf{t}$ a translation.

A physical quantity F of a crystal has the same translational symmetry as the crystal; thus $F(\mathbf{r})$ can be expanded in a Fourier series

$$F(\mathbf{r}) = \sum_{\mathbf{q}} F_{\mathbf{q}} \exp^{(i\mathbf{q}\cdot\mathbf{r})} \tag{1.2.16}$$

with $\mathbf{q}\cdot\mathbf{a}_i = 2\pi p$ where $\mathbf{a}_i$ are the basis vectors of the Bravais lattice. The vector $\mathbf{q}$ is a vector of the reciprocal lattice whose basis vectors are given by:

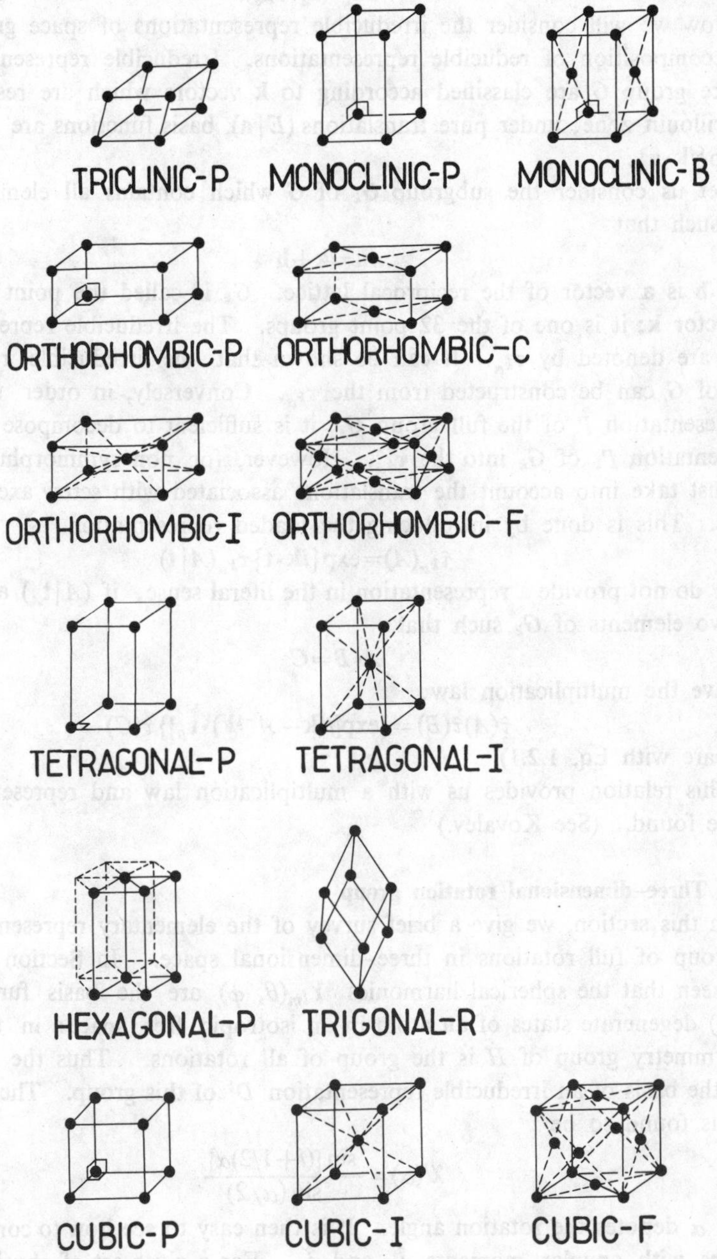

Fig. 1.2.2
The 14 Bravais lattices.

$$\mathbf{b}_1=2\pi\frac{\mathbf{a}_2\times\mathbf{a}_3}{V},\quad \mathbf{b}_2=2\pi\frac{\mathbf{a}_3\times\mathbf{a}_1}{V},\quad \mathbf{b}_3=2\pi\frac{\mathbf{a}_1\times\mathbf{a}_2}{V}$$

with

$$V=\mathbf{a}_1\cdot(\mathbf{a}_2\times\mathbf{a}_3)$$

Now we will consider the irreducible representations of space groups and the decomposition of reducible representations. Irreducible representations of a space group G are classified according to $\mathbf{k}$ vectors which are restricted to the Brillouin zone; under pure translations $(E\,|\,\mathbf{a})$, basis functions are multiplied by $\exp\{i\mathbf{k}\cdot\mathbf{a}\}$.

Let us consider the subgroup G_k of G which contains all elements $(A|\mathbf{t})$ of G such that

$$A\mathbf{k}=\mathbf{k}+\mathbf{b}$$

where $\mathbf{b}$ is a vector of the reciprocal lattice. G_k is called the point group of the vector $\mathbf{k}$; it is one of the 32 point groups. The irreducible representations of G_k are denoted by τ_{k_α}. It can be shown that the irreducible representations of G can be constructed from the τ_{k_α}. Conversely, in order to reduce a representation Γ of the full group G, it is sufficient to decompose the small representation Γ_k of G_k into the τ_{k_α}. However, for non-symmorphic groups, we must take into account the translations associated with screw axes or glide planes. This is done by introducing the loaded representation

$$\hat{\tau}_{k_\alpha}(A)=\exp\{i\mathbf{k}\cdot\mathbf{t}\}\tau_{k_\alpha}(A\,|\,\mathbf{t}) \tag{1.2.17}$$

The $\hat{\tau}$ do not provide a representation in the literal sense; if $(A\,|\,\mathbf{t}_A)$ and $(B\,|\,\mathbf{t}_B)$ are two elements of G_k such that

$$A\cdot B=C$$

we have the multiplication law:

$$\hat{\tau}(A)\hat{\tau}(B)=\{\exp[i(\mathbf{k}-A^{-1}\mathbf{k})\cdot\mathbf{t}_B]\}\hat{\tau}(C) \tag{1.2.18}$$

(compare with Eq. 1.2.1)

This relation provides us with a multiplication law and representations $\hat{\tau}$ can be found. (See Kovalev.)

1.2.4 Three-dimensional rotation group

In this section, we give a brief survey of the elementary representations of the group of full rotations in three-dimensional space. In Section 1.1.3, we have seen that the spherical harmonics $Y_{lm}(\theta, \phi)$ are the basis functions of $(2l+1)$ degenerate states of an atom in an isotropic free space: in that case, the symmetry group of $\hat{H}$ is the group of all rotations. Thus the $Y_{lm}(\theta, \phi)$ form the basis of an irreducible representation D^l of this group. The character $\chi^l(\alpha)$ is found to be

$$\chi^l(\alpha)=\frac{\sin[(l+1/2)\alpha]}{\sin(\alpha/2)} \tag{1.2.19}$$

where α denotes the rotation angle. It is then easy to see how to combine two systems with angular momenta $\hat{j}_1$ and $\hat{j}_2$. For a given set of physical values j_1 and j_2, the total system is in a $(2j_1+1)\,(2j_2+1)$ degenerate state. As long as the total system is isotropic, the total angular momentum $\hat{J}=\hat{j}_1+\hat{j}_2$ is conserved. The following question arises: what are the possible values of J for given values of j_1 and j_2? The representation associated with the total system is the direct product of D^{j_1} and D^{j_2}

$$\Delta(\alpha)=D^{j_1}(\alpha)\otimes D^{j_2}(\alpha)$$

Δ must be decomposed using the character relations. We find

$$\chi^{j_1}(\alpha)\chi^{j_2}(\alpha)=\sum_{J=|j_1-j_2|}^{j_1+j_2}\chi^J(\alpha)$$

that is

$$D^{j_1}(\alpha)\otimes D^{j_2}(\alpha)=D^{j_1+j_2}(\alpha)+D^{j_1+j_2-1}(\alpha)+\cdots+D^{|j_1-j_2|}(\alpha) \qquad (1.2.20)$$

We have confirmed the vector model rule which states that total angular momentum can take many integrally spaced values between $|j_1-j_2|$ and j_1+j_2.

1.2.5 Application to quantum mechanics

We now turn back to the quantum mechanical problem. As we have mentioned earlier, if we consider an energy level E which is l_n degenerate, the l_n eigenfunctions form an invariant subspace: they induce an irreducible representation; the associated wave functions form the basis of the representation. As a consequence, if the symmetry group of the Hamiltonian is known, we can work out the number and degeneracy of irreducible representations, which in turn give us all the possible degeneracies and symmetries of the eigenstates E_n.

Furthermore, let us consider an unperturbed Hamiltonian $\hat{H}_0$ which is invariant under G_0; we then apply a perturbation $\hat{V}$ invariant under G: since G is less symmetric than G_0, a given energy level $E_{0,n}$ may split into new levels whose separation will be given by perturbation theory, see (1.1.30). Group theory can tell us how it may split. The eigenfunctions associated with $E_{0,n}$ give an irreducible representation Γ_0^n of G. But Γ_0^n is no longer an irreducible representation of G_0: it is reducible and decomposes into irreducible representations of G. This decomposition can be easily worked out using character tables; it tells us the number and degeneracies of the energy levels that arise from $E_{0,n}$ when turning on the perturbation $\hat{V}$. Many examples will be given in the course of these lectures

On the other hand, we may have to evaluate matrix elements such as

$$V_{jj'}^{KK'}=\langle\psi_{K'}^{(j')}|\hat{V}|\psi_K^{(j)}\rangle$$

$\psi_K^{(j)}$ is the K-th basis function of the Γ^j irreducible representation. Having determined the representation Γ^v according to which $\hat{V}$ transforms, and using the basis function orthogonality, we can say that the matrix element $V_{jj'}^{KK'}$, is zero unless the representation $\Gamma^{j'*}$ is found in the decomposition of the direct product $\Gamma^v\otimes\Gamma^j$. If F^v is the basis function of Γ^v, then for a given set (j', j) the matrix elements of $\hat{V}$ are proportional to those of F^v.

1.3 QUANTUM MECHANICS OF ATOMS

Now we turn to calculations of properties of atoms. To begin with, we develop the study of hydrogen-like atoms and then we will present an elementary review of atomic structures.

1.3.1 Hydrogen-like atoms

We assume that the nucleus is at rest and has a charge $+Ze$. The Schrödinger equation that describes the motion of the electron around the nucleus is then written as:

$$\hat{\Delta}\psi+\frac{2m}{\hbar^2}\left(E+\frac{Ze^2}{r}\right)\psi=0 \tag{1.3.1}$$

This Hamiltonian has spherical symmetry. This means that energy levels induce irreducible representations of the symmetry group whose basis functions are the $Y_{lm}(\theta, \phi)$. We thus seek solutions of (1.3.1) in the form

$$\psi(r, \theta, \varphi)=R(r)Y_l^m(\theta, \varphi) \tag{1.3.2}$$

The Laplacian operator can be written as:

$$\hat{\Delta}\equiv-\frac{1}{r^2}\frac{\partial}{\partial r}\left(r^2\frac{\partial}{\partial r}\right)+\frac{\hat{l}^2}{r^2}$$

Since

$$\hat{l}^2Y_l^m(\theta, \varphi)=l(l+1)Y_l^m(\theta, \varphi)$$

the radial part $R(r)$ obeys the equation

$$\frac{d^2R}{dr^2}+\frac{2}{r}\frac{dR}{dr}-\frac{l(l+1)}{r^2}R+\frac{2m}{\hbar^2}\left(E+\frac{Ze^2}{r}\right)R=0 \tag{1.3.3}$$

We are seeking solutions corresponding to stable states with negative values of the energy E. In that case, solutions to (1.3.3) are given using the generalised Laguerre polynomials:

$$R_{nl}(r)=\text{const}\,\rho^l e^{-\rho/2}L_{n+l}^{2l+1}(\rho)$$

with

$$\rho=\frac{2Zme^2}{n\hbar^2}r=\frac{2Z\,r}{n\,a_0},\quad a_0=0.53\,\text{Å}$$

$$E_n=-\frac{mZ^2e^4}{2\hbar^2n^2} \tag{1.3.4}$$

We have thus determined the eigenfunction and the eigenvalues of $\hat{H}$. As we can see, the energy is given by the principal quantum number n. For a given n, l can take the values $0, 1 \cdots n-1$. This extra degeneracy is called accidental degeneracy; it is not predicted by the spatial symmetry arguments discussed previously. For a given l, m can have $2l+1$ values. The total degeneracy of E_n is

$$\sum_{l=0}^{n-1}(2l+1)=n^2$$

Electrons have spin 1/2. Thus the state of one electron in the hydrogen-like atom is described by the wave function

$$\psi_{n,l,m,s}(\mathbf{r})=R_{nl}(r)Y_l^m(\theta,\varphi)\chi_s \tag{1.3.5}$$

Such a state is $2n^2$-fold degenerate; when one electron is in one of these states, $\hat{H}$ takes the value E_n; $\hat{l}^2$ and $\hat{l}_z$ have the values $l(l+1)$ and m, respectively; $\hat{s}_z$ is given by χ_s $(\pm 1/2)$.

1.3.2 Elementary atomic structure

We have shown the wave functions describing a system of Fermions (particles with half-integral spin) must be totally antisymmetric with respect to particle interchange. In particular, this means that no two electrons can be in the same quantum state at the same time (Pauli principle). The lowest energy in the hydrogen-like atom corresponds to $n=1$; thus $l=0$ and we can have only 2 electrons (due to the 2 possible spin states $\pm 1/2$). This gives the $1s^2$ configuration. Going to $n=2$ levels, we can have $l=0$ and $l=1$ with twofold and sixfold degeneracy, respectively. We have the $1s^2\ 2s^2\ 2p^6$ configuration. All these shells are closed; they have a spherical symmetry and they are characterised by zero orbital angular momentum and zero spin.

Let us look at the ground state of silicon with $Z=14$ electrons. The ground state configuration is $1s^2\ 2s^2\ 2p^6\ 3s^2\ 3p^2$. This is obtained by assuming that there is no interaction between electrons. But correlations and electrostatic interactions will split the configuration energy levels and give rise to different terms. In the case of silicon, the closed shells $1s^2$, $2s^2$, $2p^6$ and $3s^2$ would not be affected; let us concentrate on the half-filled shell $3p^2$. According to Section 1.2.4, the two electron momenta would combine as

$$D^1 \otimes D^1 = D^0 + D^1 + D^2 \qquad (\mathrm{S, P, D})$$
$$D^{1/2} \otimes D^{1/2} = D^0 + D^1 \qquad (S=0,\ S=1)$$

The possible terms are ^{1}S, ^{1}P, ^{1}D, ^{3}S, ^{3}P, ^{3}D. However, ^{3}D, ^{3}S, ^{1}P are forbidden by the Pauli exclusion principle. We are thus left with the ^{3}P, ^{1}D and ^{1}S terms.

Separation between terms is $\sim 10^5$K. The ground state determination is worked out with the help of Hund's rules:

(1) S has the maximum value consistent with the Pauli principle.

(2) L has the maximum value consistent with the Pauli principle and rule 1. In the case of silicon, the ground state is the ^{3}P state, whose multiplicity is $(2L+1)\times(2S+1)=9$.

It is noteworthy that rule (1) arises from the antisymmetry of the wave function: each electron belongs to a different wave function and the repulsive electrostatic repulsion energy is thus lowered (see exchange as discussed in Section 1.1.8).

In Table 1.3.1, we give a few examples of possible terms for configurations of

Table 1.3.1
Possible terms for configurations of equivalent electrons

p, p^5	^{2}P		
p^2, p^4	^{1}SD	^{3}P	
p^3	^{2}PD	^{4}S	
d, d^9	^{2}D		
d^2, d^8	^{1}SDG	^{3}PF	
d^3, d^7	^{2}PDFGH	^{4}PF	
d^4, d^6	^{1}SDFGI	^{3}PDFGH	^{5}D
d^5	^{2}SPDFGHI	^{4}PDFG	^{6}S

equivalent atoms (with the same n and l quantum numbers). It can be seen that the absence of an electron can be regarded as a hole with the same quantum numbers as the missing electron.

The wave functions and energies $E(n, L, S)$ of different terms are calculated using self-consistent methods (Hartree-Fock). These eigenfunctions and eigenvalues are taken as starting points for introducing coupling between spin and angular momentum; this is a relativistic interaction. It can be written as

$$\hat{H}_{s,o}=A(L, S)\hat{L}\cdot\hat{S} \tag{1.3.6}$$

where $A(L, S)$ depends on the term L, S (Russell saunders coupling). Thus the total Hamiltonian is still invariant under rotations: the total angular momentum $\hat{J}=\hat{L}+\hat{S}$ is then a good quantum number. We have

$$2\hat{L}\cdot\hat{S}=\hat{J}^2-\hat{L}^2-\hat{S}^2 \tag{1.3.7}$$

The order of magnitude of A is 10^2—10^4K. It varies roughly as Z^4. But even in the case of the heaviest atoms, the spin-orbit coupling is not stronger than the electrostatic interactions.

We use the $\psi(n, L, S, J, m_J)$ as a basis; in that basis the perturbation (1.3.7) is diagonal; thus the perturbed energy levels are given by:

$$E(n, L, S, J, m_J)=E(n,L,S)+\frac{A}{2}\Big[J(J+1)-L(L+1)-S(S+1)\Big] \tag{1.3.8}$$

where n, L, S, J, m_J denotes the set of quantum numbers describing the new quantum states.

The interval between adjacent fine levels is

$$\Delta E=AJ \tag{1.3.9}$$

which is the Landé interval rule.

The ground state multiplet is such that $J=|L-S|$ if the shell is less than half full ($A>0$); but $J=L+S$ otherwise ($A<0$). A multiplet is then characterised by the values of L, S and J: for example ${}^4F_{3/2}$, $L=3$, $2S+1=4$, $J=3/2$.

In Table 1.3.2, we give the electron configuration and ground state multiplet for elements of the principal groups.

The other groups are called intermediate groups. We observe competition

Table 1.3.2
Electron configurations of the atoms of elements in the principal groups

$n=2$	^{3}Li	^{4}Be	^{5}B	^{6}C	^{7}N	^{8}O	^{9}F	^{10}Ne	$1s^2$
3	^{11}Na	^{12}Mg	^{13}Al	^{14}Si	^{15}P	^{16}S	^{17}Cl	^{18}Ar	$2s^2\,2p^6$
4	^{19}K	^{20}Ca							$3s^2\,3p^6$
4	^{29}Cu	^{30}Zn	^{31}Ga	^{32}Ge	^{33}As	^{34}Se	^{35}Br	^{36}Kr	$3d^{10}$
5	^{37}Rb	^{38}Sr							$4s^2\,4p^6$
5	^{47}Ag	^{48}Cd	^{49}In	^{50}Sn	^{51}Sb	^{52}Te	^{53}I	^{54}Xe	$4d^{10}$
6	^{55}Cs	^{56}Ba							$5s^2\,5p^6$
6	^{79}Au	^{80}Hg	^{81}Tl	^{82}Pb	^{83}Bi	^{84}Po	^{85}At	^{86}Rn	$4f^{14}5d^{10}$
7	^{87}Fr	^{88}Ra							$6s^2\,6p^4$
	$^2S_{1/2}$	$^1S_0$	$^2P_{1/2}$	$^3P_0$	$^4S_{3/2}$	$^3P_2$	$^3P_{3/2}$	$^1S_0$	

Table 1.3.3
Electron configurations of the atoms of elements in the iron group

	^{21}Sc	^{22}Ti	^{23}V	^{24}Cr	^{25}Mn	^{26}Fe	^{27}Co	^{28}Ni
Ar envelope+	$3d\,4s^2$ $^2D_{3/2}$	$3d^2\,4s^2$ $^3F_2$	$3d^3\,4s^2$ $^4F_{3/2}$	$3d^4\,4s^2$ $^7S_3$	$3d^5\,4s^2$ $^6S_{5/2}$	$3d^6\,4s^2$ $^5D_4$	$3d^7\,4s^2$ $^4F_{9/2}$	$3d^8\,4s^2$ $^3F_4$

between the *s* and *d* states when filling up the 3*d* (iron group), 4*d* and 5*d* shells (Table 1.3.3). Also the filling of the 4*f* shell is irregular due to competition between 4*f*, 5*d* and 6*s* states (Table 1.3.4).

Two series of elements play a fundamental role in the study of magnetism: the iron group (3*d*) and the rare earths (4*f*).

They are important because the half-filled shells are not the outer shells. In other compounds, these outer shells can be filled by bonding or giving electrons

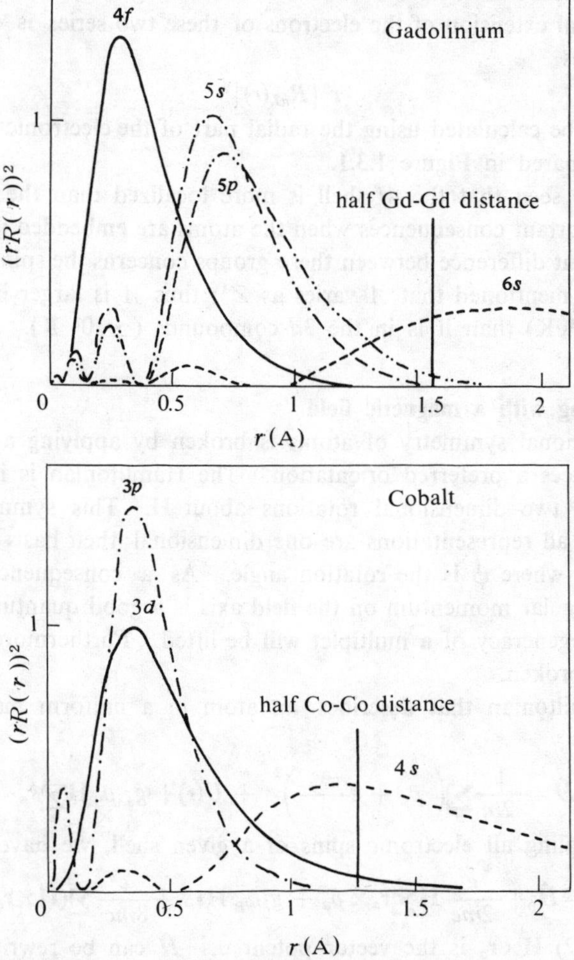

Fig. 1.3.1

Table 1.3.4
Electron configurations of the atoms of the rare-earth elements

	^{58}Ce	^{59}Pr	^{60}Nd	^{61}Pm	^{62}Sm	^{63}Eu	^{64}Gd
Xe envelope +	$4f^2\ 6s^2$	$4f^3\ 6s^2$	$4f^4\ 6s^2$	$4f^5\ 6s^2$	$4f^6\ 6s^2$	$4f^7\ 6s^2$	$4f^7\ 5d6s^2$
	$^3H_4$	$^4I_{9/2}$	$^5I_4$	$^6H_{5/2}$	^7F	$^8S_{1/2}$	$^9D_2$
	^{65}Tb	^{66}Dy	^{67}Ho	^{68}Er	^{69}Tm	^{70}Yb	
Xe envelope +	$4f^8\ 5d6s^2$	$4f^{10}\ 6s^2$	$4f^{11}\ 6s^2$	$4f^{12}\ 6s^2$	$4f^{13}\ 6s^2$	$4f^{14}\ 6s^2$	
	$^8H_{17/2}$	$^5I_8$	$^4I_{15/2}$	$^3H_6$	$^2F_{7/2}$	$^1S_0$	

to the conduction bands, but closed shells are not magnetic, as will be seen later.

The spatial extension of the electrons of these two series is different. The radial densities

$$r^2 |R_{nL}(r)|^2$$

see (1.1), can be calculated using the radial part of the electronic wave function; they are compared in Figure 1.3.1.

It can be seen that the $4f$ shell is more localized than the $3d$ shell, which will have important consequences when the atoms are embedded in a solid. The other important difference between these groups concerns the spin-orbit coupling Λ. We have mentioned that Λ varies as Z^4; thus Λ is larger in the $4f$ compounds ($\simeq 10^4$ K) than it is in the $3d$ compounds ($\simeq 10^2$ K).

1.3.3 Coupling with a magnetic field

The rotational symmetry of atoms is broken by applying a magnetic field **H**: **H** introduces a preferred orientation. The Hamiltonian is invariant under the group of two-dimensional rotations about **H**. This symmetry group is Abelian, then all representations are one dimensional; their basis functions have the form $e^{im\phi}$ where ϕ is the rotation angle. As a consequence, the projection of the angular momentum on the field axis is a good quantum number, but the $(2J+1)$ degeneracy of a multiplet will be lifted. Furthermore, time reversal symmetry is broken.

The Hamiltonian that describes an atom in a uniform magnetic field is written as:

$$\hat{H} = \frac{1}{2m} \sum_a \left(\hat{p}_a + e \frac{\mathbf{A}_a}{c} \right)^2 + U(\mathbf{r}) + g_s\, \mu_B \mathbf{H} \sum_a \hat{s}_a \tag{1.3.10}$$

Thus, by coupling all electronic spins of a given shell, we have

$$\hat{H} = \hat{H}_0 + \frac{e}{2mc} \mathbf{H} \sum_a \mathbf{r}_a \times \hat{p}_a + g_s \mu_B\, \mathbf{H} \cdot \hat{s} + \frac{e^2}{8mc^2} \sum_a (\mathbf{H} \times \mathbf{r}_a)^2 \tag{1.3.11}$$

where $\mathbf{A}_a$: $(1/2)\, \mathbf{H} \times \mathbf{r}_a$ is the vector potential. $\hat{H}$ can be rewritten in terms of $\hat{L}$ and $\hat{S}$:

$$\hat{H}=\hat{H}_0+\mu_B(\hat{L}+g_s\hat{S})\mathbf{H}+\frac{e^2}{8mc^2}\sum_a(\mathbf{H}\times\mathbf{r}_a)^2 \tag{1.3.12}$$

where $\hat{H}_0$ is the free-atom Hamiltonian.

The operator $\hat{\mu}_{at}=-\mu_B(\hat{L}+g_s\hat{S})$ is the operator of the intrinsic magnetic moment of the atom. μ_B is the Bohr magneton $\mu_B=eh/2mc$ and g_s is the anomalous g-value of the electron spin ($g_s\simeq 2.0023$). If $L=0$, $S=0$, there is no magnetic moment.

If the applied field is small, we can apply perturbation theory to investigate the lifting of multiplet degeneracy. The strong field limit (Paschen–Back effect) will be investigated later. To first order in H, we have to evaluate matrix elements of $\hat{L}$ and $\hat{S}$ in the basis $|Jm_J\rangle$ where J is diagonal, see (1.1.31). We have:

$$\langle Jm_J'|\hat{L}|Jm_J\rangle=(1-\alpha)\langle Jm_J'|\hat{J}|Jm_J\rangle$$
$$\langle Jm'_J|\hat{S}|Jm_J\rangle=\alpha\langle Jm_J'|\hat{J}|Jm_J\rangle$$

It can be shown that:

$$\alpha=\frac{J(J+1)+S(S+1)-L(L+1)}{2J(J+1)}$$

The matrix elements of the perturbation $-\hat{\mu}_{at}\,\mathbf{H}$ are diagonal in the unperturbed basis $|Jm_J\rangle$, in agreement with the group theory argument (J, m_J are good quantum numbers).

The perturbed energies are:

$$E_{J,m_J}=E_J^0-g_J\mu_B m_J H$$
$$g_J=(1-\alpha)+g_s\alpha \tag{1.3.13}$$

If we set $g_s=2$, then

$$g_J=1+\frac{J(J+1)+S(S+1)-L(L+1)}{2J(J+1)} \tag{1.3.14}$$

which is the Landé g-factor.

We can see that, according to Kramers theorem, the degeneracy of the multiplet is completely removed. The amplitude of the splitting is proportional to the applied field H.

According to (1.3.13) an atom in the state (J, m_J) possesses a mean magnetic moment $-\mu_B g_J m_J$. But, at a given temperature T, the actual magnetic moment is given by

$$\bar{\mu}_{at}=-\frac{\partial E_T}{\partial H}$$

where E_T is the average value of the energy at the temperature T. Applying Boltzmann statistics, we get

$$E_T=\sum_{m_J=-J}^{+J}\frac{E_{J,m_J}\exp(-\beta E_{J,m_J})}{\sum\exp(-\beta E_{J,m_J})} \tag{1.3.15}$$

$$E_T=E_J^0-g_J\mu_B H\frac{\sum m_J\exp(-Xm_J)}{\sum\exp(-Xm_J)},\quad X=\frac{g_J\mu_B H}{kT}$$

The second term in E_T, is the Brillouin function $\mathscr{B}_J$.

$$E_T=E_J^0-g_J\mu_B H\mathscr{B}_J(X)\quad\text{and}\quad \bar{\mu}_{at}=g_J\mu_B\mathscr{B}_J(X)$$

When X is small,

$$\mathscr{B}_J(X) \sim \frac{J(J+1)}{3} X$$

Then the energy is given by

$$E_T = E_J^0 - g_J^2 \mu_B^2 H^2 \frac{J(J+1)}{3kT}$$

and the magnetic moment $\bar{\mu}$:

$$\bar{\mu}_{at} = \frac{J(J+1)}{3kT} g_J^2 \mu_B^2 H$$

The paramagnetic susceptibility, $\chi(T) = \frac{\partial \bar{\mu}}{\partial H}$, follows a Curie law:

$$\chi(T) = g^2 \mu_B^2 \frac{J(J+1)}{3kT} \tag{1.3.16}$$

However, when $S=0$ and $L=0$ (closed shell) the magnetic moment vanishes. The only contribution arises from the term in H^2 of the Hamiltonian (1.3.12). It is a shift in energy:

$$\Delta E = \frac{e^2}{8mc^2} \sum_a \overline{(\mathbf{H} \times \mathbf{r}_a)^2} = \frac{e^2}{12mc^2} H^2 \sum_a \overline{\mathbf{r}_a^2} \tag{1.3.17}$$

The magnetic moment is defined as

$$\mu = -\frac{\partial \Delta E}{\partial H} = -\frac{e^2}{6mc^2} \sum_a \overline{\mathbf{r}_a^2} \cdot H \tag{1.3.18}$$

The magnetic susceptibility $\chi = \mu / H$ is negative and temperature independent. An atom with $L=S=0$ is diamagnetic.

REFERENCES

G. BURNS, Introduction to Group Theory with Applications, Academic Press, New York(1977).

E.U. CONDON, G.H. SHORTLEY, The Theory of Atomic Spectra, Cambridge University Press, Cambridge (1935).

A. HERPIN, Théorie du Magnétisme, Presses Universitaires de France, Paris (1968).

O.V. KOVALEV, Irreducible Representations of the Space Groups, Gordon and Breach, New York (1965).

L.D. LANDAU, E.M. LIFSHITZ, Quantum Mechanics, Pergamon Press, Oxford.

M. TINKHAM, Group Theory and Quantum Mechanics, McGraw-Hill, New York (1964).

J.H. VAN VLECK, The Theory of Electric and Magnetic Susceptibility, Oxford University Press, Oxford (1932).

CHAPTER 2

MAGNETIZATION AND SUSCEPTIBILITY MEASUREMENTS

2.1 DESCRIPTION OF A MAGNETIZATION MEASUREMENT EXPERIMENT BY AXIAL EXTRACTION IN A CONTINUOUS INTENSE MAGNETIC FIELD

2.1.1 Principle of the experiment

The magnetization is measured by axial extraction of the sample. The sample is pulled along the axis of the coil which produces the field **H** (Fig. 2.1.1), from a position 1 to a position 2. The applied field **H** and thus the magnetization **M** are assumed to be equal in the two positions. Let us assume that the sample is in any position whatever called z. Then the induction due only to the sample (because it is always possible to separate the total induction in to an external part and a sample part, the external part being independent of the sample position) gives rise to a flux in the "pick up coils" [measuring coil system (C)] which can be written as:

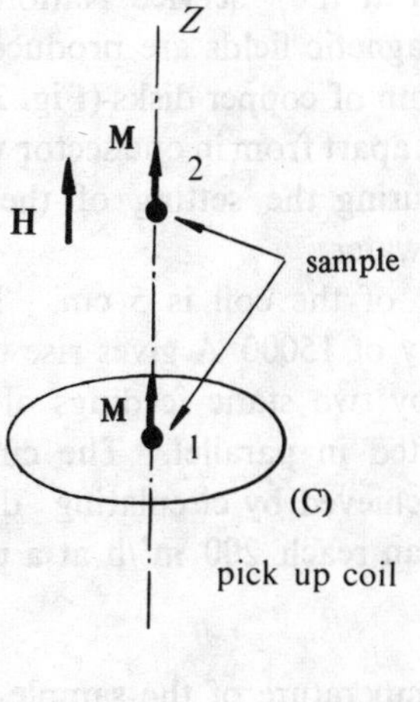

Fig. 2.1.1
Principle of the axial extraction.

$$\Phi=\sum_{S}\mathbf{B}_m d\mathbf{S}$$

As at any point the induction $\mathbf{B}_m$ is proportional to the magnetization of the sample M, we have $\Phi=K(z)M$, where $K(z)$ is a function of the position along the axis of the pick up coils. The shape of this function is drawn in Fig. 2.1.2. When the sample is moved from 1 to 2 the flux variation is:

$$\Delta\Phi=[K(z_2)-K(z_1)]\cdot M$$

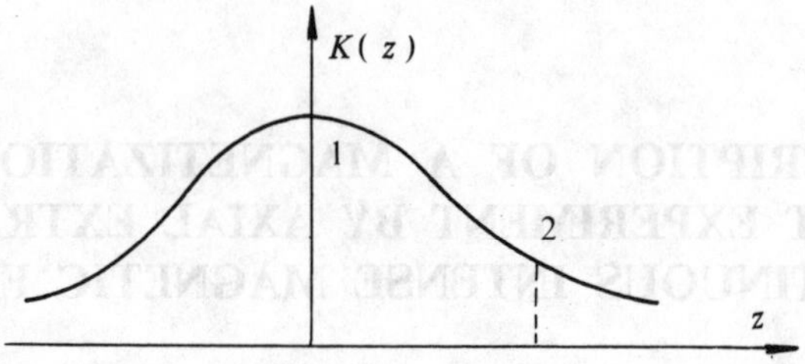

Fig. 2.1.2
Schematic variation of $K(z)$

This flux variation, which is proportional to the magnetization, is directly measured using an electronic integrator. (In some devices the sample is moved into a region where the field H is zero and far enough from the pick up coils. Then the flux due to the sample is zero in position 2 and $\Delta\Phi$ remains proportional to the magnetization).

2.1.2 The applied magnetic field (Fig. 2.1.3)

In the experiment used at the "Service National des Champs Intenses" of Grenoble, the continuous magnetic fields are produced by means of a Bitter coil. The coil is formed by a column of copper disks (Fig. 2.1.4), each cut along a radius and isolated from each other apart from in one sector where the disks are connected in series; holes are drilled during the setting of the disks in order to provide circulation of the cooling water.

The available diameter of the coil is 5 cm. The supply voltage is about 330 V; a maximum intensity of 15000 A gives rise to a field of 15 Tesla. The electric power is supplied by two static feedings of 2.5 MW each, i.e. 7500 A 330 V, which are connected in parallel. The current stability is $\pm 5\times 10^{-6}$. The cooling of the coil is achieved by circulating deionized and demineralized water, the flow of which can reach 200 m^3/h at a pressure of 25 bars.

2.1.3 The temperature

In order to vary the temperature of the sample between 1.3 K and 300 K, one uses a cryostat filled with liquid helium. The sample, the diameter of which can reach 6 mm, is in contact with a capsule where there are two thermoprobes,

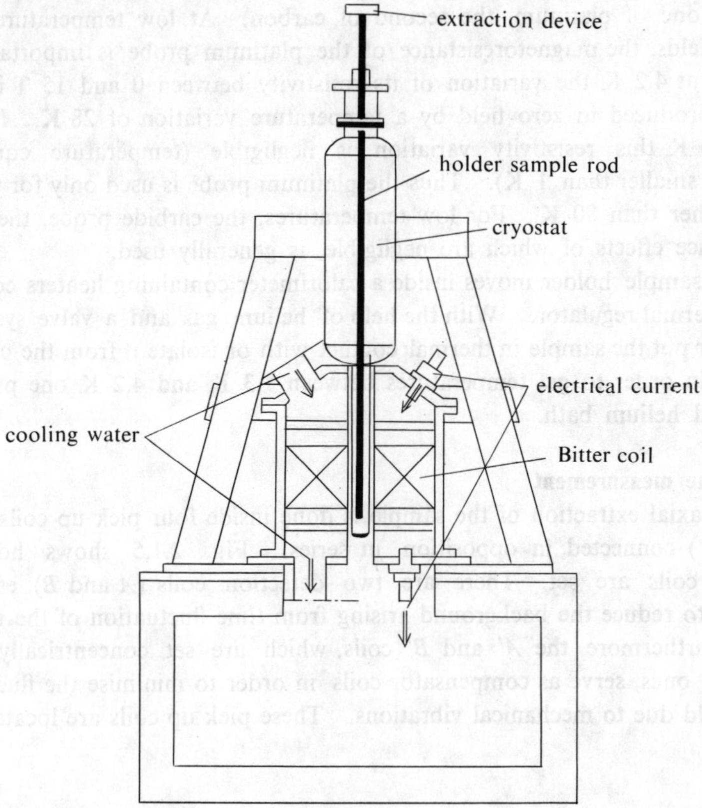

Fig. 2.1.3
Magnetization experiment in intense fields.

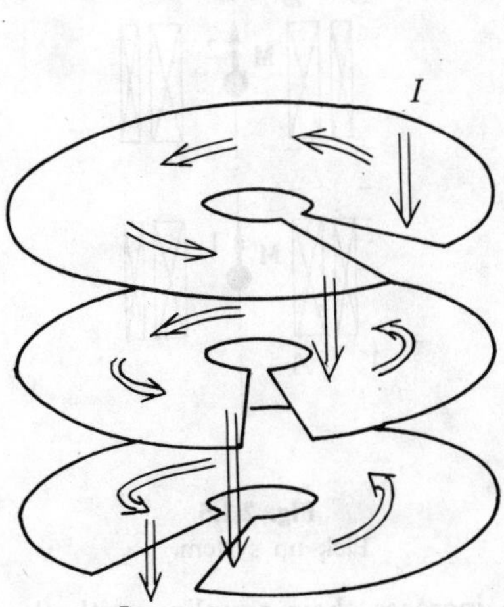

Fig. 2.1.4
Connection of the copper disks; circulation of the electric current *I*.

the first one of platinum, the second of carbon. At low temperatures and in intense fields, the magnetoresistance of the platinum probe is important. For instance, at 4.2 K the variation of its resistivity between 0 and 15 T is similar to that produced in zero field by a temperature variation of 28 K. However, above 80 K this resistivity variation is negligible (temperature equivalence variation smaller than 1 K). Thus the platinum probe is used only for temperatures higher than 80 K. For low temperatures, the carbide probe, the magnetoresistance effects of which are negligible, is generally used.

The sample holder moves inside a calorimeter containing heaters connected with a thermal regulator. With the help of helium gas and a valve system one can either put the sample in thermal contact with or isolate it from the cryogenic liquid. In order to get temperatures between 1.3 K and 4.2 K one pumps on the liquid helium bath.

2.1.4 The measurement

The axial extraction of the sample is done inside four pick up coils (*A*, *A'*, *B* and *B'*) connected in opposition in series. Fig. 2.1.5 shows how these pick up coils are set. There are two detection coils (*A* and *B*), essentially in order to reduce the background arising from time fluctuation of the magnetic field. Furthermore the *A'* and *B'* coils, which are set concentrically to the *A* and *B* ones, serve as compensator coils in order to minimise the fluctuations of the field due to mechanical vibrations. These pick up coils are located inside

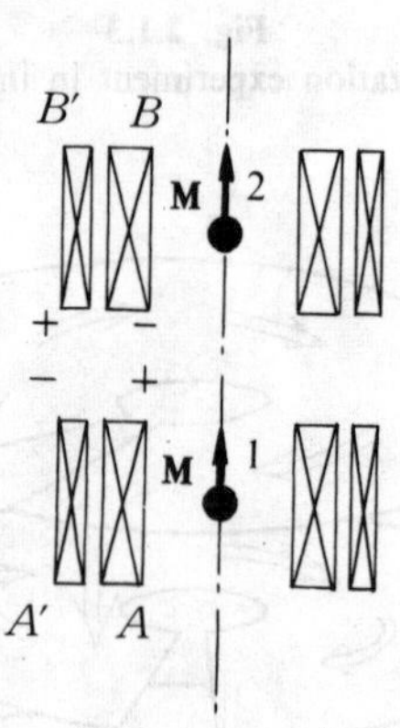

Fig. 2.1.5
Pick up system.

the cryostat in order to increase their coupling with the sample and to lower the spurious induced electronic structure. The available diameter in the pick up coils is 12 mm. The extraction length is 20 mm. In the positions 1 and

2 the magnetic field is then the same. The signal induced in the pick up coils is measured by using an electronic integrator. The sensitiveness of the system is 10^{-2} e.m.u.

The experiment allows the isothermal field dependence of magnetization of polycrystalline and single crystal samples to be plotted for temperatures between 1.3 K and 300 K and in fields up to 15 T. As an example, the field dependences of the magnetization of a single crystal of $HoNi_5$ at 4.2 K are reported in Fig. 2.1.6.

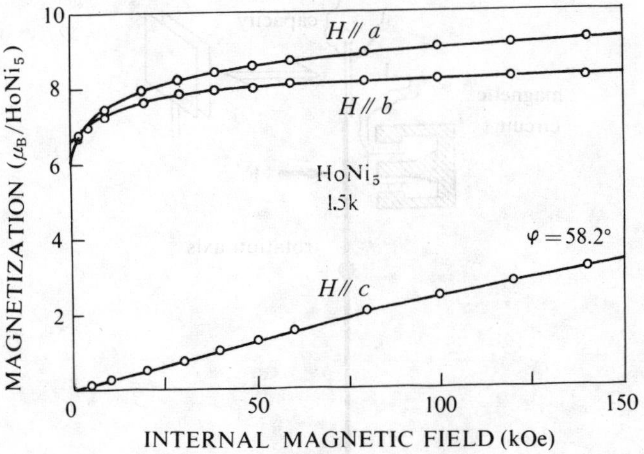

Fig. 2.1.6

$HoNi_5$: Magnetization versus magnetic field along the *a*, *b* and *c* axes of the ortho-hexagonal cell of the hexagonal structure at 4.2 K.

2.2 MAGNETIC SUSCEPTIBILITY MEASUREMENTS: A TRANSLATION BALANCE

2.2.1 Principle of the experiment

This experiment is used for the measurement of paramagnetic susceptibilities below room temperature (between 1.5 K and 300 K).

In a field **H**, the magnetic energy of a sample with magnetization **M** can be written:

$$E = -\int_0^M \mathbf{H} d\mathbf{M}$$

In the case of a paramagnetic compound of volume V:

$E = -\frac{V\mathbf{H}[\chi]\mathbf{H}}{2}$, where $[\chi]$ is the susceptibility tensor. In the case of a polycrystalline sample or of a single crystal with a symmetry axis parallel to the field, $[\chi]$ is diagonal, **M** is parallel to **H**, and the sample is subjected to a force **F** parallel to the gradient of **H**:

$$E = \frac{V\chi H^2}{2} \text{ and } \mathbf{F} = -\nabla E = \frac{V\chi\nabla H^2}{2}$$

The force acting on the sample is measured with the help of a balance. The translation balance built up in the "Laboratoire Louis Néel" is schematized in Fig. 2.2.1. The bar of the balance can rotate around an axis without friction.

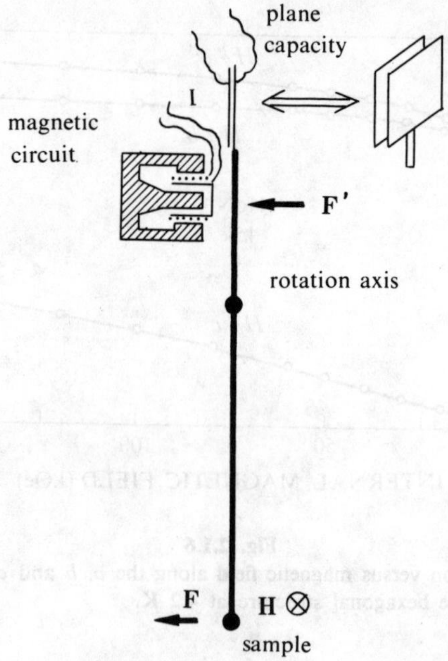

Fig 2.2.1
Principle of the translation balance.

The sample is fixed to one end of the bar and the force **F** is balanced by a counter force **F′** produced by a direct current passing through a coil set in a magnetic circuit.

2.2.2 The magnetic field

The magnetic field is produced by an electromagnet (Fig. 2.2.2) the pole face shape of which gives rise to a horizontal field gradient. The field gradient is maximum and constant in an available region of 15 mm [$H\frac{\partial H}{\partial x} = 7.5$ kOe²/cm (Fig. 2.2.3)]. The diameter of the sample being around 5 mm, the calibration of the apparatus is not modified by small modifications of the position of the sample from one experiment to another. The applied field can reach 8 kOe. The electromagnet can be removed far from the sample in order to take the zero-point reading of each measurement.

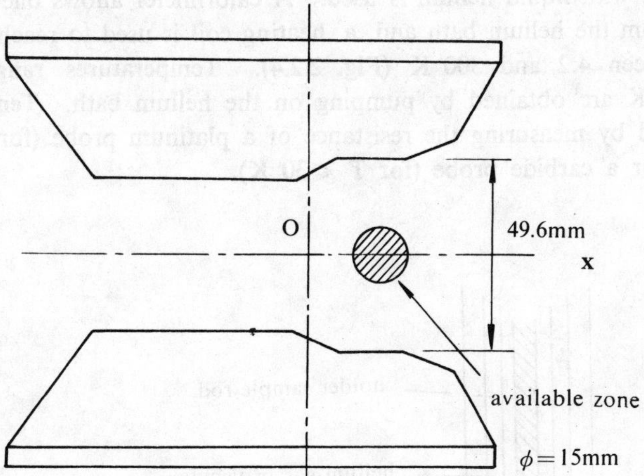

Fig. 2.2.2
Pole face shape of the electromagnet.

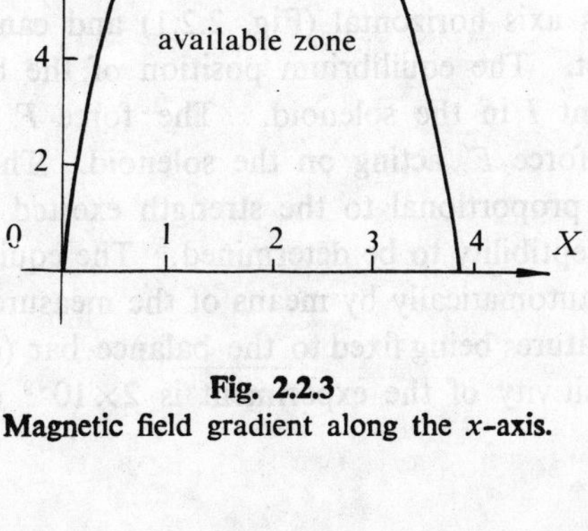

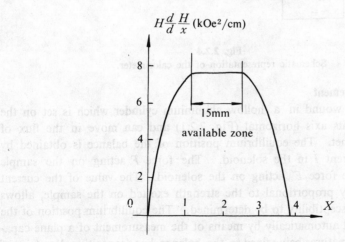

Fig. 2.2.3
Magnetic field gradient along the *x*-axis.

2.2.3 The temperature

In this experiment, measurements are performed below room temperature and a cryostat with liquid helium is used. A calorimeter allows one to isolate the sample from the helium bath and a heating coil is used to reach any temperature between 4.2 and 300 K (Fig. 2.2.4). Temperatures ranging from 1.6 K to 4.2 K are obtained by pumping on the helium bath. Temperatures are determined by measuring the resistance of a platinum probe (for 30 K $\leqslant$ T $\leqslant$300 K) or a carbide probe (for T $\leqslant$30 K).

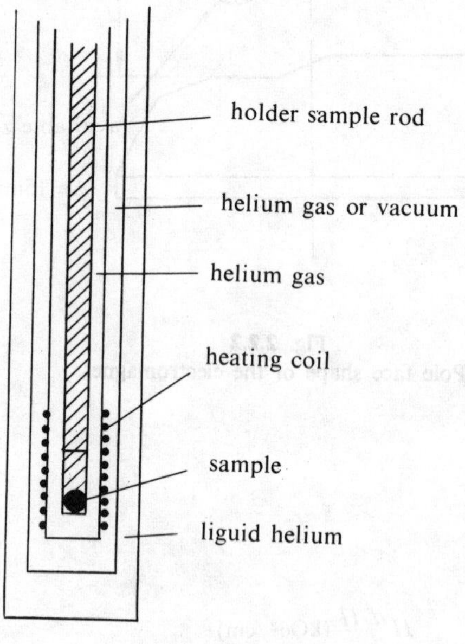

Fig. 2.2.4
Schematic representation of the calorimeter.

2.2.4 The measurement

A solenoid is wound in a hollow aluminium cylinder which is set on the balance bar with its axis horizontal (Fig. 2.2.1) and can move in the flux of a permanent magnet. The equilibrium position of the balance is obtained by adjusting the current I in the solenoid. The force F acting on the sample is balanced by the force F' acting on the solenoid. The value of the current I, which is directly proportional to the strength exerted on the sample, allows the value of its susceptibility to be determined. The equilibrium position of the balance is adjusted automatically by means of the measurement of a plane capacity, one of its armatures being fixed to the balance bar (capacitive detection of position). The sensitivity of the experiment is 2×10^{-9} e.m.u./Oe.

CHAPTER 3

THE MOLECULAR FIELD MODEL AND MAGNETIC ORDERING

It is well known that some materials become spontaneously magnetized at low temperatures because of interactions between the magnetic atoms. Such substances may be divided for convenience into five classes: ferromagnets, antiferromagnets, ferrimagnets, helimagnets and modulated structures.. As usual in such classifications the distinction occasionally becomes somewhat arbitrary. Ferromagnetic materials have been known since early history and are technologically important (see Chapter 16). Néel first proposed the concept of antiferromagnetism and of ferrimagnetism. Generalizations of these ideas led to the discovery of helimagnetism and modulated structures.

3.1 MAGNETIC COUPLING AND THE MOLECULAR FIELD APPROXIMATION

3.1.1 Exchange coupling

The correlations between two electrons lead to different energies for the parallel and antiparallel spin states. This is a result of the antisymmetry of the total wave function (this function is built from a Slater determinant). As has been seen, an antisymmetric spin state is associated with a symmetric orbital state and vice versa. The correlation effects which are of electrostatic origin lead to the splitting of energies of the antisymmetric and symmetric orbital states and hence of the symmetric (↑↑) and antisymmetric (↑↓) spin states. This is the case for all exchange interactions: direct exchange, indirect exchange (RKKY type) between $4f$ atoms, superexchange through a non-magnetic ion. In all cases the exchange interaction energy between two ions can be expressed as:

$$\mathscr{H}_{ij} = -2J_{ij}\mathbf{S}_i \cdot \mathbf{S}_j \tag{3.1.1}$$

In $3d$ based materials: $J_{ij} \simeq 10^2$ to 10^3 K. For indirect and superexchange interactions: $J_{ij} \simeq 10$ to 10^2 K. The interaction energy of the whole system will then be written:

$$\mathscr{H} = -\sum_{\substack{i,j \\ i \neq j}} J_{ij}\mathbf{S}_i \cdot \mathbf{S}_j \tag{3.1.2}$$

(the factor two disappears because the summations over i and j concern all the atoms).

For rare-earth atoms inside the same multiplet (see Chapter 1) we know that the atomic magnetic moment is:

$$\mathbf{m}=g_J\mu_B\mathbf{J}=g_J\mu_B(\mathbf{L}+\mathbf{S}) \tag{3.1.3}$$

and due to the fact that:

$$\mathbf{m}=\mu_B(2\mathbf{S}+\mathbf{L}) \tag{3.1.4}$$

we obtain:

$$\mathbf{m}=\frac{g_J\mu_B}{g_J-1}\mathbf{S} \tag{3.1.5}$$

For 3*d* transition atoms, where generally the orbital momentum **L** is almost quenched (see Chapter 8) and where the spin-orbit coupling is smaller than in 4*f* atoms:

$$\mathbf{m}=g\mu_B\mathbf{S} \tag{3.1.6}$$

where the Landé factor g is little dependent on the moment direction and almost equal to 2 (see Section 8.1.4). Generally speaking the interaction energy can be rewritten as:

$$\mathscr{H}=-\sum_{\substack{i,j\\ i\neq j}} n_{ij}\mathbf{m}_i\cdot\mathbf{m}_j=-\sum_i \mathbf{m}_i\sum_{j\neq i} n_{ij}\mathbf{m}_j \tag{3.1.7}$$

which becomes:

$$\mathscr{H}=-\sum_i \mathbf{m}_i\cdot\mathbf{H}_i \tag{3.1.8}$$

with

$$\mathbf{H}_i=\sum_{j\neq i} n_{ij}\mathbf{m}_j \tag{3.1.9}$$

$\mathbf{H}_i$ can be considered as a local molecular field. It is time fluctuating and depends on the instantaneous values of the considered magnetic moments $\mathbf{m}_j$. The assumption (inaccurate from the statistical point of view) which is the background of the mean field molecular theory, consists in neglecting the fluctuating character of the field $\mathbf{H}_i$. The average energy, which is exactly

$$\langle\mathscr{H}\rangle_T=\sum_i\langle\mathbf{m}_i\mathbf{H}_i\rangle_T \tag{3.1.10}$$

becomes then:

$$\langle\mathscr{H}\rangle_T=\sum_i\langle\mathbf{m}_i\rangle_T\langle\mathbf{H}_i\rangle_T \tag{3.1.11}$$

where $\langle\mathbf{H}_i\rangle_T$ is the molecular field $\mathbf{H}_m$, which is the same for all the equivalent atoms. We then obtain:

$$\mathbf{H}_m=\langle\mathbf{H}_i\rangle_T=\sum_{\substack{j\\ j\neq i}} n_{ij}\langle\mathbf{m}_j\rangle_T \tag{3.1.12}$$

This molecular field can also be written:

$$\mathbf{H}_m=W\mathbf{M} \tag{3.1.13}$$

where $\mathbf{M}=N\langle\mathbf{m}_j\rangle_T$ is the magnetization of the considered atoms per unit volume and N the number of these atoms per unit volume.

The energy of an infinitely small magnetization dM' in the molecular field is $-WM'dM'$. Thus, the total energy of a solid of magnetization M is:

$$-\int_0^M WM'dM'=-\frac{1}{2}WM^2 \tag{3.1.14}$$

J_{ij} is an exchange energy, it is expressed in energy units. n_{ij} is a local molecular;

field coefficient reduced to one atomic magnetic moment. If the energy is expressed per unit volume, because $\mathbf{m}_i\mathbf{m}_j$ has the dimensions of energy, n_{ij} corresponds to the inverse of a volume. W is a molecular field coefficient associated with a magnetization per unit volume; it is then a dimensionless quantity.

3.2 MOLECULAR FIELD MODEL OF ORDERED MAGNETIC SOLIDS

In this section we will briefly summarize the major features characterising the behaviour of ferro–, ferri–, antiferro–, heli– and modulated magnetic structures.

3.2.1 Ferromagnetism

(a) *The Langevin Law*

In ferromagnets the interactions between magnetic atoms favour a parallel alignment of the atomic magnetic moments. At T=0 K, the alignment is complete and the "spontaneous" magnetization M_s has its maximum possible value. As the temperature increases, the effects of kT which favour random orientations of the magnetic moments begin to be felt. M_s decreases with increasing T, gradually at first, and then more and more rapidly until it becomes zero at a characteristic temperature: the Curie temperature T_c (Fig. 3.2.1). It is clear

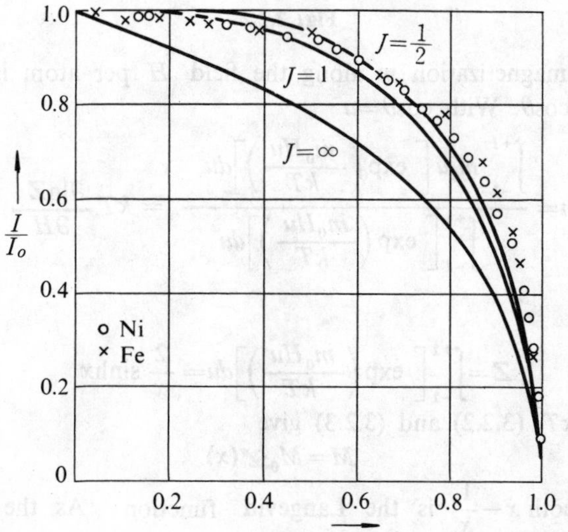

Fig. 3.2.1

that $\frac{3k}{2}T_c \simeq \frac{1}{2} WM^2$ (three degrees of freedom). Otherwise if a magnetic field H is applied, it tends to align the magnetic moments in its direction and $M(H)$ increases (if $T \neq 0$ in the classical theory).

The simplest and most naive representation of ferromagnetism uses the Langevin model; an atom, the moment $\mathbf{m}_0$ of which makes an angle θ with the applied magnetic field **H**, has a potential energy $-m_0 H \cos\theta$. Using the Boltzmann distribution, the proportion of magnetic moments whose direction is in the solid angle $d\Omega = 2\pi \sin\theta \, d\theta$ is

$$dN = \frac{\left[\exp\left(\frac{m_0 H \cos\theta}{kT}\right) 2\pi \sin\theta \, d\theta\right]}{\int_0^\pi \left[\exp\left(\frac{m_0 H \cos\theta}{kT}\right) 2\pi \sin\theta \, d\theta\right]} \tag{3.2.1}$$

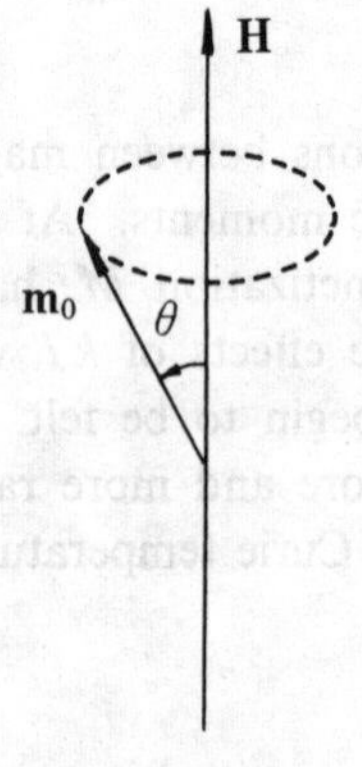

Fig. 3.2.2

The measured magnetization m along the field H per atom is equal to the average of $m_0 \cos\theta$. With $\cos\theta = u$

$$m = \frac{\int_{-1}^{+1} m_0 u \left[\exp\left(\frac{m_0 H u}{kT}\right)\right] du}{\int_{-1}^{+1} \left[\exp\left(\frac{m_0 H u}{kT}\right)\right] du} = kT \frac{\partial \ln Z}{\partial H} \tag{3.2.2}$$

with

$$Z = \int_{-1}^{+1} \left[\exp\left(\frac{m_0 H u}{kT}\right)\right] du = \frac{2}{x} \sinh x \tag{3.2.3}$$

With $x = m_0 H / kT$, (3.2.2) and (3.2.3) give

$$M = M_0 \mathcal{L}(x) \tag{3.2.4}$$

where $\mathcal{L}(x) = \coth x - \frac{1}{x}$ is the Langevin function As the exchange interactions are, in the molecular field theory, equivalent to an applied magnetic field, they will be taken into account only by making the change $H \to WM + H$

Thus:

$$x = m_0(H+WM)/kT \tag{3.2.5}$$

(3.2.4) becomes a self-consistent equation:

$$M = M_0 \mathscr{L}\left(\frac{m_0}{kT}(H+WM)\right) \tag{3.2.6}$$

giving the magnetization as a function of T and H. It can be solved graphically. Setting:

$$M/M_0 = y = \mathscr{L}(x)$$

$$x = \frac{m_0 H + W m_0 M_0 y}{kT} = \frac{M_0 H + W M_0^2 y}{NkT}$$

the reduced magnetization y is obtained by the intersection of the Langevin curve and the line of equation:

$$y = -\frac{H}{WM_0} + \frac{NkTx}{WM_0^2} \qquad \text{(Fig. 3.2.3)}$$

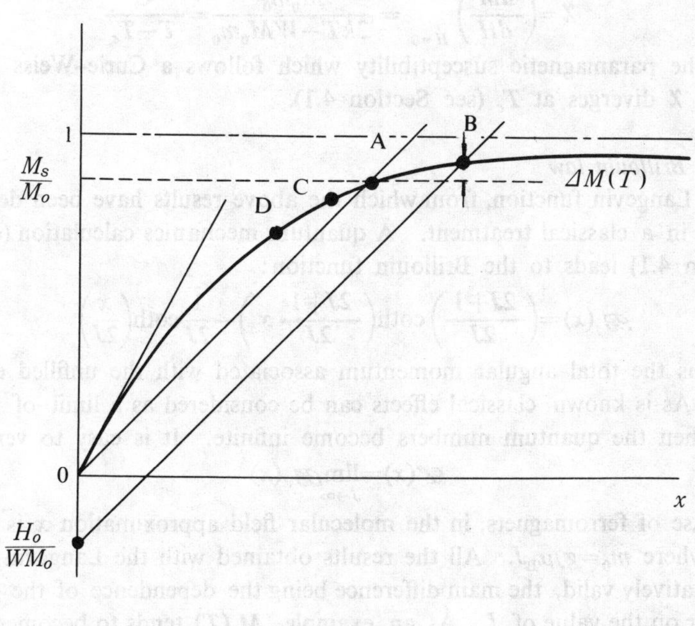

Fig. 3.2.3

In zero applied field, $H=0$, the line passes through the origin and its slope is small at low temperatures; then $y = \frac{M_s(T)}{M_0}$ has a finite value (point A). The magnetization $M_s(T)$ is called the spontaneous magnetization. If H increases from zero to a finite value $H=H_0$, $A \to B$ and $M_s(T) \to M_s(T) + \Delta M_H(T)$. It is clear that if $T \to 0$, $\Delta M_H(T) \to 0$ because the spontaneous magnetization has reached its maximum value.

If the temperature increases (in zero field), the intersection A moves on the Langevin curve towards $C, D, \cdots$, and $M_s(T)$ decreases. The spontaneous magnetization vanishes at the Curie temperature, when the slope of the line is equal to the initial slope of $\mathscr{L}(x)$. M is small and x can be considered small ($H=0$). An expansion of (3.2.4) gives:

$$\frac{M}{M_0}=\left(\frac{x}{3}-\frac{x^3}{45}\cdots\right) \tag{3.2.7}$$

and then the Curie temperature is:

$$T_c=\frac{WNm_0^2}{3k}=CW \tag{3.2.8}$$

where $C=\dfrac{Nm_0^2}{3k}$ is the Curie constant.

In the paramagnetic range there is no spontaneous magnetization. In that case, when the applied field H is small, the magnetization is also small. x being then small we can use the expansion (3.2.7). The initial susceptibility is then:

$$\chi=\left(\frac{dM}{dH}\right)_{H=0}=\frac{M_0m_0}{3kT-WM_0m_0}=\frac{C}{T-T_c} \tag{3.2.9}$$

This is the paramagnetic susceptibility which follows a Curie–Weiss law. As expected, χ diverges at T_c (see Section 4.1).

(b) *The Brillouin law*

The Langevin function, from which the above results have been deduced, is obtained in a classical treatment. A quantum mechanics calculation (described in Section 4.1) leads to the Brillouin function:

$$\mathscr{B}_J(x)=\left(\frac{2J+1}{2J}\right)\coth\left(\frac{2J+1}{2J}x\right)-\frac{1}{2J}\coth\left(\frac{x}{2J}\right) \tag{3.2.10}$$

where J is the total angular momentum associated with the unfilled electronic orbital. As is known, classical effects can be considered as a limit of quantum effects when the quantum numbers become infinite. It is easy to verify that:

$$\mathscr{L}(x)=\lim_{J\to\infty}\mathscr{B}_J(x)$$

In the case of ferromagnets, in the molecular field approximation x is given by (3.2.5), where $m_0=g_J\mu_B J$. All the results obtained with the Langevin function are qualitatively valid, the main difference being the dependence of the magnetic behaviour on the value of J. As an example, $M_s(T)$ tends to becomes squared as J decreases (Fig. 3.2.4). The Curie constant could be readily obtained by expanding $\mathscr{B}_J(x)$ as done for $\mathscr{L}(x)$ giving:

$$C=\frac{NJ(J+1)}{3k}g_J^2\,\mu_B^2=\frac{N}{3k}\mu_{eff}^2 \tag{3.2.11}$$

where $\mu_{eff}=g_J\mu_B\sqrt{J(J+1)}$ is the effective paramagnetic moment.

One must mention that in the models described before, the anisotropy is not quantitatively taken into account. Such models are valid for Gd-based materials (S state, the anisotropy is extremely small) or in $3d$ alloys which can be, in

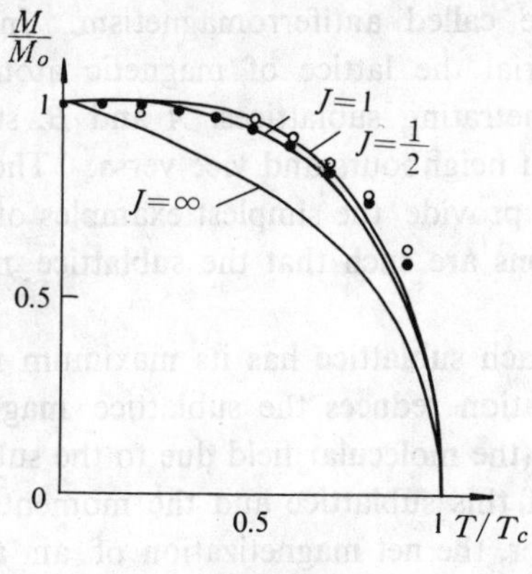

Fig. 3.2.4

first approximation, considered as localized (Fe). For other materials the Brillouin function can give only a qualitative description. Numerical calculations including the crystal field and exchange at the same order of perturbation are necessary.

3.2.2 Antiferromagnetism

In 1936, Néel predicted the existence of another kind of cooperative magnetic

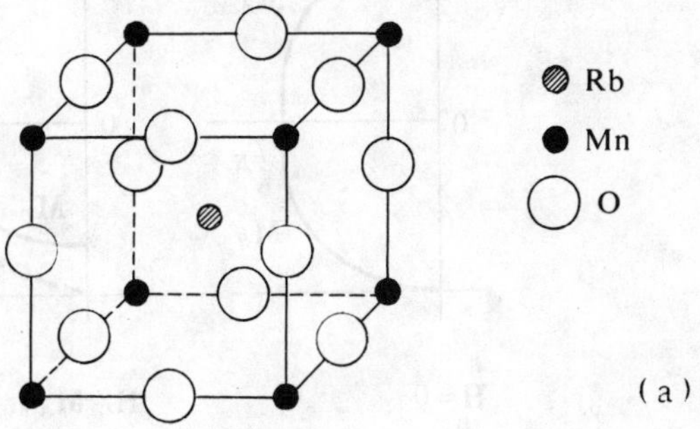

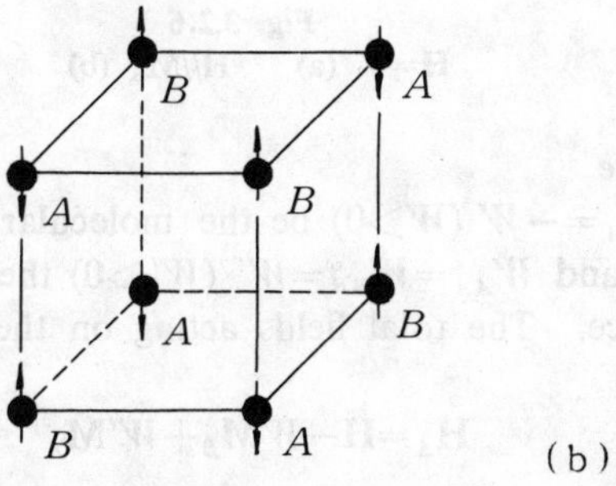

Fig. 3.2.5

(a) Crystal structure of $RbMnF_3$. (b) Antiferromagnetic ordering in simple cubic lattice of Mn ions in $RbMnF_3$.

phenomenon, which he called antiferromagnetism. In the simplest form of antiferromagnetic material the lattice of magnetic atoms can be divided into two equivalent interpenetrating sublattices, A and B, such that A atoms have only B atoms as nearest neighbours and vice versa. The simple cubic and body centered cubic lattices provide the simplest examples of such cases (Fig. 3.2.5) The magnetic interactions are such that the sublattice magnetizations are antiparallel.

At absolute zero each sublattice has its maximum magnetization and as T increases thermal activation reduces the sublattice magnetizations in the same way as in ferromagnets (the molecular field due to the sublattice A is antiparallel to the magnetization of this sublattice and the moments of B naturally orient parallel to it). However, the net magnetization of an antiferromagnet is zero at all temperatures because of the exact cancellation of the spontaneous magnetization of each sublattice (see Fig. 3.2.6 (a)). The application of a magnetic field H creates an asymmetry (Fig. 3.2.6(b)) proportional to H if the field is not too high. The antiferromagnetic susceptibility is different if the field is applied parallel or perpendicular to the direction of the magnetic moments in zero field (direction of antiferromagnetism, **D**, which is fixed by the anisotropy).

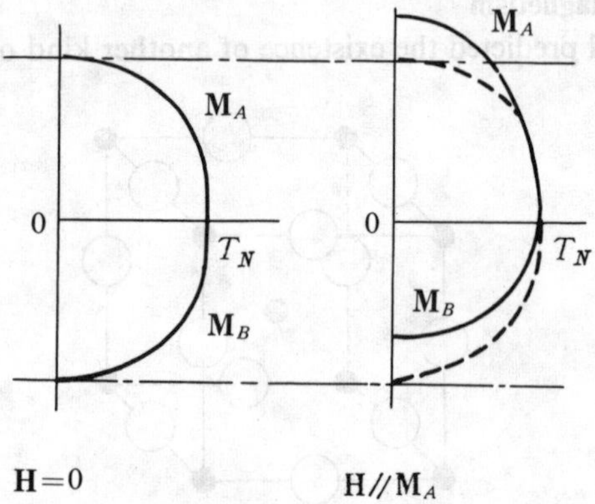

(a) (b)

Fig. 3.2.6
H=0 (a) **H//M$_A$** (b)

(a) *Néel temperature*

Let $W_{AB}=W_{BA}=-W$ ($W>0$) be the molecular field coefficient between the two sublattices and $W_{AA}=W_{BB}=W'$ ($W'>0$) the molecular field coefficient inside each sublattice. The total fields acting on the A and B sublattices are respectively:

$$\mathbf{H}_A=\mathbf{H}-W\mathbf{M}_B+W'\mathbf{M}_A \tag{3.2.12}$$

and

$$\mathbf{H}_B=\mathbf{H}-W\mathbf{M}_A+W'\mathbf{M}_B \tag{3.2.13}$$

In the paramagnetic range (no spontaneous magnetization on each sublattice) we can use the expansion of (3.2.7) for the magnetization of each sublattice. To the first order of approximation

$$\mathbf{M}_A = \frac{C_A}{T}(\mathbf{H} - W\mathbf{M}_B + W'\mathbf{M}_A) \tag{3.2.14}$$

and

$$\mathbf{M}_B = \frac{C_B}{T}(\mathbf{H} - W\mathbf{M}_A + W'\mathbf{M}_B) \tag{3.2.15}$$

with

$$C_A = \frac{N_A m_0^2}{3k} \text{ and } C_B = \frac{N_B m_0^2}{3k}$$

where N_A $(=N_B=N)$ is the number of A atoms (or B atoms) per unit volume. Here $C_A = C_B = C = \dfrac{Nm_0^2}{3k}$.

For $H=0$:

$$\mathbf{M}_A\left(1 - \frac{CW'}{T}\right) + \frac{CW}{T}\mathbf{M}_B = 0$$

and

$$\mathbf{M}_A\frac{CW}{T} + \left(1 - \frac{CW'}{T}\right)\mathbf{M}_B = 0$$

This set of equations has a non-trivial solution ($\mathbf{M}_A$ and $\mathbf{M}_B \neq 0$) only below the ordering temperature which is called the Néel temperature T_N. T_N is such that:

$$\left(1 - \frac{CW'}{T_N}\right)^2 - \left(\frac{CW}{T_N}\right)^2 = 0 \tag{3.2.16}$$

$$T_N = C(W + W') \tag{3.2.17}$$

The Néel temperature is a measure of the sum of the absolute value of the molecular field coefficients.

(b) *Perpendicular susceptibility* $\mathbf{H} \perp \mathbf{D}$

Fig. 3.2.7 (a) shows the moment and field arrangement. The field is perpendicular to the antiferromagnetism direction **D**. The sublattice magnetizations are rotated through a small angle θ until the decrease of the Zeeman energy E_Z is counterbalanced by the increase in exchange energy E_E and anisotropy energy E_A.

$$|\mathbf{M}_A| = |\mathbf{M}_B| = M$$

If K is the anisotropy constant, and θ is small:

$$E_z = -(\mathbf{M}_A + \mathbf{M}_B)\cdot\mathbf{H} = -2MH\theta$$

$$E_E = W\mathbf{M}_A\cdot\mathbf{M}_B = -WM^2(1-2\theta^2)$$

$$E_A = K\theta^2$$

Minimizing $E_T = E_Z + E_E + E_A$, one gets:

$$\theta = \frac{MH}{2WM^2 + K}$$

The measured magnetization along the field is:

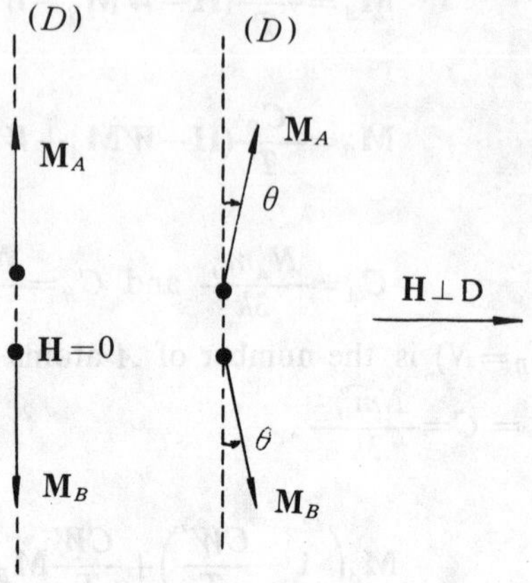

Fig. 3.2.7 (a)

$$M = M_A + M_B = 2M\theta = \frac{2M^2H}{2WM^2 + K}$$

The perpendicular susceptibility is:

$$\chi_\perp = \frac{1}{W\left(1 + \frac{K}{2WM^2}\right)} \tag{3.2.18}$$

As W does not vary much with temperature, the variations of $\chi_\perp(T)$ are essentially due to the variation of $K/2M^2$ with T, which are generally weak. Thus $\chi_\perp(T)$ is nearly constant at low temperatures (Fig. 3.2.8).

One must remark that an exact calculation needs to consider also the entropy term

$$-kT\int_0^{M(T)} \mathscr{B}_J^{-1}(x)\mathrm{d}x$$

However, the result is not affected by it.

Second remark: the exchange energy E_E contains the interactions between the sublattices A and B only. The intrasublattice couplings have not been neglected; they do not play any role because they are independent of θ.

(c) *Parallel susceptibility* **H**∥**D**

As indicated in Fig. 3.2.7 (b), all fields and moments are collinear. The sublattice magnetized parallel to **H** will have its moment increased by an amount Δ and the sublattice magnetized antiparallel to **H** will have its moment decreased by Δ (if the temperature is $T \neq 0$K for classical moments).

In the molecular field approximation, the total field acting on $\mathbf{M}_A$ is $\mathbf{H}_A = W'\mathbf{M}_A - W\mathbf{M}_B + \mathbf{H}$ and the total field acting on $\mathbf{M}_B$ is $\mathbf{H}_B = W'\mathbf{M}_B - W\mathbf{M}_A + \mathbf{H}$. Thus:

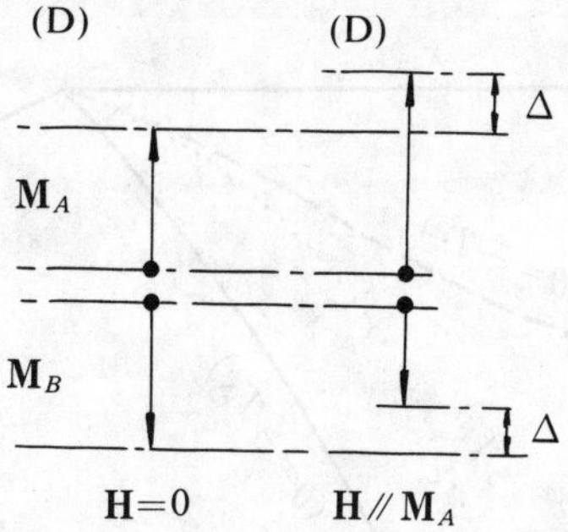

Fig. 3.2.7 (b)

$$M_A/M_0=\mathscr{B}_J\left(\frac{m_0}{kT}\,(W'\mathbf{M}_A-W\mathbf{M}_B+\mathbf{H})\right)$$
$$M_B/M_0=\mathscr{B}_J\left(\frac{m_0}{kT}\,(W'\mathbf{M}_B-W\mathbf{M}_A+\mathbf{H})\right) \quad (3.2.19)$$

Setting

$$|\mathbf{M}_A|=M_T+\Delta$$
$$|\mathbf{M}_B|=M_T-\Delta$$
$$M_T+\Delta=M_0\mathscr{B}_J\left\{\frac{m_0}{kT}\,(W'+W)\,M_T+\frac{m_0}{kT}\left[H+(W'-W)\,\Delta\right]\right\}$$

A limited expansion for small values of H and Δ leads to:

$$\Delta=\frac{m_0M_0}{kT}\,[H-(W-W')\,\Delta]\,\mathscr{B}'_J\left[\frac{m_0(W'+W)M_T}{kT}\right]$$

Knowing that $\frac{m_0M_0}{kT}\mathscr{B}'_J(0)=C$
we obtain:

$$\Delta=\frac{Cb(T)H}{T+C(W-W')b(T)}$$

with

$$b(T)=\frac{\mathscr{B}'_J\left[\frac{m_0}{kT}\,(W'+W)M_T\right]}{J'(0)}$$

Thus

$$\chi_{//}=\frac{2\Delta}{H}=\frac{2Cb(T)}{T+C\,(W-W')b(T)} \quad (3.2.20)$$

The parallel susceptibility decreases with T and vanishes at 0K (Fig. 3.2.8). As this calculation accounts for the entropy, it is valid at all temperatures. In the vicinity of T_N, $b(T)$ is close to 1 and $\chi_{//}\simeq\frac{1}{W}\simeq\chi_\perp$ because near T_N, K cancels faster than M^2.

As (3.2.20) holds at all temperatures, it is easy to see that there is only a slope discontinuity of the susceptibility at T_N.

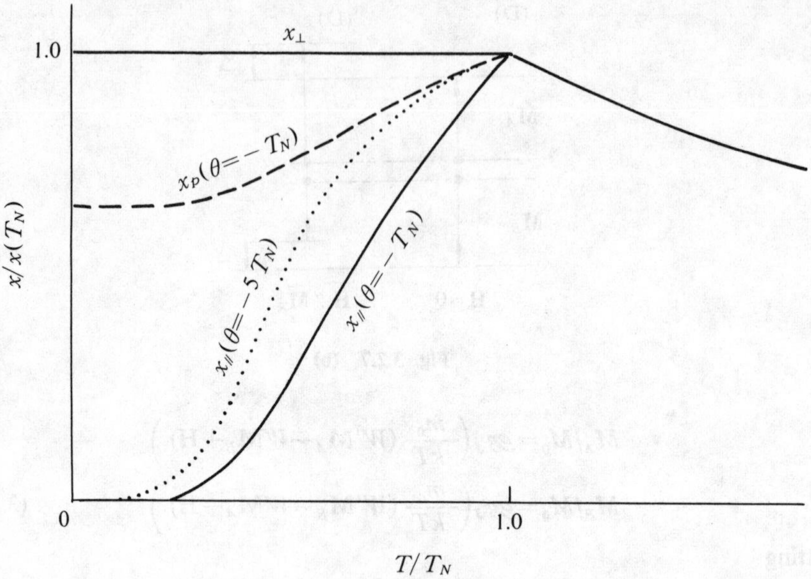

Fig. 3.2.8

Parallel and perpendicular susceptibilities for the two-sublattice antiferromagnet. ---- Powder susceptibility for the two-sublattice antiferromagnet. ····Parallel susceptibility for $\theta=-5T_N$. All curves are calculated by the molecular field method.

3.2.3 Ferrimagnetism

Contrary to the case of antiferromagnets, the different sublattices of a ferrimagnet are not compensated. This requires non-equivalent magnetic sublattices and/or atoms. The first prediction and theoretical description of ferrimagnetism was given by Néel. His model was used to explain the magnetic properties of ferrites.

We consider two different types of magnetic sites A and B having different spins ($M_A \neq M_B$). The effective field (molecular field+applied field H) acting on the atoms A is:

$$\mathbf{H}_A=\mathbf{H}-W_{AB}\mathbf{M}_B+W_{AA}\mathbf{M}_A=\mathbf{H}-W(\mathbf{M}_B-\alpha\mathbf{M}_A) \tag{3.2.21}$$

where $W=-W_{AB}=-W_{BA}(W>0)$ and $\alpha W=W_{AA}$.

Similarly:

$$\mathbf{H}_B=\mathbf{H}-W_{AB}\mathbf{M}_A+W_{BB}\mathbf{M}_B=\mathbf{H}-W(\mathbf{M}_A-\beta\mathbf{M}_B) \tag{3.2.22}$$

with $W_{BB}=\beta W$.

The magnetic energy is (for $H=0$):

$$E=W(\mathbf{M}_A\mathbf{M}_B)-\frac{1}{2}\,(W_{AA}\,M_A^2+W_{BB}\,M_B^2) \tag{3.2.23}$$

Low-temperature behaviour

In order to simplify this complex problem, as a first step let us choose $\alpha=\beta=0$, i.e. one neglects the interactions inside each sublattice. In this case, using the formula (4.2.22) one obtains the ordering temperature:

$$T_c = W\sqrt{C_A C_B}$$

With C_A and C_B given respectively by (4.2.19) and (4.2.21). At T_c the spontaneous magnetization which appears can be written:

$$M_A = -\frac{C_A}{T} W M_B$$

and

$$M_B = -\frac{C_B}{T} W M_A$$

which leads to $M_A = \sqrt{\frac{C_A}{C_B}} M_B$.

At lower temperatures:

$$M_A = N_A m_A \mathscr{B}_A\left(-\frac{W m_A M_B}{kT}\right)$$

$$M_B = N_B m_B \mathscr{B}_B\left(-\frac{W m_B M_A}{kT}\right)$$

At very low temperatures:

$$M_A^0 = N_A m_A$$

and

$$M_B^0 = N_B m_B$$

which leads to:

$$M = N_A m_A - N_B m_B \tag{3.2.24}$$

The thermal variations of $M_A(T)$ and $M_B(T)$, which one can numerically calculate, are similar to that of the spontaneous magnetization of a ferromagnet. However, $M(T)$ can have different characteristic variations which are called, following Néel, Q, P, N, L and M. All these variations have a zero derivative at $T=0$ and tend towards zero around T_c. These variations are drawn in Fig. 3.2.9.

In the case N, at a certain temperature below T_c the resulting magnetization reverses (Fig. 3.2.10) (compensation point T_{c0}). However, we must note that the measured macroscopic magnetization remains parallel to the applied field (dashed curve) due to domain wall motion.

Let us examine the condition for such a behaviour to be observed, by studying the variation of the magnetization near the Curie temperature. The expansion of the Brillouin function to third order

($\coth x = \frac{1}{x} + \frac{x}{3} - \frac{x^3}{45} + \cdots$) leads to:

$$M_A = -\frac{WC_A}{T} M_B (1 - \alpha_A M_B^2) \tag{3.2.25}$$

and

$$M_B = -\frac{WC_B}{T} M_A (1 - \alpha_B M_A^2) \tag{3.2.26}$$

where α_A and α_B are constants.

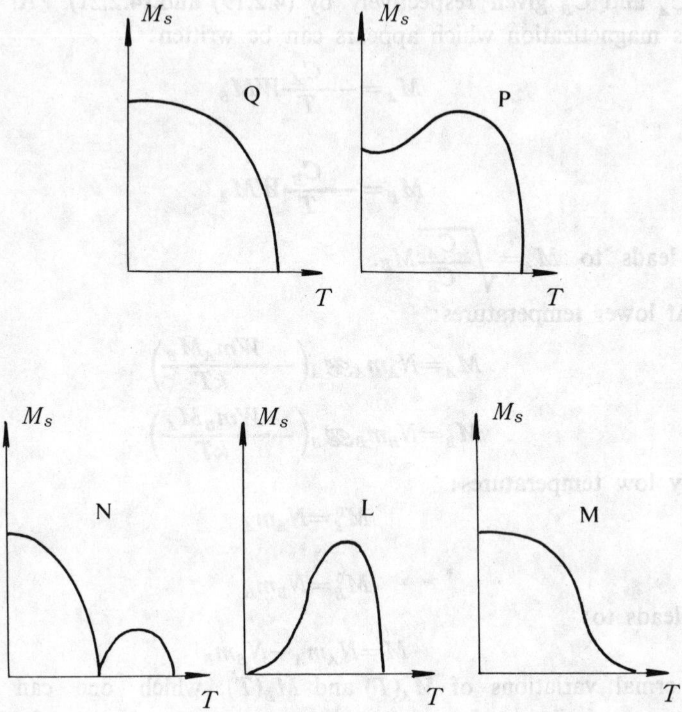

Fig. 3.2.9

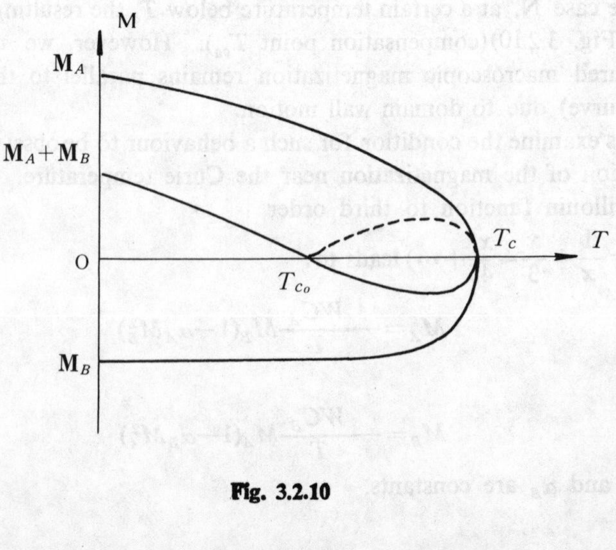

Fig. 3.2.10

From (3.2.25) and (3.2.26) one obtains:

$$M_A^2 = \frac{2C_A}{(\alpha_A C_B + \alpha_B C_A)} \frac{(T_c - T)}{T_c} \tag{3.2.27}$$

and

$$M_B^2 = \frac{2C_B}{(\alpha_A C_B + \alpha_B C_A)} \frac{(T_c - T)}{T_c} \tag{3.2.28}$$

The total magnetization, such that positive values are in the same direction as M_A magnetization, is then:

$$M = M_A - M_B = \frac{\sqrt{2}}{\sqrt{C_A \alpha_B + C_B \alpha_A}} \sqrt{\frac{T_c - T}{T_c}} (\sqrt{C_A} - \sqrt{C_B})$$

The bulk magnetization is parallel to the sublattice magnetization which has the higher Curie constant. The magnetization changes sign when:

$$N_A m_A > N_B m_B \qquad (M > 0 \text{ at } T = 0)$$

and

$$N_A m_A^2 < N_B m_B^2 \qquad (M < 0 \text{ around } T_c)$$

or vice versa.

Let $x = m_A/m_B$ and $y = N_A/N_B$. Bulk magnetization is zero at low and high temperatures, respectively, when $xy = 1$ and $x^2 y = 1$. In Fig. 3.2.11 we show the regions corresponding to each behaviour.

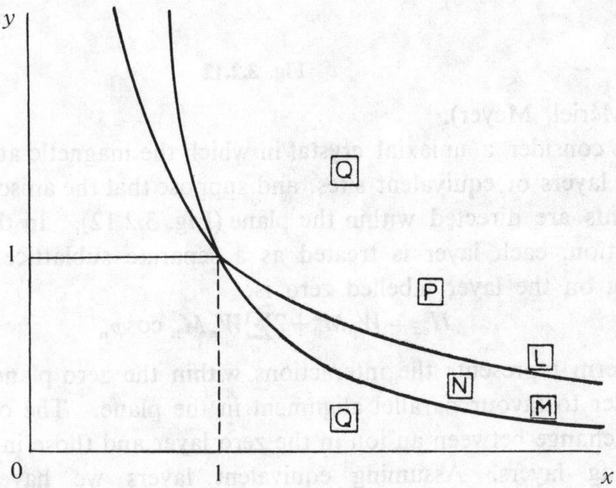

Fig. 3.2.11

3.2.4 Helimagnetism

The classes of magnetic ordering considered in the above sections are the simplest, involving only two or three sublattices collinearly magnetized. Neutron diffraction experiments have revealed a much wider variety of patterns. In fact when long-range interactions act, there can result remarkable helical and modulated patterns. The first observed case of helical structure was $MnAu_2$

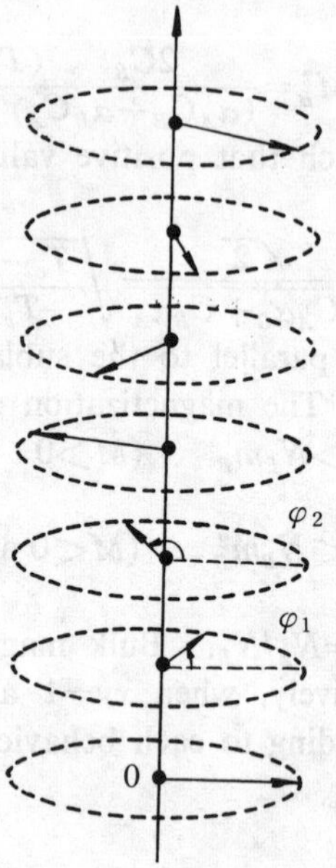

Fig. 3.2.12

(Herpin, Mériel, Meyer).

Let us consider a uniaxial crystal in which the magnetic atoms are arranged in parallel layers of equivalent sites, and suppose that the anisotropy is such that the moments are directed within the plane (Fig. 3.2.12). In the molecular field approximation, each layer is treated as a separate sublattice. The molecular field acting on the layer labelled zero is:

$$H_{ex}=W_0M_0+2\sum_n W_nM_n\cos\varphi_n \tag{3.2.29}$$

The first term represents the interactions within the zero plane, presumed positive in order to favour parallel alignment in the plane. The other terms represent the exchange between an ion in the zero layer and those in both 2nd, 3rd,... neighbouring layers. Assuming equivalent layers we have $|M_i|=M_s$ and $\varphi_2=2\varphi_1$, $\varphi_3=3\varphi_1$.

$$H_{ex}=M_s(W_0+2\sum_n W_n\cos n\varphi)=M_sW(\varphi) \tag{3.2.30}$$

The exchange energy is

$$E_E=-\int_0^{M_s}H_{ex}dM=-W(\varphi)M_s^2/2 \tag{3.2.31}$$

For $W(\varphi)>0$ (ferromagnetic arrangement in each layer), E_E is minimum if $W(\varphi)$ is maximum, that is to say, if

$$\sum_n nW_n\sin n\varphi=0 \tag{3.2.32}$$

The case $\varphi=0$ corresponds to ferromagnetism ($W_n>0$). The case $\varphi=\pi$ corresponds to antiferromagnetism ($W_1<0$ and all other W's are zero). When $W_2\neq 0$, but higher coefficients are zero, helical order occurs with a turn angle from layer to layer:

$$\cos\varphi_0=-W_1/4W_2 \tag{3.2.33}$$

Obviously this requires $|W_1|<4|W_2|$ with $W_1>0$ and $W_2<0$. Physically there is competition between positive and negative interactions, making both ferromagnetism and antiferromagnetism unstable. The exchange energy is lowered by opening of the angle between the magnetic moments (Fig. 3.2.13).

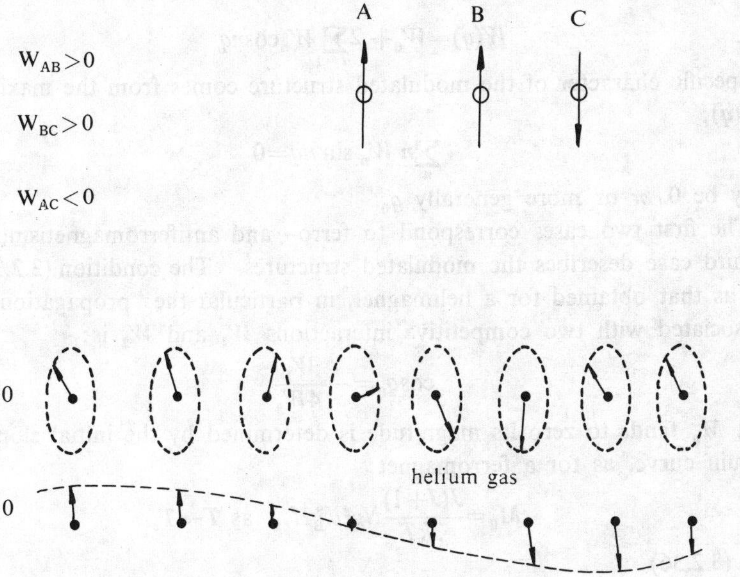

Fig. 3.2.13

The Néel temperature can be obtained as above from the divergence of the paramagnetic susceptibility. As the molecular field is $M_s W(\varphi_0)$

$$T_N=\frac{J(J+1)}{3k}W(\varphi_0)M_s^2 \tag{3.2.34}$$

Modulated structure

In the above case, the anisotropy is such that the moments are within the different layers ($K<0$ if the anisotropy energy is written as $E_A=K\sin^2\theta$, where θ is the angle between the uniaxial direction and the moment direction).

If we have the same problem of competition between positive and negative interactions with, in addition, a strong uniaxial anisotropy ($K>0$), the only means to reduce the exchange energy between two moments is to reduce the modulus of the magnetic moment. In this case the different magnetic layers cannot be considered as equivalent:

$$H_{ex}=W_0M_0+\sum_n W_n(M_n+M_{-n}) \tag{3.2.35}$$

We can represent the variation of M_n from one layer to the next along the uniaxial axis as a Fourier series:

$$M_n=\sum_q a_q\cos(nq+\alpha_q) \tag{3.2.36}$$

where q is the wave number of the Fourier component and n the index of the layer. (3.2.35) becomes:

$$H_{ex}=\sum_{q=0}^{\infty} a_q W(q)\cos\alpha_q \tag{3.2.37}$$

with

$$W(q)=W_0+2\sum_{n=1} W_n\cos nq \tag{3.2.38}$$

The specific character of the modulated structure comes from the maximization of $W(q)$:

$$\sum_n n\, W_n \sin nq=0 \tag{3.2.39}$$

q may be 0, π or more generally q_0.

The first two cases correspond to ferro– and antiferromagnetism, whereas the third case describes the modulated structures. The condition (3.2.39) is the same as that obtained for a helimagnet, in particular the "propagation vector" q_0 associated with two competitive interactions W_1 and W_2 is:

$$\cos q_0=-\frac{W_1}{4W_2} \tag{3.2.40}$$

When M_n tends to zero its magnitude is determined by the initial slope of the Brillouin curve, as for a ferromagnet:

$$M_0=\frac{J(J+1)}{3kT}Ng^2\mu_B^2 H_{ex} \quad \text{as } T\to T_c \tag{3.2.41}$$

using (3.2.36)

$$T_c=\frac{J(J+1)}{3k}Ng^2\mu_B^2\frac{\sum_q a_q W(q)\cos\alpha_q}{\sum_q a_q\cos\alpha_q} \tag{3.2.42}$$

The Néel temperature T_N is equal to the maximum value of the above temperature. This clearly corresponds to that pattern of order for which all the Fourier components take the same (maximum) value of $W(q)$, i.e. $W(q_0)$. On cooling a sample from high temperatures, therefore, the first spontaneous order appears at the Néel point such that:

$$T_N=\frac{J(J+1)}{3k}W(q_0)\,Ng^2\,\mu_B^2 \tag{3.2.43}$$

and has the form of a pure sine-wave modulation with the propagation vector q_0.

To investigate the nature of the ordering at lower temperatures, M_n must be expanded to higher powers of H_{ex}/kT than in Equation (3.2.41). It is then found that harmonics of odd degree enter the Fourier sum for M_n and the sinusoidal variation becomes progressively squared. Physically this result comes from the fact that just below T_N, $|\mathbf{M}_n|$ can be small due to high thermal activation, whereas at lower temperatures $|\mathbf{M}_n|$ tends to saturate and thus, the inhomogeneous reductions of magnetization, characteristic of the modulated structure, vanish. This occurs when there is an intrinsic magnetic moment. However, if the modulation persists down to 0K, the ground state (in the absence of applied or exchange magnetic fields) has to be non-magnetic (see Chapter 7), for instance a singlet. In that case the magnetization is induced by the molecular field.

We have treated above two extreme cases of uniaxial anisotropy ($K>0$ and $K<0$) and found a sinusoidal modulation in one case and a helical structure in the other. More general cases of anisotropy can be handled in a similar fashion and so have the effect of an applied field. Calculations of these general kinds apply most directly to the rare-earth metals and alloys where long-range interactions favour these structures.

3.3 THE METHOD OF VILLAIN AND YOSHIMORI

In the previous sections we have always considered a splitting into several sublattices. The powerful method of Villain and Yoshimori does not take into account this hypothesis. However, they assume that the magnetic atoms are disposed on a Bravais lattice and the interactions are treated in the molecular field approximation. Furthermore, they do not introduce the anisotropy energy. The mean magnetic moment at the temperature T is:

$$\mathbf{m}_i=\frac{\mathbf{H}_i^{\mathrm{eff}}}{|\mathbf{H}_i^{\mathrm{eff}}|}\, m_0\, \mathscr{B}_J\left(\frac{m_0 H_i^{\mathrm{eff}}}{kT}\right) \tag{3.3.1}$$

with

$$\mathbf{H}_i^{\mathrm{eff}}=\mathbf{H}+\sum_j n_{ij}\mathbf{m}_j \tag{3.3.2}$$

At high temperatures, (3.3.1) can be linearized:

$$\mathbf{m}_i=\frac{C}{T}\left(\mathbf{H}+\sum_j n_{ij}\,\mathbf{m}_j\right) \tag{3.3.3}$$

The critical temperature (Curie or Néel temperature) is the highest temperature for which the linear system (3.3.3) admits a non-trivial solution ($\langle m_i\rangle \neq 0$), when $H=0$. The solutions of equations:

$$T\mathbf{m}_i=C\sum_j n_{ij}\mathbf{m}_j \tag{3.3.4}$$

are such that:

$$\mathbf{m}_j=\sum_q \mathbf{m}_q \exp^{(i\mathbf{q}\cdot\mathbf{R}_j)} \tag{3.3.5}$$

Putting (3.3.5) in (3.3.4):

$$T\sum_q \mathbf{m}_q=\sum_{q,j}\mathbf{m}_q C n_{ij}\exp^{[i\mathbf{q}(\mathbf{R}_j-\mathbf{R}_i)]} \tag{3.3.6}$$

Introducing the Fourier transform exchange interaction:

$$J(\mathbf{q})=C\sum_j n_{ij}\exp^{[i\mathbf{q}(\mathbf{R}_j-\mathbf{R}_i)]} \tag{3.3.7}$$

(3.3.7) gives for each **q**:

$$T\mathbf{m}_q = J(\mathbf{q})\mathbf{m}_q \tag{3.3.8}$$

This relation is always satisfied if $\mathbf{m}_q = 0$, but $\mathbf{m}_q = 0$ is valid only in the paramagnetic region. So, $\mathbf{m}_q$ is non-zero only for **q** belonging to a set of $\mathbf{q}_0$ values for which $\mathbf{m}_q \neq 0$. The $\mathbf{q}_0$ value for which $J(\mathbf{q})$ is maximum gives the more stable configuration and:

$$T_N = J(\mathbf{q}_0) \tag{3.3.9}$$

Then the exchange energy:

$$E_E = -Nm_0^2 J(\mathbf{q}_0)$$

is minimum. Thus the obtained solutions of (3.3.4) are stable and can be written

$$\mathbf{m}_j = \frac{2}{N}(\boldsymbol{\alpha}\cos\mathbf{q}_0 \cdot \mathbf{R}_j + \boldsymbol{\beta}\sin\mathbf{q}_0 \cdot \mathbf{R}_j) \tag{3.3.10}$$

where $\boldsymbol{\alpha}$ and $\boldsymbol{\beta}$ are real and constant vectors. The ferromagnetic solution corresponds to $\mathbf{q}_0 = 0$. The cases $\mathbf{q}_0 \neq 0$ describe antiferromagnetic, helimagnetic and modulated structures.

It would be interesting to find again, by this method, the results of preceding sections which treated particular cases.

REFERENCES

B. COQBLIN, The Electronic Structure of Rare-Earth Metals and Alloys, Academic Press, New York (1977).

A. HERPIN, Théroie du Magnétisme, Presses Universitaires de France, Paris (1968).

A. HERPIN, P. MERIEL, A.J.P. MEYER, *C. R. Acad. Sci.*, **246**, 3170 (1958).

J. S. SMART, Effective Field Theories of Magnetism, Studies in Physics and Chemistry Series, W.B. Saunders Co., Philadelphia (1966).

CHAPTER 4

THE PARAMAGNETIC STATE

4.1 LOCALIZED MAGNETIC MOMENTS WITHOUT INTERACTIONS

Let us consider a compound with one type of magnetic atoms without interactions. Let their ground state, in the absence of a magnetic field, be defined by the quantum number J (or S in the case of Gd): the degeneracy is $2J+1$ and each state is characterized by $|J, M_J\rangle$ such that $\hat{J}_Z|J, M_J\rangle = M_J|J, M_J\rangle$ with $M_J = J, J-1, J-2, \cdots, -J$. Let us apply a magnetic field. The ground state is split into $2J+1$ levels. These energy levels are the eigenstates of the perturbing Hamiltonian $\hat{H} = -\hat{m}_Z H_Z = -g_J \mu_B \hat{J}_Z H_Z$, where $\hat{J}_Z$ is the total angular momentum operator, g_J is the Landé g-factor and $\hat{m}_Z$ the magnetic moment operator (Section 1.3.3).

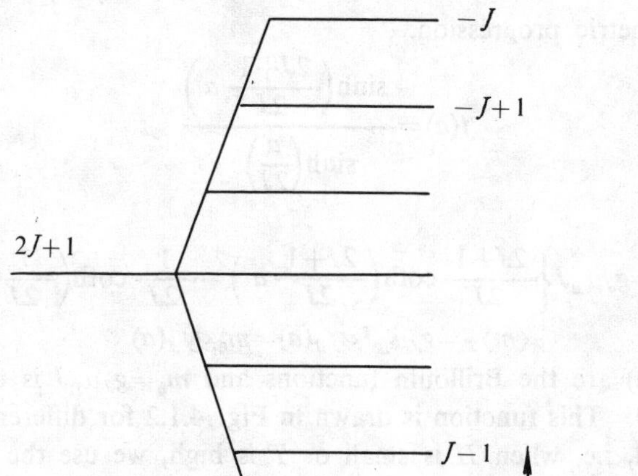

Fig. 4.1.1

Zeeman effect on the ground state multiplet of the free ion.

$$E_M = -g_J \mu_B H_Z \langle J,M|J_Z|J,M\rangle \tag{4.1.1}$$

$$E_M = -g_J \mu_B H_Z M \tag{4.1.2}$$

At $T=0$, only the ground state is occupied and the magnetization per atom is $m=g_J\mu_B J$.

At $T\neq 0$, we have to consider the thermal population of the excited states. The probability p_i of occupation of each state of energy E_i is given by the Boltzmann law:

$$p_i=\frac{\exp(-E_i/kT)}{\sum_i \exp(-E_i/kT)} \tag{4.1.3}$$

The value of magnetization per atom at finite temperature T can then be written:

$$\langle m\rangle_T=\sum_i m_i p_i=\frac{\sum_{M=-J}^{+J} g_J\mu_B M\exp(g_J\mu_B H_Z M/kT)}{\sum_{M=-J}^{+J} \exp(g_J\mu_B H_Z M/kT)} \tag{4.1.4}$$

With $a=g_J\mu_B H_Z J/kT$, this relation becomes:

$$\langle m\rangle_T=g_J\mu_B J\frac{\sum_{M=-J}^{+J}\frac{M}{J}\exp\left(a\frac{M}{J}\right)}{\sum_{M=-J}^{+J}\exp\left(a\frac{M}{J}\right)} \tag{4.1.5}$$

$$\langle m\rangle_T=g_J\mu_B J\frac{1}{f}\frac{df}{da} \tag{4.1.6}$$

with:

$$f(a)=\sum_{M=-J}^{+J} e^{a\frac{M}{J}} \tag{4.1.7}$$

$$f(a)=e^{-a}\left(1+e^{\frac{a}{J}}+\left(e^{\frac{a}{J}}\right)^2+\dots+\left(e^{\frac{a}{J}}\right)^{2J}\right) \tag{4.1.8}$$

which is a geometric progression.

$$f(a)=\frac{\sinh\left(\frac{2J+1}{2J}a\right)}{\sinh\left(\frac{a}{2J}\right)} \tag{4.1.9}$$

This leads to:

$$\langle m\rangle_T=g_J\mu_B J\left\{\frac{2J+1}{2J}\coth\left(\frac{2J+1}{2J}a\right)-\frac{1}{2J}\coth\left(\frac{1}{2J}a\right)\right\} \tag{4.1.10}$$

$$\langle m\rangle_T=g_J\mu_B J\mathscr{B}_J(a)=m_0\mathscr{B}_J(a) \tag{4.1.11}$$

where the $\mathscr{B}_J(a)$ are the Brillouin functions and $m_0=g_J\mu_B J$ is the saturation moment at $T=0$. This function is drawn in Fig. 4.1.2 for different values of J. When a is small, i.e. when H is small or T is high, we use the expansion:

$$\coth x=\frac{1}{x}+\frac{x}{3}+O(x^3)\dots \tag{4.1.12}$$

Then:

$$\frac{\langle m\rangle_T}{m_0}=\frac{1}{3}\left[\left(\frac{2J+1}{2J}\right)^2-\left(\frac{1}{2J}\right)^2\right]a=\frac{J+1}{3J}a \tag{4.1.13}$$

$$N\langle m\rangle_T=\frac{N(J+1)}{3J}(g_J\mu_B J)\frac{g_J\mu_B JH}{kT}=C\frac{H}{T} \tag{4.1.14}$$

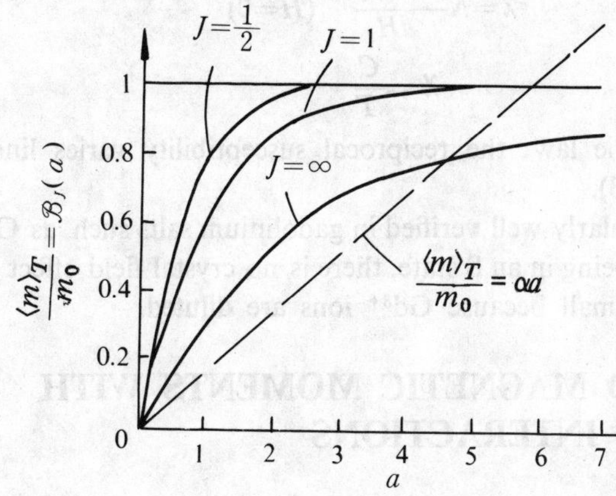

Fig. 4.1.2
Brillouin function.

where N is the number of magnetic atoms per unit volume and C the Curie constant:

$$C = \frac{N g_J^2 J(J+1) \mu_B^2}{3k} \tag{4.1.15}$$

$g_J \mu_B \sqrt{J(J+1)}$ is the paramagnetic moment.

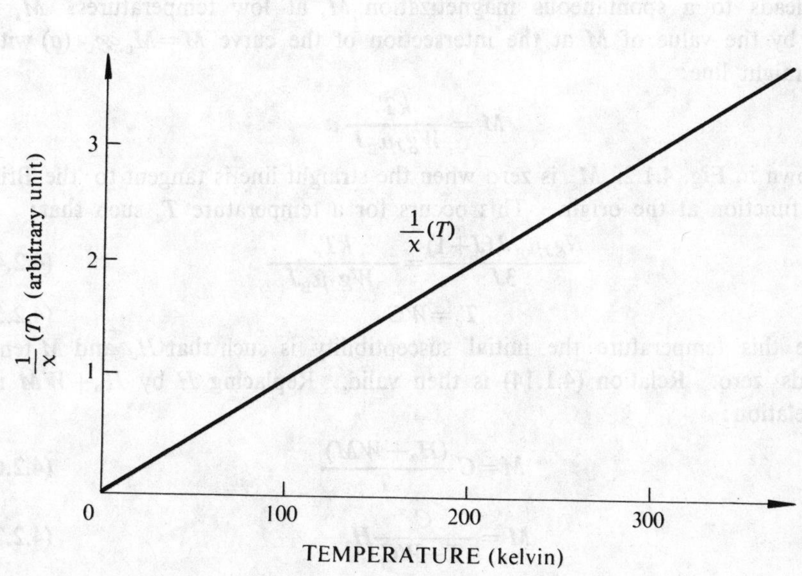

Fig. 4.1.3
Curie's law.

The initial susceptibility is defined by:

$$\chi = N\frac{d\langle m\rangle_T}{dH} \quad (H=0) \tag{4.1.16}$$

then

$$\chi = \frac{C}{T} \tag{4.1.17}$$

and we have the Curie law: the reciprocal susceptibility varies linearly with temperature (Fig. 4.1.3).

This law is particularly well verified in gadolinium salts such as $Gd_2(SO_4)_3 \cdot 8H_2O$, where, Gd^{3+} being in an S state, there is no crystal field effect and where interactions are very small because Gd^{3+} ions are diluted.

4.2 LOCALIZED MAGNETIC MOMENTS WITH EXCHANGE INTERACTIONS

4.2.1 Ferromagnetic compounds

In the molecular field approximation the exchange interactions are equivalent to a magnetic field:

$$H_m = WM \tag{4.2.1}$$

The total field H acting on the atoms is then:

$$H = H_m + H_a = WM + H_a \tag{4.2.2}$$

where H_a is the applied magnetic field, W the molecular field coefficient and M the magnetization per unit volume ($M = N\langle m\rangle_T$). For a given value of T and H_a, magnetization is obtained from relation (4.1.11), where:

$$a = g_J\mu_B J(H_a + WM)/kT \tag{4.2.3}$$

This leads to a spontaneous magnetization M_s at low temperatures. M_s is given by the value of M at the intersection of the curve $M = M_0\mathscr{B}_J(a)$ with the straight line:

$$M = \frac{kT}{Wg_J\mu_B J}a$$

as shown in Fig. 4.1.2. M_s is zero when the straight line is tangent to the Brillouin function at the origin. This occurs for a temperature T_c such that:

$$\frac{Ng_J\mu_B J(J+1)}{3J} = \frac{kT_c}{Wg_J\mu_B J} \tag{4.2.4}$$

$$T_c = WC \tag{4.2.5}$$

Above this temperature the initial susceptibility is such that H_a and M tend towards zero. Relation (4.1.14) is then valid. Replacing H by $H_a + WM$ in this relation:

$$M = C\frac{(H_a + WM)}{T} \tag{4.2.6}$$

$$M = \frac{C}{T - WC}H_a \tag{4.2.7}$$

$$\chi = \frac{dM}{dH_a}\ (H_a = 0) = \frac{C}{T - WC} \tag{4.2.8}$$

$$\frac{1}{\chi}=\frac{1}{\chi_0}-W \tag{4.2.9}$$

where χ_0 is the susceptibility without exchange. The result is that the thermal variation of the reciprocal susceptibility is parallel to that without exchange interaction but it is shifted by an amount proportional to the exchange interaction. In Fig. 4.2.1 we report the reciprocal susceptibility of $(Gd_{0.5}Y_{0.5})Ni$.

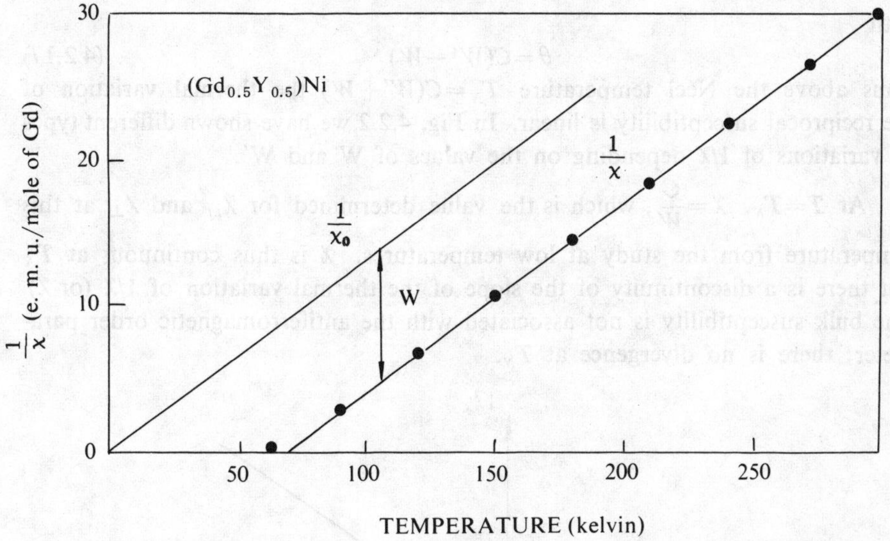

Fig. 4.2.1

4.2.2 Antiferromagnetic compounds

Let us consider a compound where the magnetic atoms, which are identical, are distributed in two antiparallel sublattices A and B with magnetization $\mathbf{M}_A$ and $\mathbf{M}_B$. When there is no applied magnetic field, $|\mathbf{M}_A|=|\mathbf{M}_B|$. Let $W_{AB}=W_{BA}=-W$ ($W>0$) be the molecular field coefficient between the two sublattices and $W_{AA}=W_{BB}=W'$ ($W'>0$) the molecular field coefficient inside each sublattice. In the presence of an applied magnetic field $\mathbf{H}_0$ the field acting on each sublattice is:

$$\mathbf{H}_A=\mathbf{H}_0-W\mathbf{M}_B+W'\mathbf{M}_A \tag{4.2.10}$$

$$\mathbf{H}_B=\mathbf{H}_0-W\mathbf{M}_A+W'\mathbf{M}_B \tag{4.2.11}$$

At each temperature the magnetizations $\mathbf{M}_A$ and $\mathbf{M}_B$ are given by the Brillouin function:

$$\mathbf{M}_A=\mathbf{M}_A^0\,\mathscr{B}_J\left(\frac{m_0|\mathbf{H}_A|}{kT}\right) \quad \text{and} \quad \mathbf{M}_B=\mathbf{M}_B^0\,\mathscr{B}_J\left(\frac{m_0|\mathbf{H}_B|}{kT}\right) \tag{4.2.12}$$

When $\mathbf{H}_A$ and $\mathbf{H}_B$ are small:

$$\mathbf{M}_A=\frac{C}{T}(\mathbf{H}_0-W\mathbf{M}_B+W'\mathbf{M}_A) \quad \text{and} \quad \mathbf{M}_B=\frac{C}{T}(\mathbf{H}_0-W\mathbf{M}_A+W'\mathbf{M}_B) \tag{4.2.13}$$

with

$$C=\frac{Nm_0^2}{3k} \tag{4.2.14}$$

N=number of atoms of each sublattice per unit volume (cm³). This leads to

$$\mathbf{M}=\mathbf{M}_A+\mathbf{M}_B=\frac{2C}{T-\theta}\mathbf{H} \tag{4.2.15}$$

$$\frac{1}{\chi}=\frac{T-\theta}{2C} \tag{4.2.16}$$

with

$$\theta=C(W'-W) \tag{4.2.17}$$

Thus above the Néel temperature $T_N=C(W'+W)$ the thermal variation of the reciprocal susceptibility is linear. In Fig. 4.2.2 we have shown different types of variations of $1/\chi$ depending on the values of W and W′.

At $T=T_N$, $\chi=\frac{C}{W}$, which is the value determined for $\chi_{//}$ and $\chi_\perp$ at this temperature from the study at low temperatures. χ is thus continuous at T_N but there is a discontinuity of the slope of the thermal variation of $1/\chi$ (or χ). The bulk susceptibility is not associated with the antiferromagnetic order parameter: there is no divergence at T_N.

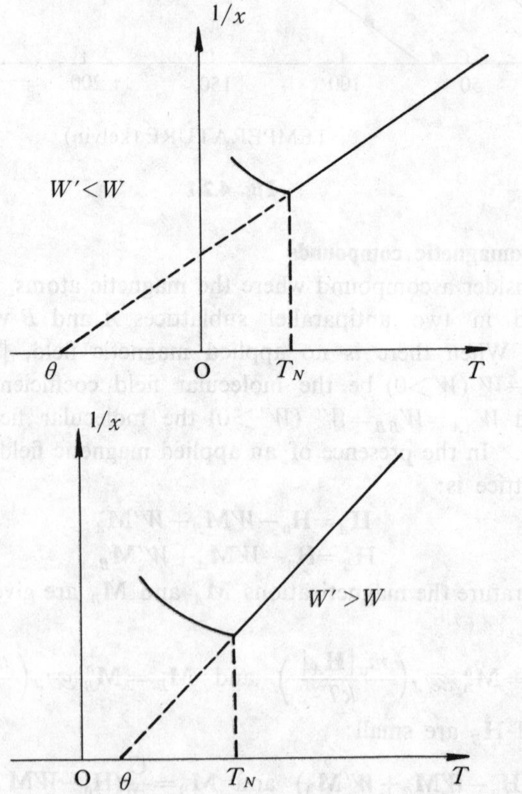

Fig. 4.2.2

4.2.3 Ferrimagnetic compounds

(a) *Case of two sublattices with localized magnetic moments*

In this case $\mathbf{M}_A \neq \mathbf{M}_B$ and $N_A \neq N_B$. Let W be the molecular field coefficient between the two sublattices and $W_{AA}=\alpha W$ and $W_{BB}=\beta W$. In the paramagnetic range, when measuring the susceptibility, $\mathbf{H}_0$, $\mathbf{M}_A$ and $\mathbf{M}_B$ are small enough so that:

$$\mathbf{M}_A=\frac{C_A}{T}(\mathbf{H}_0-W\mathbf{M}_B+W\alpha\mathbf{M}_A) \tag{4.2.18}$$

with

$$C_A=\frac{N_A m_A^2}{3k} \tag{4.2.19}$$

and

$$\mathbf{M}_B=\frac{C_B}{T}(\mathbf{H}_0-W\mathbf{M}_A+W\beta\mathbf{M}_B) \tag{4.2.20}$$

with

$$C_B=\frac{N_B m_B^2}{3k} \tag{4.2.21}$$

We can deduce the total magnetization:

$$\mathbf{M}=\mathbf{M}_A+\mathbf{M}_B=\frac{(C_A+C_B)T-C_AC_BW(2+\alpha+\beta)}{T^2-TW(C_A\alpha+C_B\beta)-C_AC_BW^2(1-\alpha\beta)}\mathbf{H}_0=\chi\mathbf{H}_0 \tag{4.2.22}$$

$1/\chi$ takes the following hyperbolic form:

$$\frac{1}{\chi}=\frac{T+\theta_p}{C}-\frac{\gamma}{T-\theta} \tag{4.2.23}$$

where $C=C_A+C_B$ is the mean value of the Curie constant of the assembly of m_A and m_B moments.

$$\theta=W(2+\alpha+\beta)\frac{C_AC_B}{C_A+C_B} \tag{4.2.24}$$

$$\gamma=W^2\frac{C_AC_B}{(C_A+C_B)^3}\Big[C_A(1+\alpha)-C_B(1+\beta)\Big]^2 \tag{4.2.25}$$

$$\theta_p=W\frac{2C_AC_B-\alpha C_A^2-\beta C_B^2}{C_A+C_B} \tag{4.2.26}$$

The two asymptotes of the hyperbola are as follows.
At high temperature:

$$\frac{1}{\chi}=\frac{T+\theta_p}{C} \tag{4.2.27}$$

The asymptote $\dfrac{1}{\chi}=\dfrac{T+\theta_p}{C}$ passes through the temperature axis for $T=-\theta_p$; this temperature is called the "asymptotic Curie point".

Around the ordering temperature there is a vertical asymptote

$$T=\theta \tag{4.2.28}$$

The ordering temperature T_c is defined as the temperature where $1/\chi$ passes through zero (χ becomes infinite). This leads to a second degree equation, in which we take only one solution:

$$T_c = \frac{W}{2}(\alpha C_A + \beta C_B + 4C_A C_B + (\alpha C_A - \beta C_B)^2) \tag{4.2.29}$$

A typical temperature dependence of the reciprocal susceptibility is shown in Fig. 4.2.3.

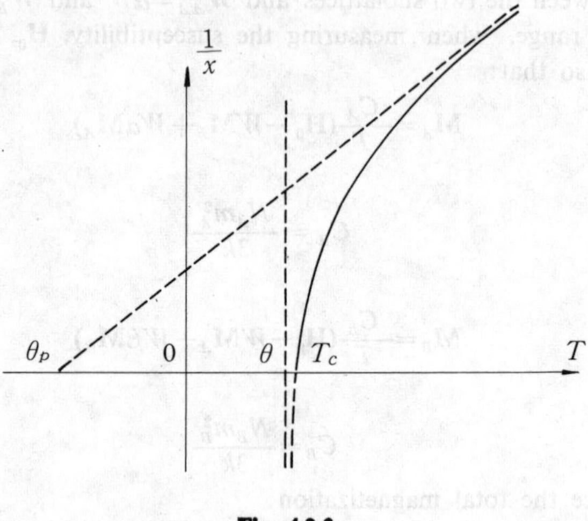

Fig. 4.2.3

Schematic representation of the paramagnetic reciprocal susceptibility χ^{-1} in a ferrimagnet.

(b) *One of the two sublattices is described by the itinerant model* (RCo_2 *compounds*; R=*rare earth*)

Let A be the sublattice described by the localized model. Let B be the sublattice described by the collective itinerant model (see Chapter 10):

$$\mathbf{M}_A = \frac{C_A}{T}(\mathbf{H}_0 + W\alpha\mathbf{M}_A - W\mathbf{M}_B) \tag{4.2.30}$$

$$\mathbf{M}_B = \chi_{B,0}(\mathbf{H}_0 + W\beta\mathbf{M}_B - W\mathbf{M}_A) \tag{4.2.31}$$

When the magnetization of atoms A is zero (i.e. yttrium), then the total susceptibility is the exchange enhanced susceptibility:

$$\chi_Y = \frac{M_B}{H_0} = \chi_{B,0}/(1 - W\beta\chi_{B,0}) \tag{4.2.32}$$

These three equations all lead to the temperature dependence of the reciprocal susceptibility of the whole compound:

$$\frac{1}{\chi} = \frac{T - \theta_B}{C_A + \chi_Y(T - EC_A)} \tag{4.2.33}$$

with

$$E = W\alpha + 2W. \tag{4.2.34}$$

The magnetic ordering temperature is given by:

$$\theta_B = (W\alpha + W^2\chi_Y)C_A \tag{4.2.35}$$

The variation of $1/\chi$ is rather similar to that determined in the case where the two sublattices are described by the localized model.

In the Fig. 4.2.4 we report the thermal variation of the reciprocal susceptibility of some RCo_2 compounds where the Co moment has to be described by either the localized or the itinerant model.

In fact both models account for the experimental results. However, other experimental studies (polarized neutron studies) have shown that Co has a collective itinerant character.

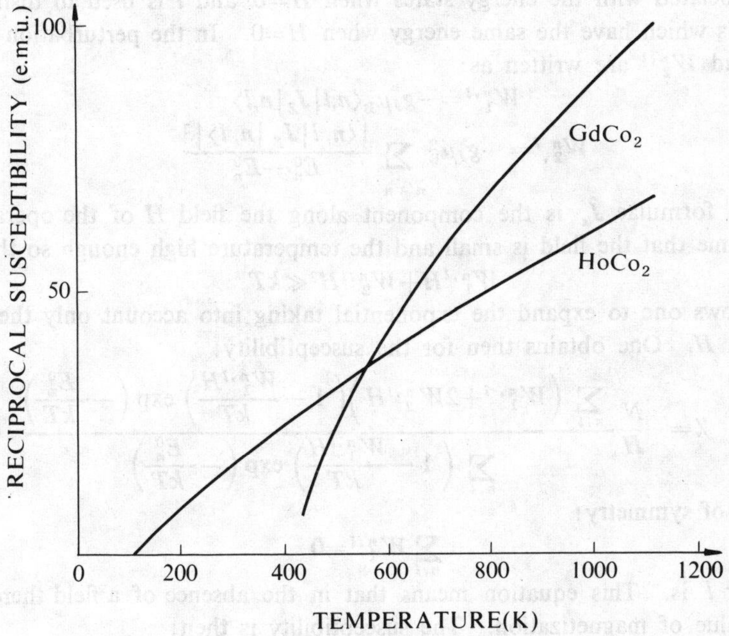

Fig. 4.2.4

4.3 CRYSTAL FIELD EFFECTS ON LOCALIZED MAGNETIC MOMENTS: VAN VLECK SUSCEPTIBILITY

4.3.1 System without exchange interaction

We are concerned in this section essentially with rare-earth ions where the kinetic orbital momentum is different from zero. As seen previously, the crystal field effects on the free ion lead to the splitting of the ground state multiplet. Each energy level E_n^0 is associated with a representation Γ_n of the symmetry group of the magnetic atom sites and to the states $|n, l\rangle$.

The magnetic moment m being defined as:

$$\langle m\rangle_T = -\frac{\partial E}{\partial H} \tag{4.3.1}$$

where E is the mean value of the energy of one atom at finite temperature T, the susceptibility of N atoms will be:

$$\chi = N\frac{\langle m\rangle_T}{H} = \frac{N}{H}\frac{\sum \frac{\partial E}{\partial H}\exp\left(-\frac{E}{kT}\right)}{\sum \exp\left(-\frac{E}{kT}\right)} \tag{4.3.2}$$

In the presence of a magnetic field the energy levels E_n^0 are split and the new energy levels $E_{n,l}$ (H) can be expanded up to the second order of perturbation:

$$E_{n,l}(H) = E_n^0 + W_1^{n,l}H + W_2^{n,l}H^2 + \cdots \tag{4.3.3}$$

n is associated with the energy states when $H=0$ and l is used to distinguish the levels which have the same energy when $H=0$. In the perturbation theory $W_1^{n,l}$ and $W_2^{n,l}$ are written as:

$$W_1^{n,l} = -g_J\mu_B\langle n,l|J_z|n,l\rangle \tag{4.3.4}$$

$$W_2^{n,l} = -g_J\mu_B^2 \sum_{\substack{l' \\ n'\neq n}} \frac{|\langle n,l|J_z|n,l\rangle|^2}{E_{n'}^0 - E_n^0} \tag{4.3.5}$$

In these formulae $\hat{J}_z$ is the component along the field H of the operator $\hat{J}$. We assume that the field is small and the temperature high enough so that:

$$W_1^{n,l}H + W_2^{n,l}H^2 \ll kT \tag{4.3.6}$$

This allows one to expand the exponential taking into account only the terms linear in H. One obtains then for the susceptibility:

$$\chi = -\frac{N}{H}\frac{\sum_{n,l}\left(W_1^{n,l} + 2W_2^{n,l}H\right)\left(1 - \frac{W_1^{n,l}H}{kT}\right)\exp\left(-\frac{E_n^0}{kT}\right)}{\sum_{n,l}\left(1 - \frac{W_1^{n,l}H}{kT}\right)\exp\left(-\frac{E_n^0}{kT}\right)} \tag{4.3.7}$$

Because of symmetry:

$$\sum_{n,l} W_1^{n,l} = 0 \tag{4.3.8}$$

whatever l is. This equation means that in the absence of a field there is no mean value of magnetization. The susceptibility is then:

$$\chi = \frac{N\langle m\rangle_T}{H} = -\frac{N}{kT}\frac{\sum_{n,l}\left(W_1^{n,l\,2} - 2kTW_2^{n,l}\right)\exp\left(-\frac{E_n^0}{kT}\right)}{\sum_{n,l}\exp\left(-\frac{E_n^0}{kT}\right)} \tag{4.3.9}$$

This formula is due to Van Vleck. It is quite general (on condition that H is small). We obtain the formula (4.1.14) if there is no crystal field effect.

We now apply this foruula in the case of two rare-earth compounds: $Pr_2(SO_4)_3 \cdot 8H_2O$ and $Nd_2(SO_4)_3 \cdot 8H_2O$.

(a) *Praseodymium*

In the ionic state Pr^{3+} has 2 electrons and the ground state multiplet is characterized by $L=5$, $S=1$ and then $J=4$. In $Pr_2(SO_4)_3 \cdot 8H_2O$, Pr^{3+} ions lie in a site of cubic symmetry. One can show from group theory that the $2J+1 = 9$ levels of the free ion are split by the cubic crystal field into a singlet Γ_1, one doublet Γ_3 and two triplets Γ_4 and Γ_5. The wave functions which diagonalize the crystal field Hamiltonian are shown in Table 4.3.1 In this Table

Δ is the overall crystal field splitting. The splitting of the ground state multiplet is shown in Fig. 4.3.1.

Table 4.3.1

Level	Degeneracy	$\psi^i_{\Gamma_n}$	E^0_n	$\frac{W_1^{n,l}}{(g_J\mu_B)}$	$\frac{W_2^{n,l}}{(g_J\mu_B)^2}$
Γ_1	1	$\frac{\sqrt{5}}{2\sqrt{6}}\|4,4\rangle+\frac{\sqrt{5}}{2\sqrt{6}}\|4,-4\rangle+\frac{\sqrt{7}}{2\sqrt{3}}\|4,0\rangle$	$-\frac{14}{27}\Delta$	0	$\frac{20}{21\Delta}$
Γ_4	3	$\frac{\sqrt{2}}{2}\|4,4\rangle-\frac{\sqrt{2}}{2}\|4,-4\rangle$	$-\frac{7}{27}\Delta$	0	$\frac{32}{35\Delta}$
		$\frac{1}{2\sqrt{2}}\|4,3\rangle+\frac{\sqrt{7}}{2\sqrt{2}}\|4,-1\rangle$		$-\frac{1}{2}$	$\frac{7}{80\Delta}$
		$\frac{\sqrt{7}}{2\sqrt{2}}\|4,1\rangle+\frac{1}{2\sqrt{2}}\|4,-3\rangle$		$+\frac{1}{2}$	$-\frac{7}{80\Delta}$
Γ_3	2	$\frac{\sqrt{7}}{2\sqrt{6}}\|4,4\rangle+\frac{\sqrt{7}}{2\sqrt{6}}\|4,-4\rangle-\frac{\sqrt{5}}{2\sqrt{3}}\|4,0\rangle$	$\frac{2}{27}\Delta$	0	$\frac{4}{15\Delta}$
		$\frac{\sqrt{2}}{2}\|4,2\rangle+\frac{\sqrt{2}}{2}\|4,-2\rangle$		0	$+\frac{4}{15\Delta}$
Γ_5	3	$\frac{\sqrt{2}}{2}\|4,2\rangle-\frac{\sqrt{2}}{2}\|4,-2\rangle$	$\frac{13}{27}\Delta$	0	$+\frac{4}{15\Delta}$
		$\frac{\sqrt{7}}{2\sqrt{2}}\|4,3\rangle+\frac{1}{2\sqrt{2}}\|4,-1\rangle$		$+\frac{5}{2}$	$+\frac{7}{80\Delta}$
		$\frac{-1}{2\sqrt{2}}\|4,1\rangle+\frac{\sqrt{7}}{2\sqrt{2}}\|4,-3\rangle$		$-\frac{5}{2}$	$+\frac{7}{80\Delta}$

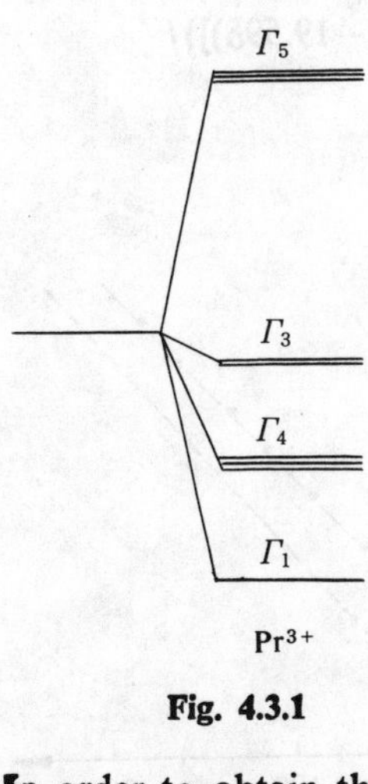

Fig. 4.3.1

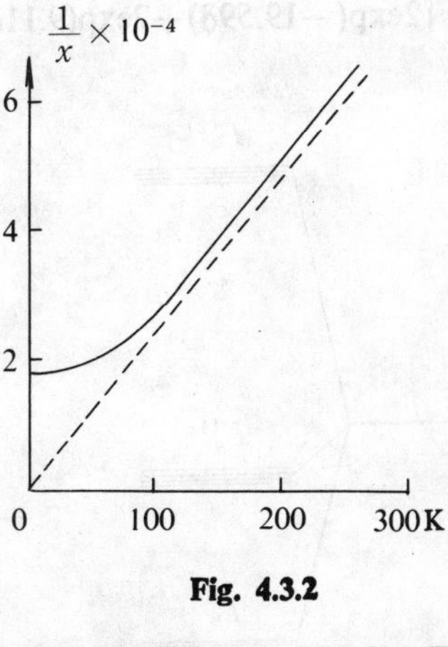

Fig. 4.3.2

In order to obtain the susceptibility one uses the formula (4.3.9). The first-order term $W_1^{n,l}$ is different from zero only for the triplets. Using the values of Table 4.3.1, one gets:

$$\chi = \frac{2Ng_J^2\mu_B^2}{\Delta/27} \times \frac{-\frac{53}{120}\exp(-13\delta)+\frac{61}{56}\exp(7\delta)+\frac{5}{21}\exp(14\delta)+\delta[25\exp(-13\delta)+\exp(7\delta)]}{3\exp(-13\delta)+2\exp(2\delta)+3\exp(7\delta)+\exp(14\delta)} \tag{4.3.10}$$

where $\delta=\Delta/27kT$.

The susceptibility calculated with this formula is in good agreement with the experimental results as shown in Fig. 4.3.2. The constant Δ (overall splitting of crystal field effects) which gives the best agreement is $\Delta=545$ Kelvin.

It is worth noting that the ground state in the crystal field is a non–magnetic singlet. Thus the magnetic moment and hence the susceptibility go to zero when the temperature is lowered.

(b) *Neodymium*

In the ionic state, Nd^{3+} has 3 electrons and the ground state multiplet $^4I_{9/2}$ is characterized by $L=6$, $S=3/2$ and $J=9/2$(cf 1.3.2). This ion is a Kramers ion because it has an odd number of electrons in the $4f$ shell. Kramers theorem says that for such ions the degeneracy of each level in the absence of magnetic field is even. Especially, singlet states are impossible. In a crystal field with cubic symmetry, the ground state multiplet is split into a doublet Γ_6 and two quadruplets $\Gamma_8^{(1)}$ and $\Gamma_8^{(2)}$, the ground state being a doublet as shown in Fig. 4.3.3; it is a Kramers doublet. All the levels have a Zeeman effect. The calculation is the same as for praseodymium. It leads to:

$$\chi=\frac{2Ng_J^2\mu_B^2}{\Delta} \times\{15.73\exp(20.95\delta)-9.715\exp(9.11\delta)-4.304\exp(-19.59\delta) +\delta[245.8\exp(20.95\delta)-163.4\exp(9.11\delta)-68.1\exp(-19.59\delta)]\}/ \{2\exp(-19.59\delta)+2\exp(9.11\delta)+\exp(20.95\delta)\} \tag{4.3.11}$$

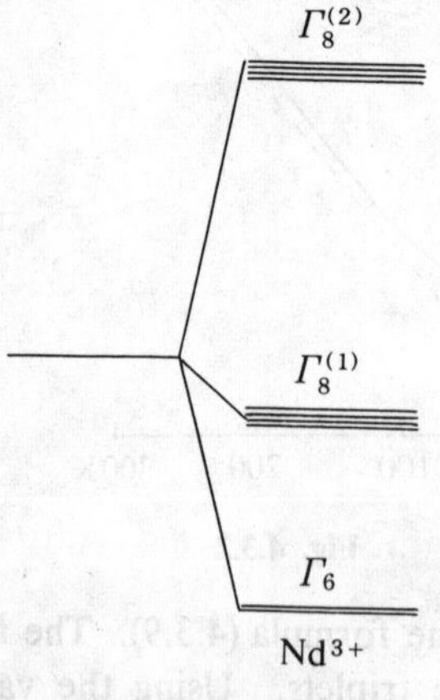

Fig. 4.3.3

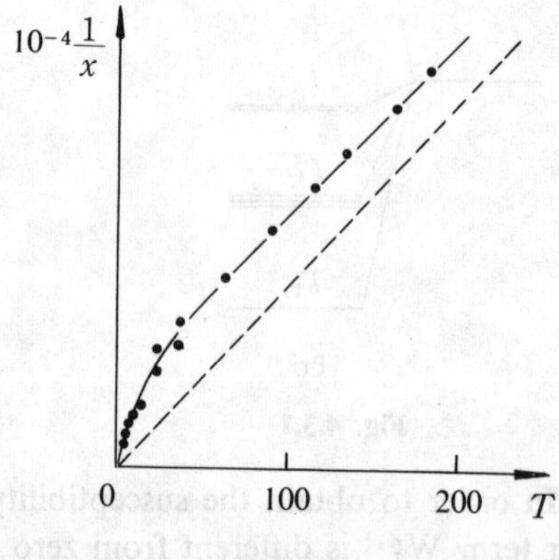

Fig.4.3.4

where $\delta = \frac{\Delta}{40.54\,kT}$, Δ being the overall splitting of the $^4I_{9/2}$ ground state multiplet by the crystal field. As shown in Fig. 4.3.4 the agreement between the experimental points and the calculated curve is good (Δ=1200 Kelvin). $1/\chi$ vanishes at $T=0$; the higher slope at the origin corresponding to a magnetic moment of the ground state multiplet smaller than that of the free ion.

In Figs. 4.3.2 and 4.3.4 the dashed lines are the asymptotes of the thermal variation of the reciprocal susceptibilities for high temperatures. They correspond to the variation expected in the absence of crystal field effects (Curie's law). The fact that these asymptotes pass through the origin shows that there are no exchange interactions in the $Pr_2(SO_4)_3 \cdot 8H_2O$ and $Nd_2(SO_4)_3 \cdot 8H_2O$ compounds.

4.3.2 System with exchange interactions: ferromagnetic compounds

Above the ordering temperature, the initial susceptibility is obtained for small values of H and so of the magnetization M. The formula (4.3.9) is thus always valid on condition that one replaces H by $H+WM$. The susceptibility in the absence of interaction, i.e. the susceptibility of a magnetic moment in the total field acting on it, is:

$$\chi = \frac{M}{H+WM} \tag{4.3.12}$$

This leads to:

$$\chi H + WM\chi = M \tag{4.3.13}$$

and

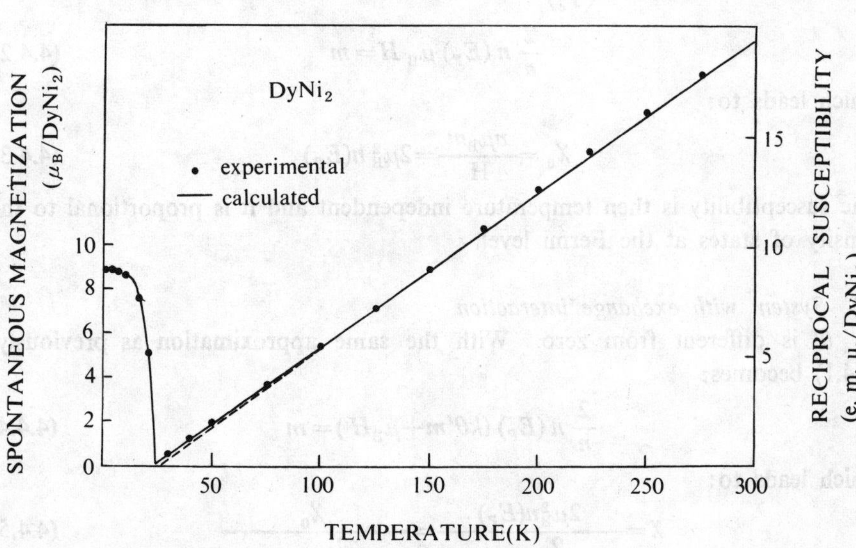

Fig. 4.3.5

$$H=\frac{M}{\chi}-WM \tag{4.3.14}$$

If χ_e is the measured susceptibility, one obtains:

$$\frac{1}{\chi_e}=\frac{1}{\chi}-W \tag{4.3.15}$$

As in the case when there are no crystal field effects, the exchange interactions lead to a shift of thermal variation of the susceptibility. This shift is a measure of the exchange interactions. The magnetic ordering occurs for the value of the temperature (T_c) where the reciprocal susceptibility goes to zero. This ordering temperature can be different from that which would be observed in the absence of crystal field effects. As an example, the thermal variation of the reciprocal susceptibility of $DyNi_2$ is shown in Fig. 4.3.5.

4.4 ITINERANT ELECTRON MAGNETISM: PAULI PARAMAGNETISM

The susceptibility of a system of itinerant electrons can be discussed from formula (10.2.4) of Chapter 10:

$$\frac{2}{n}\,n(E_F)\,(k\theta' m+\mu_B H)=m\left[1+\alpha\left(\frac{T}{T_c}\right)^2\right]+\gamma m^3\cdots \tag{4.4.1}$$

(a) *System without exchange interaction*

In this case $\theta'=0$. To the first oıder of approximation, considering that the splitting of the two subbands is small and that $n(E_F)$ is constant near the Fermi level, the terms $\alpha\left(\frac{T}{T_c}\right)^2$ and γ can be neglected. Then (4.4.1) becomes:

$$\frac{2}{n}\,n(E_F)\,\mu_B\,H=m \tag{4.4.2}$$

which leads to:

$$\chi_0=\frac{n\mu_B m}{\mathrm{H}}=2\mu_B^2\,n(E_F) \tag{4.4.3}$$

The susceptibility is then temperature independent and it is proportional to the density of states at the Fermi level.

(b) *System with exchange interaction*

θ' is different from zero. With the same approximation as previously, (4.4.1) becomes:

$$\frac{2}{n}\,n(E_F)\,(k\theta' m+\mu_B H)=m \tag{4.4.4}$$

which leads to:

$$\chi=\frac{2\mu_B^2 n(E_F)}{1-\frac{2}{n}n(E_F)k\theta'}=\frac{\chi_0}{1-\frac{2}{n}n(E_F)k\theta'} \tag{4.4.5}$$

Taking into account that $\theta' = \frac{n\bar{U}}{2k}$, (18.45) becomes:

$$\chi = \frac{\chi_0}{1 - \bar{U}n(E_F)} \tag{4.4.6}$$

In a paramagnetic compound the Stoner criterion $\bar{U}n(E_F) > 1$ is not satisfied and the value of the denominator lies between 0 and 1. The interactions ($\bar{U}$) tend to decrease the denominator and thus to increase the susceptibility: the susceptibility is enhanced by the exchange interactions.

When the density of states at the Fermi level is far from constant the term α in (4.4.1) is no longer negligible and the susceptibility becomes hardly temperature dependent. The effect is well illustrated in YCo_2: the thermal variation of its susceptibility is shown in Fig. 10.4.1.

CHAPTER 5

DETERMINATION OF MAGNETIC STRUCTURES

It will be shown in the following chapters that various types of interactions may couple magnetic ions in a solid. And furthermore, for a given type of interaction, say Heisenberg bilinear exchange $-J_{ij}\hat{\mathbf{S}}_i \cdot \hat{\mathbf{S}}_j$, we may expect competition between nearest neighbour interactions. It is clear that the resulting magnetic ordering, if any, will reflect this competition; in turn, the determination of the magnetic order will give us valuable information about the different couplings.

A large variety of magnetic structures has been observed in nature, which is due to different combinations of interactions. But how can we determine magnetic structures? This can be done by carrying out neutron diffraction experiments. Since neutrons have a spin ($S=1/2$) they couple to magnetic moments; they also interact with nuclei. Hence we can obtain diffraction patterns from the magnetic system and from the underlying lattice.

First we present an introduction to magnetic scattering of neutrons; then we will present some possible types of magnetic ordering.

5.1 MAGNETIC SCATTERING OF NEUTRONS

Consider a beam of neutrons in the quantum state described by $|\sigma,\mathbf{k}\rangle$; σ is the polarisation, and $\mathbf{k}$ the wave vector. They are scattered by the sample under investigation. Measurements are made by setting a counter which defines a solid angle $d\Omega$, and measuring the scattered neutrons as a function of their energy and direction. The results are expressed in terms of the partial cross section $\dfrac{d^2\sigma}{d\Omega\, dE}$, which is defined by (total number of neutrons scattered per second, into the solid angle $d\Omega$ with final energy between E and $E+dE)/\Phi d\Omega dE$, where Φ is the incident neutron flux.

Incident neutrons have the wave vector $\mathbf{k}$; scattered neutrons have the wave vector $\mathbf{k}'$ that lies in the solid angle $d\Omega$ (Fig. 5.1.1). If we denote by $|\lambda\rangle$ the state of the scattering system, we have:

$$\frac{d^2\sigma}{d\Omega\, dE}=\frac{|\mathbf{k}'|}{|\mathbf{k}|}\left(\frac{m_n}{2\hbar^2\pi}\right)^2 \quad |\langle\sigma'\mathbf{k}'\lambda'|\hat{V}|\sigma\mathbf{k}\lambda\rangle|^2\delta(E_\lambda-E_{\lambda'}+E_0-E) \quad (5.1.1)$$

where $E_0(E_\lambda)$ and $E(E_{\lambda'})$ are initial and final energies of the neutrons (scatterer) respectively. $\hat{V}$ represents the interaction potential between neutrons and the scattering system. $\hat{V}$ contains a nucleus neutron interaction, which gives rise to

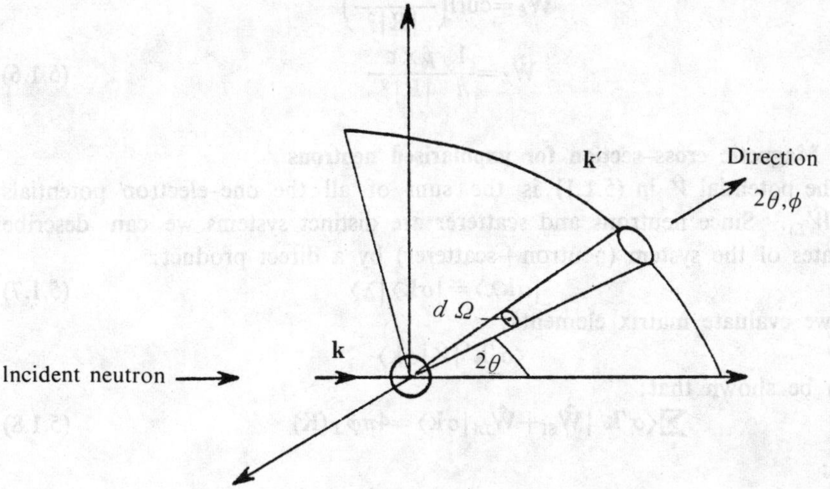

Fig. 5.1.1
Geometry for scattering experiment.

nuclear scattering, and a magnetic interaction.

5.1.1 Interaction neutron–electron

Neutrons have a magnetic moment operator related to the spin by:

$$\hat{\mu}_n = -\gamma \mu_n \hat{\sigma} \tag{5.1.2}$$

where: $\gamma = 1.913$ and $\mu_N = \dfrac{e\hbar}{2m_p}$ is the nuclear magneton. $\hat{\sigma}$ is the Pauli spin operator.

Electrons have a magnetic dipole moment

$$\hat{\mu}_e = -2\mu_B \hat{\mathbf{s}} \tag{5.1.3}$$

where μ_B is the Bohr magneton.

The neutron magnetic moment is subjected to the magnetic field $\hat{\mathbf{B}}(\mathbf{R})$ created by the electron. In the dipolar approximation $\hat{\mathbf{B}}(\mathbf{R})$ decomposes into two parts: a spin part $\hat{\mathbf{B}}_s$ due to magnetic dipole moment and an "orbital" part $\hat{\mathbf{B}}_L$ due to momentum $\hat{p}$:

$$\hat{\mathbf{B}}_s(\mathbf{R}) = \frac{\mu_0}{4\pi} \operatorname{curl} \frac{\mu_e \times \mathbf{u}}{|\mathbf{R}|^2} \tag{5.1.4}$$

$$\hat{\mathbf{B}}_L(\mathbf{R}) = -\frac{\mu_0}{4\pi} \frac{2\mu_B}{\hbar} \frac{\hat{p} \times \mathbf{u}}{|\mathbf{R}|^2}$$

where $\mathbf{u}$ is a unit vector parallel to $\mathbf{R}$. $\mathbf{R}$ is the position of the neutron with respect to the electron; μ_0 is the vacuum permeability.

Thus the potential interaction $\hat{V}$ can be written as follows:

$$\hat{V} = -\hat{\mu}_n \hat{\mathbf{B}} = \frac{\mu_0}{4\pi} \gamma \, \mu_N \, 2\mu_B \, \hat{\sigma} \, (\hat{\mathbf{W}}_S + \hat{\mathbf{W}}_L) \tag{5.1.5}$$

where

$$\hat{\mathbf{W}}_S = \mathrm{curl}\left(\frac{\hat{\mathbf{s}} \times \mathbf{u}}{|\mathbf{R}|^2}\right)$$

$$\hat{\mathbf{W}}_L = \frac{1}{\hbar}\frac{\hat{p} \times \mathbf{u}}{|\mathbf{R}|^2} \tag{5.1.6}$$

5.1.2 Magnetic cross-section for unpolarised neutrons

The potential $\hat{V}$ in (5.1.1) is the sum of all the one-electron potentials $\hat{W}_{\mathrm{Si}} + \hat{W}_{\mathrm{Li}}$. Since neutrons and scatterer are distinct systems we can describe the states of the system (neutron+scatterer) by a direct product:

$$|\sigma \mathbf{k} \lambda\rangle = |\sigma \mathbf{k}\rangle |\lambda\rangle \tag{5.1.7}$$

First we evaluate matrix elements:

$$\langle \sigma' \mathbf{k}' | \hat{V} | \sigma \mathbf{k}\rangle$$

It can be shown that:

$$\sum_i \langle \sigma' \mathbf{k}' | \hat{\mathbf{W}}_{\mathrm{Si}} + \hat{\mathbf{W}}_{\mathrm{Li}} | \sigma \mathbf{k}\rangle = 4\pi \hat{\varphi}_\perp(\hat{\mathbf{K}}) \tag{5.1.8}$$

where:

$$\hat{\varphi}_\perp(\mathbf{K}) = \sum_i \exp(\mathrm{i}\mathbf{K}\cdot\mathbf{r}_i)\left\{\hat{K} \times (\hat{\mathbf{s}}_i \times \hat{\mathbf{K}}) + \frac{\mathrm{i}}{\hbar|\mathbf{K}|}(\hat{p}_i \times \hat{\mathbf{K}})\right\}$$

K is the scattering vector defined in Fig. 5.1.2:

$$\mathbf{K} = \mathbf{k} - \mathbf{k}' \tag{5.1.9}$$

and $\hat{\mathbf{K}}$ is a unit vector in the direction of **K**.

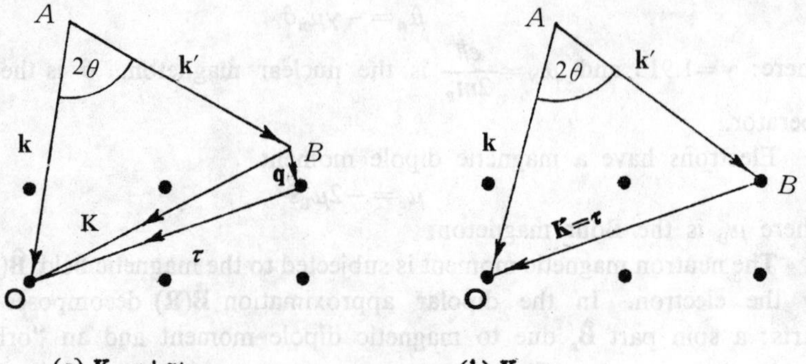

(a) $\mathbf{K} = \boldsymbol{\tau} + \mathbf{q}$; (b) $\mathbf{K} = \boldsymbol{\tau}$

Fig. 5.1.2 Scattering triangle.

We can simplify out some of the constants in (5.1.4), (5.1.5) and (5.1.8):

$$\frac{m_n}{2\pi\hbar^2} \cdot \frac{\mu_0}{4\pi} \cdot \gamma \cdot \frac{e\hbar}{2m_p} \cdot 2\frac{e\hbar}{2m_e} \cdot 4\pi = \gamma r_0 \frac{m_n}{m_p} \simeq \gamma r_0 \tag{5.1.10}$$

where

$$r_0 = \frac{\mu_0}{4\pi}\frac{e^2}{m_e} \tag{5.1.11}$$

is the classical electron radius ($r_0 = 0.28 \times 10^{-12}$cm). Writing the energy difference

(E_0-E) as $\hbar\omega$, we arrive at:

$$\left(\frac{d^2\sigma}{d\Omega dE}\right)_{\substack{\lambda\to\lambda' \\ \sigma\to\sigma'}} =(\gamma r_0)^2\frac{|\mathbf{k}'|}{|\mathbf{k}|}|\langle\sigma'\lambda'|\hat{\sigma}\cdot\hat{\varphi}_\perp(\mathbf{K})\,|\sigma\lambda\rangle|^2\delta(E_\lambda-E_{\lambda'}+\hbar\omega) \quad (5.1.12)$$

For simplicity we consider the spin part of $\hat{Q}_\perp(\mathbf{K})$.

$$\hat{\mathbf{Q}}_{\perp s}(\mathbf{K})=\sum_i\exp(i\mathbf{K}\cdot\mathbf{r}_i)\{\hat{\mathbf{K}}\times(\hat{s}_i\times\hat{\mathbf{K}})\} \quad (5.1.13)$$

Consider a vector $\mathbf{V}$; its projection perpendicular to the vector $\mathbf{K}$ is $\mathbf{V}_\perp$:

$$\mathbf{V}_\perp=\hat{\mathbf{K}}\times(\mathbf{V}\times\hat{\mathbf{K}})$$

The $\hat{\mathbf{Q}}_{\perp s}$ vector is the projection perpendicular to $\hat{\mathbf{K}}$ of a vector $\hat{Q}_s(\mathbf{K})$

$$\hat{\mathbf{Q}}_s(\mathbf{K})=\sum_i\exp(i\mathbf{K}\cdot\mathbf{r}_i)\hat{s}_i \quad (5.1.14)$$

which is proportional to the Fourier transform of the spin magnetization operator $\hat{m}_s(\mathbf{r})$

$$\hat{m}_s(\mathbf{r})=-2\mu_B\sum_i\delta(\mathbf{r}-\mathbf{r}_i)\hat{s}_i \quad (5.1.15)$$

The same holds when we include orbital effects. We have:

$$\hat{\mathbf{Q}}(\mathbf{K})=-\frac{1}{2\mu_B}\hat{\mathbf{M}}(\mathbf{K})=-\frac{1}{2\mu_B}\int\exp(i\mathbf{K}\cdot\mathbf{r})\,\hat{m}(\mathbf{r})d\mathbf{r} \quad (5.1.16)$$

and

$$\hat{\mathbf{Q}}_\perp(\mathbf{K})=\mathbf{K}\times(\hat{\mathbf{Q}}(\mathbf{K})\times\hat{\mathbf{Q}})=\hat{\mathbf{Q}}(\mathbf{K})-(\hat{\mathbf{Q}}(\mathbf{K})\cdot\hat{\mathbf{K}})\hat{\mathbf{K}}$$

The important result is that a neutron scattering experiment gives information about Fourier components of magnetic moments.

The quantity in (5.1.12) must be summed over the final states σ' and λ' and averaged over the initial states $\sigma\lambda$. In what follows, we assume an unpolarised neutron beam: the $\hat{\sigma}^z$ component of the neutron spin can take the values $\pm 1/2$ with equal probability $p=1/2$. We evaluate:

$$\begin{aligned} A&=\sum_{\sigma\sigma'}p_\sigma|\langle\sigma'\lambda'|\hat{\sigma}\cdot\hat{\mathbf{Q}}_\perp|\sigma\lambda\rangle|^2\\ &=\sum_{\sigma\sigma'}p_\sigma\langle\sigma'\lambda'|\hat{\sigma}\cdot\hat{\mathbf{Q}}_\perp|\sigma\lambda\rangle^*\langle\sigma'\lambda'|\sigma\cdot\hat{\mathbf{Q}}_\perp|\sigma\lambda\rangle \quad (5.1.17)\\ &=\sum_{\sigma\sigma'}p_\sigma\langle\sigma\lambda|\hat{\mathbf{Q}}_\perp^{+}\cdot\hat{\sigma}^{+}|\sigma'\lambda'\rangle\langle\sigma'\lambda'|\hat{\sigma}\cdot\hat{\mathbf{Q}}_\perp|\sigma\lambda\rangle \end{aligned}$$

where A^+ is the Hermitian conjugate of A

$$\langle j|A|i\rangle=\langle i|A^+|j\rangle^*$$

We recall that operators corresponding to physical quantities (position, momentum, energy, z–component of magnetization) are Hermitian.

The $\hat{\sigma}$ operators are given in terms of Pauli matrices in Chapter 1 (1.1.27). These calculations, with $p_{1/2}=p_{-1/2}=1/2$, lead to:

$$A=\sum_\alpha\langle\lambda|\hat{Q}_{\perp\alpha}^{+}|\lambda'\rangle\langle\lambda'|\hat{Q}_{\perp\alpha}|\lambda\rangle \quad (5.1.18)$$

where α is a coordinate. The cross–section in (5.1.12) must be summed over the final states λ' and averaged over the initial states λ of the scatterer. This leads to:

$$\frac{d^2\sigma}{d\Omega dE}=(\gamma r_0)^2\frac{|\mathbf{k}'|}{|\mathbf{k}|}\sum_{\lambda\lambda'}p_\lambda\sum_\alpha\langle\lambda|\hat{Q}_{\perp\alpha}^{+}|\lambda'\rangle\langle\lambda'|\hat{Q}_{\perp\alpha}|\lambda\rangle\delta(E_\lambda-E_{\lambda'}+\hbar\omega) \quad (5.1.19)$$

where p_λ is the probability that the scatterer is in the state $|\lambda\rangle$; if we make use of (5.1.14):

$$\frac{d^2\sigma}{d\Omega dE}=(\gamma r_0)^2\frac{|\mathbf{k}'|}{|\mathbf{k}|}\sum_{\alpha\beta}(\delta_{\alpha\beta}-\hat{K}_\alpha\hat{K}_\beta)$$
$$\times\sum_{\lambda\lambda'}p_\lambda\langle\lambda|\hat{Q}_\alpha^+(\mathbf{K})|\lambda'\rangle\langle\lambda'|\hat{Q}_\beta(\mathbf{K})|\lambda\rangle\delta(E_\lambda-E_\beta+\hbar\omega) \tag{5.1.20}$$

Now we consider a localized system; the electrons are localized around fixed nuclei in the lattice (we thus neglect any coupling between spins and lattice vibrations). In that case, we can write:

$$\hat{\mathbf{Q}}_s(\mathbf{K})=\sum_{li}\exp(i\mathbf{K}\cdot\mathbf{R}_{li})\sum_p\exp(i\mathbf{K}\cdot\mathbf{r}_p)\hat{\mathbf{s}}_p \tag{5.1.21}$$

where $\mathbf{R}_{li}$ locates the i–th nucleus in the l–th cell. The matrix element of $\hat{Q}_s$ can be expressed as:

$$\langle\lambda'|\hat{\mathbf{Q}}_s|\lambda\rangle=\sum_{li}\langle\lambda'|\hat{\mathbf{Q}}_s\rangle\lambda\rangle_{li}$$
$$\langle\lambda'|\hat{Q}_s|\lambda\rangle_{li}=\langle\lambda'|\exp(i\mathbf{K}\cdot\mathbf{R}_{li})\sum_p\exp(i\mathbf{K}\cdot\mathbf{r}_p)\hat{\mathbf{s}}_p|\lambda\rangle$$
$$=\exp(i\mathbf{K}\cdot\mathbf{R}_{li})f_i(\mathbf{K})\langle\lambda'|\hat{\mathbf{S}}_{li}|\lambda\rangle \tag{5.1.22}$$

where $\hat{\mathbf{S}}_{li}$ is the spin operator of the i–th atom and

$f_i(\mathbf{K})=\int s_i(\mathbf{r})\exp(i\mathbf{K}\cdot\mathbf{r})\,dr$ represents the Fourier transform of magnetic electron density $s_i(\mathbf{r})$; $f_i(\mathbf{K})$ is known as the spin form factor of the i–th atom. If we include orbital effects, a form similar to (5.1.22) can be obtained by replacing $f_i(\mathbf{K})$ by:

$$\frac{1}{2}gf_i(\mathbf{K})=g_SJ_0+g_L(J_0+J_2)$$

$$J_n=4\pi\int_0^\infty j_n(Kr)\,s_i(r)r^2dr$$

where g_S, g_L and g are the spin, orbital and Landé factors respectively; $j_n(Kr)$ is a Bessel function; this result is valid only for small $|\mathbf{K}|$ values and is known as the dipole approximation. $\hat{\mathbf{J}}$ is the total moment operator. Thus the cross–section (5.1.21) is written:

$$\frac{d^2\sigma}{d\Omega dE}=\left(\frac{\gamma r_0}{2}\right)^2\frac{|\mathbf{k}'|}{|\mathbf{k}|}\sum_{\alpha\beta}(\delta_{\alpha\beta}-\hat{K}_\alpha\hat{K}_\beta)$$
$$\times\sum_{l'i'}\sum_{li}g_{i'}f_{i'}^*(\mathbf{K})g_if_i(\mathbf{K})\exp(-i\mathbf{K}\cdot\mathbf{R}_{l'i'})\exp(i\mathbf{K}\cdot\mathbf{R}_{li})$$
$$\times\sum_{\lambda\lambda'}p_\lambda\langle\lambda|\hat{J}^+_{l'i',\alpha}|\lambda'\rangle\langle\lambda'|\hat{J}_{li,\beta}|\lambda\rangle\delta(E_{\lambda'}-E_\lambda+\hbar\omega) \tag{5.1.23}$$

A δ–function $\delta(x)$ can be written as:

$$\delta(x)=\frac{1}{2\pi}\int_{-\infty}^{+\infty}\exp(ikx)\,dk$$

Thus

$$\delta(E_\lambda-E_{\lambda'}+\hbar\omega)=\frac{1}{2\pi\hbar}\int_{-\infty}^{+\infty}\exp[i(E_{\lambda'}-E_\lambda)\,t/\hbar]\exp(-i\omega t)dt \tag{5.1.24}$$

E_λ is the eigenvalue of the Hamiltonian $\hat{H}$ of the magnetic system in the state described by $|\lambda\rangle$, then

$$\exp(i\hat{H}t/\hbar)|\lambda\rangle=\exp(iE_\lambda t/\hbar)|\lambda\rangle \tag{5.1.25}$$

Introducing time–dependent operators:

$$\hat{\mathbf{J}}_{li}(t)=\exp(i\hat{H}t/\hbar)\hat{\mathbf{J}}_{li}\exp(-i\hat{H}t/\hbar) \tag{5.1.26}$$

and using (5.1.25), the sum over λ and λ' in (5.1.24) is expressed as:

$$\frac{1}{2\pi\hbar}\int e^{-i\omega t}dt\sum_{\lambda\lambda'}p_\lambda\langle\lambda|\hat{J}_{l'i',\alpha}(0)|\lambda'\rangle\langle\lambda'|\hat{J}_{li,\beta}(t)|\lambda\rangle \tag{5.1.27}$$

The sum over λ' represents the product of the two operators $\hat{J}_{l'i',\alpha}(0)$ and $\hat{J}_{li,\beta}(t)$; thus we have

$$\frac{1}{2\pi\hbar}\int e^{-i\omega t}dt\sum_{\lambda}p_\lambda\langle\lambda|\hat{J}^{+}_{l'i',\alpha}(0)\hat{J}_{li,\beta}(t)|\lambda\rangle$$

Now we recall that p_λ is the probability that the scattering system (i.e. the spin system) is in the state $|\lambda\rangle$. The thermal average value of the operator $\hat{A}$ is given by:

$$\langle A\rangle_T=\sum_\lambda p_\lambda\langle\lambda|\hat{A}|\lambda\rangle$$

Thus, the magnetic cross-section for unpolarised neutrons is given by:

$$\begin{aligned}\frac{d^2\sigma}{d\Omega dE}&=\left(\frac{\gamma r_0}{2}\right)^2\frac{1}{2\pi\hbar}\frac{|\mathbf{k}'|}{|\mathbf{k}|}\sum_{\alpha\beta}(\delta_{\alpha\beta}-\hat{K}_\alpha\hat{K}_\beta)\\&\times\sum_{li,l'i'}(g_ig_{i'})f_i(\mathbf{K})f_{i'}(\mathbf{K})\exp i\mathbf{K}\cdot(\mathbf{R}_{li}-\mathbf{R}_{l'i'})\\&\times\int_{-\infty}^{+\infty}\langle\hat{J}^{+}_{l'i',\alpha}(0)\hat{J}_{li,\beta}(t)\rangle_T e^{-i\omega t}dt\end{aligned} \tag{5.1.28}$$

5.1.3 Elastic scattering

The magnetic cross-section (5.1.28) contains the time-dependent term

$$G_{nm}(t)=\langle\mathbf{\hat{J}}^{+}_{n}(0)\mathbf{\hat{J}}_m(t)\rangle_T$$

Let us consider the time dependence. At first, if the spin operators commute with the Hamiltonian $\hat{H}$ in (5.1.26), then there is no time dependence, the scattering is purely elastic $\left(\int e^{-i\omega t}dt=2\pi\delta(\omega)\right)$. This is the case in paramagnetic substances when there is no applied magnetic field and there is no correlation between different spins:

$$\langle\hat{J}_{l'i',\alpha}^{+}\hat{J}_{li,\beta}\rangle_T=\langle\hat{J}_{l'i',\alpha}\rangle_T\langle\hat{J}_{li,\beta}\rangle_T\equiv0$$

if $l'i'\neq li$. The non-vanishing terms arise from the same site correlations:

$$\begin{aligned}\langle\hat{J}^{+}_{li,\alpha}\hat{J}_{li,\beta}\rangle_T&=\delta_{\alpha\beta}\langle\hat{J}^{+}_{i,\alpha}\hat{J}_{i,\alpha}\rangle_T\\&=\frac{1}{3}\delta_{\alpha\beta}\langle\hat{J}^2_i\rangle_T=\frac{1}{3}J_i(J_i+1)\delta_{\alpha\beta}\end{aligned}$$

Thus the elastic cross section for a paramagnet is:

$$\begin{aligned}\frac{d\sigma}{d\Omega}&=\left(\frac{\gamma r_0}{2}\right)^2\sum_{\alpha\beta}(\delta_{\alpha\beta}-\hat{K}_\alpha\hat{K}_\beta)\sum_{li}g_i^2f_i^2(\mathbf{K})\frac{J_i(J_i+1)}{3}\delta_{\alpha\beta}\\&=\frac{2}{3}\left(\frac{\gamma r_0}{2}\right)^2N\sum_i g_i^2f_i^2(\mathbf{K})J_i(J_i+1)\end{aligned} \tag{5.1.29}$$

The scattering is incoherent.

However, in general, the correlation function $G_{nm}(t)$ does depend on time; it can be expressed as

$$G_{nm}(t)=G_{nm}(\infty)+G'_{nm}(t) \tag{5.1.30}$$

The term $G_{nm}(\infty)$ is responsible for the inelastic scattering which will be considered in a subsequent chapter. Let us concentrate on the elastic part:

$$G_{nm}(\infty)=\lim_{t\to\infty}\langle\hat{\mathbf{J}}_n^+(0)\hat{\mathbf{J}}_m(t)\rangle_T=\langle\hat{\mathbf{J}}_n^+\rangle_T\langle\hat{\mathbf{J}}_m\rangle_T$$

Let us denote by $\mathbf{m}_n$ (a vector) the thermal average of $g_n\hat{J}_n$. The elastic cross-section is then written as

$$\frac{d\sigma}{d\Omega}=\left(\frac{\gamma r_0}{2}\right)^2\sum_{\alpha\beta}(\delta_{\alpha\beta}-\hat{K}_\alpha\hat{K}_\beta)$$
$$\times\sum_{l'i'}f_{i'}(\mathbf{K})m^*_{l'i',\alpha}e^{-i\mathbf{K}\cdot\mathbf{R}_{l'i'}}\sum_{li}f_i(\mathbf{K})m_{li,\beta}e^{i\mathbf{K}\cdot\mathbf{R}_{li}}$$

Then it is useful to introduce a magnetic structure factor $\mathbf{F}(\mathbf{K})$:

$$\mathbf{F}(\mathbf{K})=\sum_{li}f_i(\mathbf{K})\mathbf{m}_{li}e^{i\mathbf{K}\cdot\mathbf{R}_{li}} \tag{5.1.31}$$

The elastic magnetic scattering cross-section takes the form:

$$\frac{d\sigma}{d\Omega}=\left(\frac{\gamma r_0}{2}\right)^2\sum_{\alpha\beta}(\delta_{\alpha\beta}-\hat{K}_\alpha\hat{K}_\beta)F^*_\alpha(\mathbf{K})F_\beta(\mathbf{K}) \tag{5.1.32}$$

or

$$\frac{d\sigma}{d\Omega}=\left(\frac{\gamma r_0}{2}\right)^2\left\{|\mathbf{F}(\mathbf{K})|^2-\frac{|\mathbf{K}\cdot\mathbf{F}(\mathbf{K})|^2}{|\mathbf{K}|^2}\right\}$$

with

$$\left(\frac{\gamma r_0}{2}\right)\simeq 0.27\times 10^{-14}\mathrm{m}.$$

In a crystalline magnetic compound, there is a long-range order of the magnetic moments, this means that the magnetization is periodic, even if it is incommensurable with the underlying lattice. Thus the $\mathbf{m}_{l,i}$ can be expressed as:

$$\mathbf{m}_{l,i}=\sum_{\{\mathbf{q}\}}\mathbf{m}_q^i\exp(i\mathbf{q}\cdot\mathbf{R}_l) \tag{5.1.33}$$

where $\mathbf{q}$ is restricted to the first Brillouin zone; $\{\mathbf{q}\}$ denotes a set of vectors $\mathbf{q}_p$ belonging to the star of $\mathbf{q}$ (see Chapter 1). If $\mathbf{q}$ is not equivalent to $-\mathbf{q}$, then $+\mathbf{q}$ and $-\mathbf{q}$ are in the summation (5.1.34).

Inserting (5.1.33) in (5.1.31) yields

$$\mathbf{F}(\mathbf{K})=\sum_{i,\{\mathbf{q}\}}f_i(\mathbf{K})\mathbf{m}_q^i e^{i\mathbf{K}\cdot\mathbf{r}_i}\sum_l e^{i\mathbf{R}_l\cdot(\mathbf{K}+\mathbf{q})}$$

But

$$\sum_l e^{i\mathbf{R}_l\cdot(\mathbf{K}+\mathbf{q})}=\frac{(2\pi)^3}{V_0}\sum_\tau\delta(\mathbf{K}+\mathbf{q}-\boldsymbol{\tau})$$

where V_0 is the unit cell volume. Then

$$\mathbf{F}(\mathbf{K})=\frac{(2\pi)^3}{V_0}\sum_{i\{\mathbf{q}\},\tau}f_i(\mathbf{K})\mathbf{m}_q^i e^{i\mathbf{K}\cdot\mathbf{r}_i}\delta(\mathbf{K}+\mathbf{q}-\boldsymbol{\tau}) \tag{5.1.34}$$

Due to the delta function in (5.1.34), magnetic scattering will be observed at some particular points in reciprocal space. The observed scattered intensity is given as

$$I_m(K)=\sum_{\mathbf{h}}I_m(\mathbf{h})\delta(\mathbf{K}-\mathbf{h}) \tag{5.1.35}$$

The easiest way to determine those $\mathbf{h}$ vectors (or the $\mathbf{q}$ vectors) in the Brillouin zone is to perform a powder diffraction experiment, the difference between spectra at low temperatures (ordered phase) and high temperatures (paramagnetic or disordered phase) yields magnetic peaks (Fig. 5.1.3) whose positions provide a et.rmination of the **q** vectors.

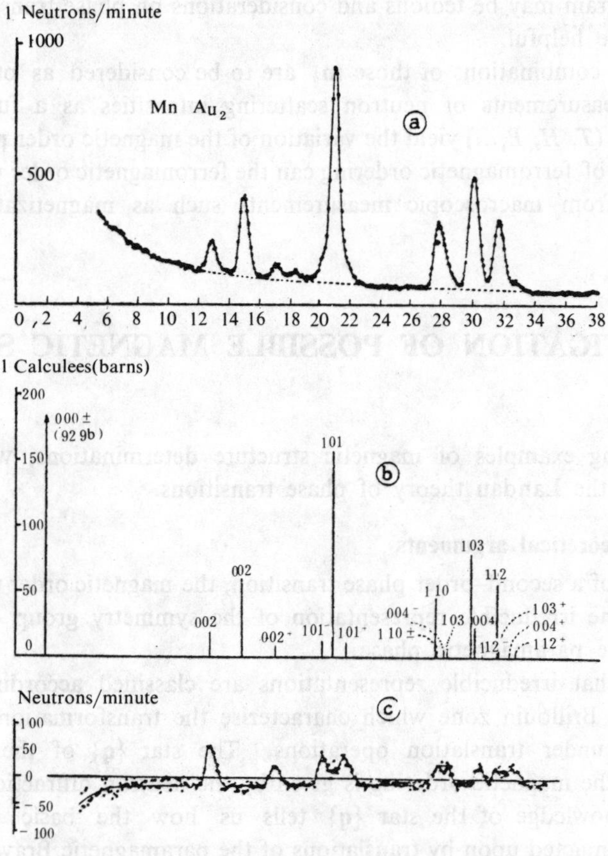

Fig. 5.1.3

Neutron scattering from $MnAu_2$. (a) Spectrum at 293 K, (b) calculated intensities, (c) difference between spectra at 293 K and 423 K (After Herpin et al. 1968)

The knowledge of $\{\mathbf{q}\}$ gives us all the information about the translational symmetry of the magnetic phase (5.1.33). However, the determination of the different $\mathbf{m}_q^i$ is obtained by a direct comparison of the observed intensities $I_m(\mathbf{K})$ with the calculated intensities $I(\mathbf{K})$:

$$I(\mathbf{K}) = RC(\mathbf{K}) \frac{d\sigma}{d\Omega} \qquad (5.1.36)$$

where $\frac{d\sigma}{d\Omega}$ is the cross–section (5.1.32), R is an instrumental factor and $C(\mathbf{K})$ a function which contains the Lorentz factor, absorption and extinction corrections… .

In the case of a Bravais lattice (one site per cell), it is relatively easy to determine the direction of $\mathbf{m}_q$ and the number of vectors $\mathbf{q}$ which enter the summation (5.1.33). In the case of a non–Bravais lattice (several equivalent sites per cell) such a program may be tedious and considerations on phase transitions and group theory are helpful.

Some linear combinations of those $\mathbf{m}_q^i$ are to be considered as order parameters, thus measurements of neutron scattering intensities as a function of external variable (T, H, P,...) yield the variation of the magnetic order parameter. Only in the case of ferromagnetic ordering can the ferromagnetic order parameter be determined from macroscopic measurements such as magnetization measurements.

5.2 INVESTIGATION OF POSSIBLE MAGNETIC STRUCTURES

Before giving examples of magnetic structure determinations, we discuss some results of the Landau theory of phase transitions.

5.2.1 Group theoretical arguments

In the case of a second–order phase transition, the magnetic order parameter transforms as one irreducible representation of the symmetry group G_0 of the high–temperature paramagnetic phase.

We know that irreducible representations are classified according to the $\mathbf{k}$ vectors in the Brillouin zone which characterise the transformations of their basis functions under translation operations. The star $\{\mathbf{q}\}$ of the $\mathbf{q}$ vectors associated with the magnetic ordering is given by the neutron diffraction pattern (5.1.35). The knowledge of the star $\{\mathbf{q}\}$ tells us how the basic pattern is transformed when acted upon by translations of the paramagnetic Bravais lattice.

In order to determine the inner features of this basic pattern we must compare the observed magnetic intensities $I_m(\mathbf{k})$ with those obtained from various models; those models can be obtained from the knowledge of the irreducible representations $\Gamma^{q,m}$ of G_0. The magnetisation $\mathbf{m}_{l,i}$ induces a representation Γ of G_0; since we are interested in representations associated with the star $\{\mathbf{q}\}$, we can restrict ourselves to the loaded representation Γ of the group G_q of the vector $\mathbf{q}$, which is induced by the components of $\mathbf{m}_q^i$. We reduce Γ to $\Gamma^{q,m}$. In general, the basis functions of $\Gamma^{q,m}$ are linear combinations of the $\mathbf{m}_{q\alpha}^i$; these basic functions can be used as a trial basis for the magnetic structure. The couplings between different $\mathbf{m}_{q\alpha}^i$ (coefficients of the linear combinations) are to be obtained from a comparison with the observed neutron scattering intensities.

5.2.2 An example: f.c.c. lattice—Antiferromagnetism of type II

Many magnetic compounds have a f.c.c. crystallographic structure. The

Brillouin zone of a f.c.c. lattice is represented in Fig. 5.2.1; there are four high-symmetry points

$\Gamma=(0, 0, 0)$; $X=(0, 0, 1)$; $L=(1/2, 1/2, 1/2)$; and $W=(1/2, 1\ 1/2, 0)$.

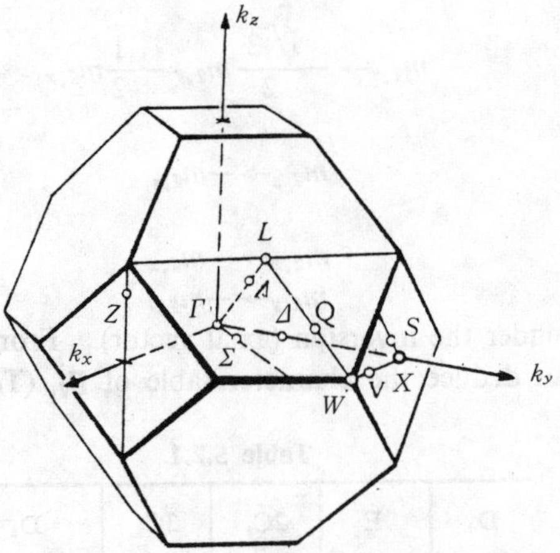

Fig. 5.2.1
Brillouin zone of f.c.c. lattice.

Let us consider the space group O_h^5 (symmorphic—one Bravais lattice). A powder diffraction experiment gives the value of the wave vector **q** (5.1.35) associated with the magnetic structure. If magnetic intensity appears at scattering $\mathbf{K}=\boldsymbol{\tau}$, then $\mathbf{q}=(0, 0, 0)$; the structure is ferromagnetic. If the **q** vector is at the X point, we have an antiferromagnetic structure of type I, the L point is associated with type II antiferromagnetism and the W point gives type III antiferromagnetism.

Suppose that scattering takes place for wave vector **K**, $\mathbf{K}=\boldsymbol{\tau}+\mathbf{q}$ with $\mathbf{q}=(1/2, 1/2; 1/2)$. The point group G_q is D_{3d}, obtained from D_3 by the direct product $D_3\times C_i$ with $C_i\equiv(E,i)$. Characters for D_3 are shown in Table 5.2.1.

There are 4 **q** vectors in the star $\{1/2, 1/2, 1/2\}$:

$$\begin{aligned}\mathbf{q}_1&=(1/2, 1/2, 1/2)\\ \mathbf{q}_2&=(-1/2, 1/2, 1/2)\\ \mathbf{q}_3&=(-1/2, -1/2, 1/2)\\ \mathbf{q}_4&=(1/2, -1/2, 1/2)\end{aligned} \tag{5.2.1}$$

Any order parameter that belongs to $\mathbf{q}_\alpha$ should transform as a basis of the irreducible representation of D_{3d}. In particular, consider the representation Γ_{q_1} induced by $\mathbf{M}_{q_1}$

Since G is symmorphic, the representation Γ_{q_1} is similar to the point group representations. The generators of the group D_{3d} are:

E, $C_3(1,1,1)$, $C_2(1,\bar{1},0)$ and i.

We take the z-axis along the (1,1,1) direction, the x-axis along the $(1,\bar{1},0)$ direction and the y-axis along the $(1,1,\bar{2})$ direction.

Under $C_3(1,1,\bar{2})$ we have: $m_{q,z} \to m_{q,z}$

whereas:

$$m_{q,x} \to -\frac{1}{2} m_{q,x} + \frac{\sqrt{3}}{2} m_{q,y}$$

$$m_{q,y} \to -\frac{\sqrt{3}}{2} m_{q,y} - \frac{1}{2} m_{q,x}$$

Under $C_2\ (\bar{1},1,0)$

$$m_{q,z} \to -m_{q,z}$$

and

$$m_{q,x} \to -m_{q,x}$$

$$m_{q,y} \to -m_{q,y}$$

$\mathbf{M}_{q_1}$ is invariant under the inversion (axial vector). From these transformation properties, we can deduce the character table of Γ_{q_1} (Table 5.2.1).

Table 5.2.1

D_3	E	$2C_3$	$3C_2$	D_3^+
Γ_1	1	1	1	S^z
Γ_2	1	1	−1	S^z
Γ_3	2	−1	0	$[-S^y, S^x]$
Γ_{q_1}	3	0	1	

Thus Γ_{q_1} decomposes into

$$\Gamma_{q_1} = \Gamma_2^+ + \Gamma_3^+ \tag{5.2.2}$$

Γ_2^+ is a one-dimensional representation whose basis function is S^z; Γ_3 is a doubly degenerate representation whose basis functions are S^x, S^y. Thus, in the case of an ordinary second-order phase transition, the Fourier component $\mathbf{M}_{q_1}$ can be either aligned along $\mathbf{q}_1$ or perpendicular to $\mathbf{q}_1$. The distinction can be made very easily: if $\mathbf{M}_{q_1}$ is parallel to $\mathbf{q}_1$, then the component of $\mathbf{M}_{q_1}$ perpendicular to $\mathbf{q}_1$ is zero, and according to (5.1.32) the scattered intensity for $\mathbf{K}$ parallel to $\mathbf{q}_1$ is zero.

Suppose that this is the case. The magnetic moment distribution is then:

$$m(\mathbf{r}) = \sum_{i=1,2,3,4} m_{q_i,z} \exp(i\mathbf{q}_i \cdot \mathbf{r}) \tag{5.2.3}$$

The $\mathbf{q}_i$ vectors are defined in (5.2.1).

We want to know what are the possible sets of coefficients $m_{q_i,z}$ which are normalised:

$$\sum_{i=1}^{4} |m_{q_i,z}|^2 = m_0^2$$

We can build 3 fourth order invariants:

$$\sum_{i=1}^{4} |m_{q_i,z}|^4, \left(\sum_{i=1}^{4} | m_{q_i,z} |^2 \right)^2, \quad m_{q_1,z} \cdot m_{q_2,z} \cdot m_{q_3,z} \cdot m_{q_4,z}$$

The thermodynamic potential Φ contains a fourth-order term Φ_4 which is a linear combination of all the fourth-order invariants:

$$\Phi_4 = B_1 \sum_{i=1}^{4} |m_{q_i,z}|^4 + B_2 \left(\sum_{i=1}^{4} | m_{q_i,z} |^2 \right)^2 + B_3 m_{q_1,z} \cdot m_{q_2,z} \cdot m_{q_3,z} \cdot m_{q_4,z}$$

This term has to be minimised with respect to the $m_{q_i,z}$. The physical origin of the different terms has to be related to the Hamiltonian of the spin system. Fourth-order terms in spin operators can be due to quadrupolar interactions, one ion anisotropy, ... Depending on the relative strength of B_1, B_2, B_3 (we neglect higher-order terms in the thermodynamic potential), we may have multi-**q** structures

1-**q** structure:

$$m_{q_1,z} = m_0, \quad m_{q_2,z} = m_{q_3,z} = m_{q_4,z} = 0$$

with permutations 1, 2, 3, 4.

2-**q** structure:

$$m_{q_1,z} = \pm m_{q_2,z} = \frac{m_0}{\sqrt{2}}, \quad m_{q_3,z} = m_{q_4,z} = 0$$

with permutations

3-**q** structure: (5.2.4)

$$m_{q_1,z} = \pm m_{q_2,z} = \pm m_{q_3,z} = \frac{m_0}{\sqrt{3}}, \quad m_{q_4,z} = 0$$

with permutations.

4-**q** structure:

$$m_{q_1,z} = \pm m_{q_2,z} = \pm m_{q_3,z} = \pm m_{q_4,z} = \frac{m_0}{2}$$

The $\pm$ solutions correspond to a phase shift induced by the (1/2, 1/2, 0) translations.

The different permutations correspond to magnetic domains. Only the 4-**q** structure does not create **q**-domains: the structure has cubic symmetry. However, as in many cases, the magnetic sites are equivalent and the magnetic moments must have the same amplitude:

$$|\mathbf{m}(\mathbf{R}_n)|^2 = |m_0|^2 \tag{5.2.5}$$

This condition cannot be satisfied by the 2-**q** and 3-**q** structures with $\mathbf{M}_q // \mathbf{q}$. Thus the only possible structures are the 1-**q** structure and the 4-**q** structure, when only fourth-order terms are taken into account. They are represented in Fig. 5.2.2.

Can we distinguish these two structures in a neutron scattering experiment? There is one Bravais lattice; thus (5.1.32) can be written as:

$$\frac{d\sigma}{d\Omega} = \left(\frac{\gamma r_0}{2}\right)^2 g^2 f^2(\mathbf{K}) \sum_{\alpha\beta} (\delta_{\alpha\beta} - \hat{K}_\alpha \hat{K}_\beta) F^*_\alpha(\mathbf{K}) F_\beta(\mathbf{K})$$

$$\mathbf{F}(\mathbf{K}) = \frac{(2\pi)^3}{V_0} \sum_{i,\tau} \mathbf{m}_{q_i,z} \delta(\mathbf{K} + \mathbf{q}_i - \boldsymbol{\tau}) \tag{5.2.6}$$

Let $\mathbf{K} = \boldsymbol{\tau} + \mathbf{q}_i$; in the case of the 1-**q** structure we have:

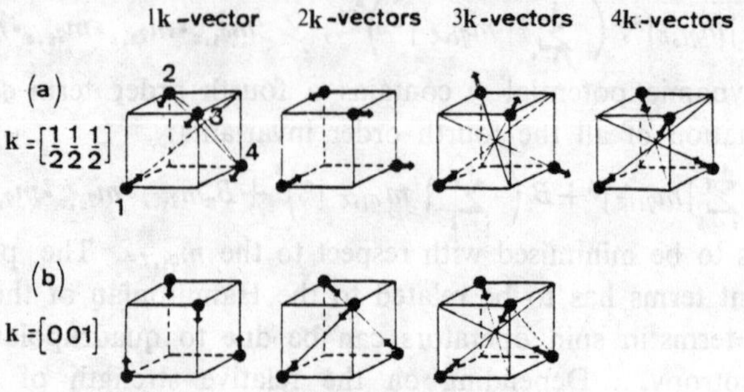

Fig. 5.2.2

— **Typical examples of the most symmetrical multiaxial structures for a face-centred cubic lattice and a wave vector k=($\frac{1}{2}\frac{1}{2}\frac{1}{2}$) (a) or k=(001) (b). The ions (1), (2), (3) and (4) are located respectively at (000), (0$\frac{1}{2}\frac{1}{2}$), ($\frac{1}{2}$0$\frac{1}{2}$) and ($\frac{1}{2}\frac{1}{2}$0) (From Rossat-Mignod).**

$$\frac{d\sigma}{d\Omega}=N\frac{(2\pi)^3}{V_0}\left(\frac{\gamma r_0}{2}\right)^2 g^2f^2(\mathbf{K})\,|m_{qi,z}|^2\sin^2\alpha_i\cdot x_i \tag{5.2.7}$$

where α_i is the angle of $\mathbf{m}_{qi}$ with $\mathbf{K}$ and x_i is the relative volume of domain $\mathbf{q}_i$. In the case of 4–**q** structure, all the Fourier components $\mathbf{m}_{qi}$ are coupled; but at a given scattering vector $\mathbf{K}=\boldsymbol{\tau}+\mathbf{q}_i$, neutrons see only one component $\mathbf{m}'_{qi}$; the intensity is then given by:

$$\frac{d\sigma}{d\Omega}=N\frac{(2\pi)^3}{V_0}\left(\frac{\gamma r_0}{2}\right)^2 g^2f^2(\mathbf{K})\,|m'_{qi,z}|^2\sin^2\alpha_i \tag{5.2.8}$$

Comparison of (5.2.7) and (5.2.8) shows that if the $\mathbf{q}_i$ domains are equally distributed ($x_i=1/4$), the two structures give the same intensities (with $\mathbf{m}'_{q_i}=$ 1/2 $\mathbf{m}_{qi}$) (see (5.2.4)) and thus cannot be distinguished. However, the symmetry of the 4–**q** structure is cubic; the 1–**q** structure has trigonal symmetry. Thus if any trigonal distortion is observable, we can conclude a 1–**q** structure. It is also possible to vary the domain population x_i by applying an external field (magnetic field, uniaxial stress...).

5.2.3 Non–collinear magnetic structures

Simple collinear structures are characterised by a wave vector **q** which corresponds to a symmetry point of the Brillouin zone, and a magnetic site of high symmetry.

Apart from the coupling between Fourier components $\mathbf{m}_{qi}$ that we have described in Section 5.2.1, we can find many non–collinear structures due to the anisotropy. In rare–earth compounds the crystal field anisotropy takes a fundamental part in determining the moment direction, therefore the symmetry of rare–earth sites will be an important parameter in the understanding of magnetic structures of rare–earth intermetallics.

We may have a non–collinear magnetic structure if the unit cell contains several rare–earth sites. This situation occurs in rare–earth nickel intermetallics, for example, RNi_3 compounds (R=Nd, Tb, Dy, Er) are non–collinear ferromagnets because the two rare–earth sites have orthogonal easy axes. However, in RCo_3 the rare earth–cobalt interactions are large enough to align all the magnetic moments along the easy axis of the rare–earth site which has the largest anisotropy.

Even if the unit cell contains only one rare–earth site a non–collinear structure is possible when the site symmetry is low enough.

5.2.4 Incommensurate magnetic structures

The long–range and oscillatory variation of some exchange interactions leads to magnetic structures which are incommensurate with the underlying lattice. Such incommensurate structures illustrate the important role of the anisotropy.

Incommensurate structures are characterised by a wave vector **q** along a symmetry line of the Brillouin zone. To define the structure, we must determine the little group G_q. If a strong anisotropy leads to an easy plane of magnetisation, the Fourier component $\mathbf{m}_q$ transforms as a two–dimensional representation and we have a helical order:

$$\mathbf{m}_q = \frac{m_0}{2} (\mathbf{u} - i\mathbf{v}) \exp(i\varphi_q) \tag{5.2.9}$$

u, **v** are two orthogonal vectors perpendicular to **q**. In general, **q** is perpendicular to the easy plane (rare earth metals, $MnAu_2$).

Otherwise, $\mathbf{m}_q$ transforms as a one–dimensional representation:

$$\mathbf{m}_q = \frac{A_q}{2} \exp(i\varphi_q)\mathbf{u} \tag{5.2.10}$$

and we have a sine–wave modulation propagating along **q** with a polarisation along **u**. **u** can be either perpendicular or parallel to **q**. These types of structures will be described in the next section.

5.3 EXAMPLES OF STRUCTURE DETERMINATION

5.3.1 $MnAu_2$—Helimagnetism

$MnAu_2$ has a body centred tetragonal structure. We assume that the space group is D_{4h}^{17}. Above T_N=366 K, it is paramagnetic. Powder diffraction reveals (Fig. 5.3.1) that the magnetic scattering appears at

$$\mathbf{K} = \boldsymbol{\tau} + \mathbf{q}$$

with $\mathbf{q} = (0, 0, q_z)$, q_z is not a simple fractional number, it varies with temperature and pressure. At T=300 K and P=0 kbar, q_z=0.29.

The point group G_q is C_{4v}. It is easily seen that the representation Γ induced by $\mathbf{m}_q$ decomposes as:

$$\Gamma = \Gamma_5 + \Gamma_2 \tag{5.3.1}$$

Thus $\mathbf{m}_q$ is either parallel to **q** (Γ_2) or perpendicular to **q**(Γ_5). Since magnetic intensity is observed at $\mathbf{K} = (0, 0, \boldsymbol{\tau}) \pm \mathbf{q}$, which is parallel to **q**, we know that $\mathbf{m}_q$ is perpendicular to **q**.

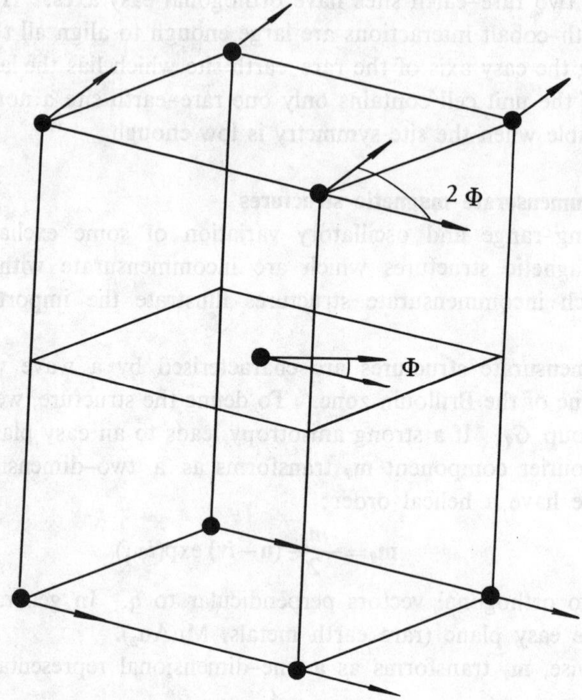

Fig. 5.3.1
Magnetic structure of $MnAu_2$.

There are two **q** vectors in the star $\{\mathbf{q}\}$: $+\mathbf{q}$ and $-\mathbf{q}$. Thus there is only one second–order invariant $\mathbf{m}_q \cdot \mathbf{m}_{-q}$, and–only one fourth–order invariant $|\mathbf{m}_q \cdot \mathbf{m}_{-q}|^2$. The magnetic moment at site $\mathbf{R}_n$ (only one Bravais lattice) is given by:

$$\mathbf{m}(\mathbf{R}_n)=\mathbf{m}_q \exp(-i\mathbf{q}\cdot\mathbf{R}_n)+\mathbf{m}_{-q}\exp(-i\mathbf{q}\cdot\mathbf{R}_n) \tag{5.3.2}$$

with $\mathbf{m}_{-q}=\mathbf{m}_q^*$, ($\mathbf{m}(\mathbf{R}_n)$ is a real quantity); the general form of $\mathbf{m}_q$ is:

$$\mathbf{m}_q=\frac{m_0}{2}(\mathbf{u}-i\mathbf{v})\exp i\varphi_q \tag{5.3.3}$$

where **u** and **v** are 2 vectors parallel to (100) and (010). Thus $\mathbf{m}(\mathbf{R}_n)$ is:

$$\mathbf{m}(\mathbf{R}_n)=m_0[\cos(\mathbf{q}\cdot\mathbf{R}_n+\varphi_q)\mathbf{u}+\sin(\mathbf{q}\cdot\mathbf{R}_n+\varphi_q)\mathbf{v}] \tag{5.3.4}$$

which describes a helical order with the moment in the basal plane as shown in Fig. 8.3.1. The pitch of the helix Φ is given by q_z:

$$\Phi=\pi q_z \simeq 52° \tag{5.3.5}$$

This type of ordering can be accounted for by assuming a strong ferromagnetic coupling in the basal plane; exchange interactions between the first layer J_1 and second layer J_2 must satisfy the relation

$$|J_2| \gg 4|J_1| \tag{5.3.6}$$

This will be established in a following chapter.

5.3.2 $CeAl_2$ $\frac{1}{m}$ Sinusoidally modulated structure

At room temperature $CeAl_2$ has a non symmorphic space group O_h^7 (Fd3m); there are two Bravais lattices of Ce atoms located on site 1: (0,0,0) and site 2: (1/4, 1/4, 1/4) positions. Powder neutron diffractions have demonstrated the onset of magnetic order associated with a wave vector $\mathbf{q}=\frac{2\pi}{a}(1/2+x, 1/2-x, 1/2)$ ($\mathbf{k}_3$ using Kovalev's notation); the group G_q contains only the elements E, identity and $(C_{2\bar{x}y}\,|\,1/4\ 1/4\ 1/4)$, a 180° rotation about $(\bar{1}, \bar{1}, 0)$ followed by a (1/4, 1/4, 1/4) translation. The star $\{\mathbf{q}\}$ consists of 24 vectors. The application of the 48 point symmetry operations contained in O_h^7 creates 24 non–equivalent $\mathbf{q}_i$ vectors. However, $+\mathbf{q}$ and $-\mathbf{q}$ are non–equivalent, but $\mathbf{m}_q^i$ and $\mathbf{m}_{-q}^i$ must couple in order to yield a real magnetic moment distribution. We are then left with 12 non–equivalent sets of $\pm\mathbf{q}_i$ vectors. For simplicity we will neglect any coupling between different $\pm\mathbf{q}_i$ vectors, only $+\mathbf{q}_i$ and $-\mathbf{q}_i$ enter the summation (5.1.33). The 12 sets of $\pm\mathbf{q}_i$ correspond to 12 magnetic **K**–domains.

Now let us consider the representation Γ of G_q which is induced by the six Fourier components

$$m_{q\,x}^1, m_{q\,y}^1, m_{q\,z}^1, m_{q\,x}^2, m_{q\,y}^2, m_{q\,z}^2.$$

The x,y,z axes are taken along the $(1, \bar{1}, 0)$, $(1, 1, \bar{2})$ and (1, 1, 1) directions respectively. When acted upon by an element $O\equiv(A\,|\,\mathbf{t}_a)$ of $\mathbf{C}_c$, $\mathbf{m}_q^i$ transforms as follows: first $(A\,|\,\mathbf{t}_a)$ sends the sublattice i to the sublattice j, if j is not in the same primitive cell as i, then it should be sent back by a lattice translation **a**, this introduces a phase shift $\exp(i\,\mathbf{q}\cdot\mathbf{a})$. Then the point symmetry operation A "rotates" $\mathbf{m}_q^i$. Since $(A\,|\,\mathbf{t}_a)$ belongs to the group of $\mathbf{q}$, the index $\mathbf{q}$ is not modified. We can write:

$$(A\,|\,\mathbf{t}_a)\mathbf{m}_q^i=\exp(i\mathbf{q}\cdot\mathbf{a})A\mathbf{m}_q^{O^{-1}(i)} \tag{5.3.7}$$

However, we must use the multiplier representation $\Gamma(O)$ defined in (1.2.3). We have

$$\Gamma(O)\mathbf{m}_q^i=\exp(i\mathbf{q}\cdot\mathbf{t}_a)\exp(i\mathbf{q}\cdot\mathbf{a})A\mathbf{m}_q^{O^{-1}(i)} \tag{5.3.8}$$

Let us consider the operation $O\equiv(C_{2\bar{x}y}\,|\,1/4\ 1/4\ 1/4)$; O permutes the two Bravais lattices 1 and 2, without introducing a phase shift ($\mathbf{a}=0$). Thus (5.3.8) can be written as:

$$(C_{2\bar{x}y}\,|\,\tfrac{1}{4}\tfrac{1}{4}\tfrac{1}{4})\mathbf{m}_q^1=\sigma^3 C_{2\bar{x}y}\mathbf{m}_q^2$$

$$\sigma=\exp i\frac{\pi}{4}$$

The two matrices of Γ are thus given by:

$$\Gamma(E\,|\,0)=\begin{vmatrix}1&0&0&0&0&0\\0&1&0&0&0&0\\0&0&1&0&0&0\\0&0&0&1&0&0\\0&0&0&0&1&0\\0&0&0&0&0&1\end{vmatrix}$$

$$\Gamma(C_{2\bar{x}y}|\tfrac{1}{4}\,\tfrac{1}{4}\,\tfrac{1}{4})=\begin{vmatrix} 0 & 0 & 0 & \sigma^3 & 0 & 0 \\ 0 & 0 & 0 & 0 & -\sigma^3 & 0 \\ 0 & 0 & 0 & 0 & 0 & -\sigma^3 \\ \sigma^3 & 0 & 0 & 0 & 0 & 0 \\ 0 & -\sigma^3 & 0 & 0 & 0 & 0 \\ 0 & 0 & -\sigma^3 & 0 & 0 & 0 \end{vmatrix}$$

The characters of Γ are given in Table 5.3.1 with those of the irreducible representations $\hat{\tau}_1$ and $\hat{\tau}_2$.

Table 5.3.1

G_q	(E|0)	($C_{2\bar{x}y}$|1/4 1/4 1/4)
$\hat{\tau}_1$	1	σ^3
$\hat{\tau}_2$	1	$-\sigma^3$
Γ	6	0

Γ can be reduced:

$$\Gamma=3(\hat{\tau}_1+\hat{\tau}_2)$$

By projecting linear combinations of $\mathbf{m}^i_{q\alpha}$ (see (1.2.12)) we can find basic functions associated with $\hat{\tau}_1$ and $\hat{\tau}_2$:

$$\hat{\tau}_1:\quad \alpha(m^1_{qx}+m^2_{qx})+\beta(m^1_{qy}-m^2_{qy})+\gamma(m^1_{qz}-m^2_{qz})$$

$$\hat{\tau}_2:\quad \alpha(m^1_{qx}-m^2_{qx})+\beta(m^1_{qy}+m^2_{qy})+\gamma(m^1_{qz}+m^2_{qz})$$

The two representations $\hat{\tau}_1$ and $\hat{\tau}_2$ correspond to different couplings between the two Bravais lattices. In the case of a second-order phase transition, the order parameter $\mathbf{m}^i_q$ belongs to one irreducible representation; if the transition is associated with $\hat{\tau}_1$ then:

$$m^1_{qx}-m^2_{qx}=m^1_{qy}+m^2_{qy}=m^1_{qz}+m^2_{qz}=0$$

If $\hat{\tau}_2$ becomes critical, we have:

$$m^1_{qx}+m^2_{qx}=m^1_{qy}-m^2_{qy}=m^1_{qz}-m^2_{qz}=0$$

Turning back to the magnetic moments (5.1.34):

$$\mathbf{m}(1)=\mathbf{m}^1_q \qquad \mathbf{m}(2)=\mathbf{m}^2_q$$

we have the relations:

$$m_x(1)=\pm m_x(2)$$
$$m_y(1)=\mp m_y(2)$$
$$m_z(1)=\mp m_z(2)$$

The sign $+(-)$ corresponds to $\hat{\tau}_1$ ($\hat{\tau}_2$) respectively. Magnetization measurements have shown that the easy axis is along [111], then we have $m^1_{qx}=m^1_{qy}=m^2_{qx}=m^2_{qy}=0$. The only possibilities for the coupling are $m^1_{qz}=-m^2_{qz}$ and $m^1_{qz}=m^2_{qz}$. The magnetic structure factor (5.1.34) is then expressed as:

$$\mathbf{F}_{\mp}(\mathbf{K})=\frac{(2\pi)^3}{V_0}f(\mathbf{K})\sum_{\{\mathbf{q}\},\tau}\mathbf{m}_{\pm q,z}(1\mp e^{i\mathbf{K}\cdot\mathbf{r}_2})\,\delta(\mathbf{K}+\mathbf{q}-\boldsymbol{\tau})$$

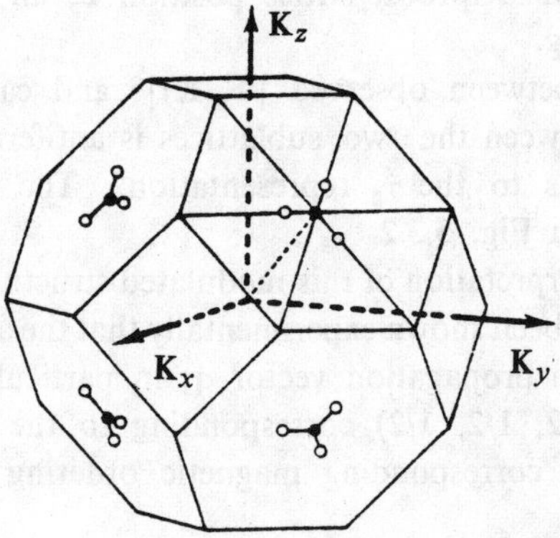

(a)

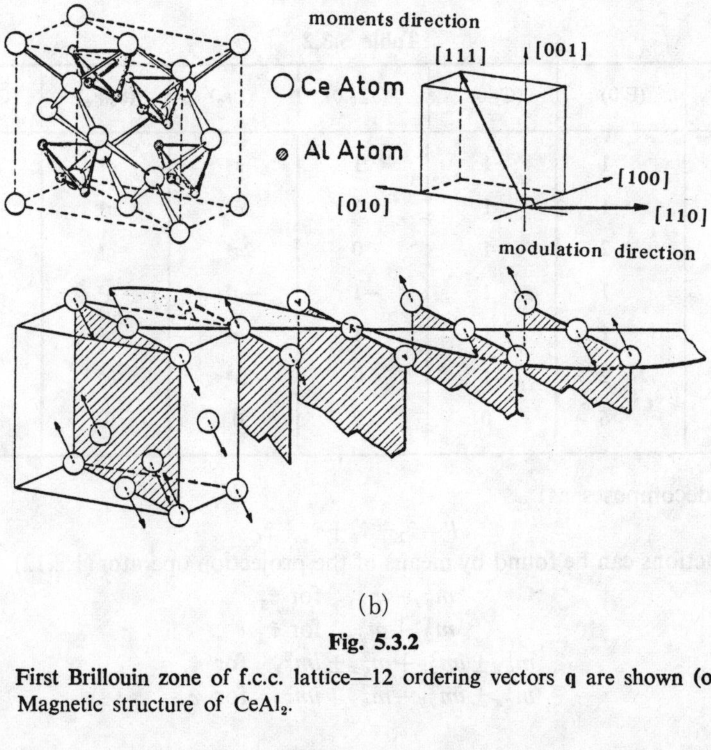

(b)

Fig. 5.3.2

(a) First Brillouin zone of f.c.c. lattice—12 ordering vectors q are shown (open dots).
(b) Magnetic structure of $CeAl_2$.

or

$$\mathbf{F}_{\mp} = \frac{(2\pi)^3}{V_0} f(\mathbf{K}) \sum_{\tau} \mathbf{m}_{\pm qz} (1 \mp e^{i\mathbf{K}\cdot\mathbf{r}_2})\, \delta(\mathbf{K} \pm \mathbf{q} - \boldsymbol{\tau}) \tag{5.3.9}$$

for a single $-\mathbf{q}$ structure with $\mathbf{r}_2 = (1/4,\ 1/4,\ 1/4)$. Magnetic intensity will be observed around each reciprocal lattice position $\boldsymbol{\tau}$; all the 24 $\mathbf{q}$ vectors contribute to the scattering.

A comparison between observed $|\mathbf{F}_0(\mathbf{K})|^2$ and calculated $|\mathbf{F}_c(\mathbf{K})|^2$ shows that the coupling between the two sublattices is antiferromagnetic $m^1_{qz} = -m^2_{qz}$ and this corresponds to the $\hat{\tau}_2$ representation. The corresponding magnetic structure is shown in Fig. 5.3.2.

The physical interpretation of this modulated structure is discussed in Chapter 12. However, it has been shown experimentally that the application of hydrostatic pressure modifies the propagation vector $\mathbf{q}$; in particular, above 20 kbars the propagation $\mathbf{q}$ is (1/2, 1/2, 1/2) corresponding to the L point (filled dots in Fig. 5.3.2 (a)). The corresponding magnetic ordering is antiferromagnetic of type II.

The star of $\{\mathbf{q}\}$ contains 4 vectors as discussed in Sect. 5.2.1. The group G_q is isomorphous to D_{3d}. G_q contains 12 elements:

$(E|0)$, $(C_{3z}|0)$, $(C^2_{3z}|0)$, $(\sigma_{\bar{x}y}|0)$, $(\sigma_{\bar{y}z}|0)$, $(\sigma_{\bar{x}z}|0)$ and
$(I|r_2)$, $(C_{2\bar{x}y}|r_2)$, $(C_{2\bar{y}z}|r_2)$, $(C_{2\bar{x}z}|r_2)$, $(S_{6z}|r_2)$, $(S^2_{6z}|r_2)$

The transformation matrices $\Gamma\ (A|\tau)$ of $(m^1_{qx},\ m_{qy},\ m^1_{qz},\ m^2_{qx},\ m^2_{qy},\ m^2_{qz})$ are easily obtained. The characters are given in Table (5.3.2).

Table 5.3.2

	$(E\|0)$	$(C_3\|0)$	$(\sigma_{\bar{x}y}\|0)$	$(I\|r_2)$	$(S_6\|r_2)$	$(C_{2\bar{x}y}\|r_2)$
$\hat{\tau}_1$	1	1	1	σ^3	σ^3	σ^3
$\hat{\tau}_3$	1	1	−1	σ^3	σ^3	$-\sigma^3$
$\hat{\tau}_5$	2	−1	0	$2\sigma^3$	$-\sigma^3$	0
$\hat{\tau}_2$	1	1	−1	$-\sigma^3$	$-\sigma^3$	$-\sigma^3$
$\hat{\tau}_4$	1	1	1	σ^3	σ^3	σ^3
$\hat{\tau}_6$	2	−1	0	$-2\sigma^3$	σ^3	0
Γ	6	0	2	0	0	0

Thus Γ decomposes as:

$$\Gamma = \hat{\tau}_1 + \hat{\tau}_5 + \hat{\tau}_4 + \hat{\tau}_6$$

Basic functions can be found by means of the projection operator (1.2.12). We get:

$$m^1_{qz} - m^2_{qz} \quad \text{for } \hat{\tau}_1$$
$$m^1_{qz} + m^2_{qz} \quad \text{for } \hat{\tau}_4$$
$$m^1_{qx} \pm i m^1_{qy} + m^2_{qx} \pm i m^2_{qy} \quad \text{for } \hat{\tau}_5$$
$$m^1_{qx} \pm i m^1_{qy} - m^2_{qx} \mp i m^2_{qy} \quad \text{for } \hat{\tau}_6$$

Again we can construct structure factors (5.1.34), however, it is observed that there is no scattered intensity when **K** is parallel to **q**, when $\mathbf{K}=\boldsymbol{\tau}-\mathbf{q}$ with $\boldsymbol{\tau}=(\pm h, \pm h, h)$. From (5.1.32) we know that **F** (**K**) is parallel to **q**, that is

$$m^1_{qx}=m^1_{qy}=m^2_{qx}=m^2_{qy}=0$$

Again, we are left with two possibilities corresponding to the $\hat{\tau}_1$ and $\hat{\tau}_4$ representations. Comparisons with observed intensities show that the coupling between the two Bravais lattices is antiferromagnetic, i.e. corresponds to the $\hat{\tau}_1$ representation.

REFERENCES

E.F. BERTAUT, in Magnetism, Vol. III, p. 150, ed. by G. T. Rado, H. Suhl, Academic Press, New York (1963).
E.F. BERTAUT, *J. Physique*, **C1**, 462 (1971).
A.P. CRACKNELL, Magnetism in Crystalline Materials, Pergamon Press, Oxford (1975).
A. HERPIN, Theorie du Magnetisme, p. 501, Presses Universitaires de France, Paris (1968).
D.F. JOHNSTON, *Proc. Phys. Soc.*, London **88,** 37 (1966).
D. MUKAMEL, S. LRINSKY, *Phys. Rev.* B **13**, 5065 (1976).
J. ROSSAT-MIGNOD, *J. Physique*, **C5**, 95 (1979).
G.L. SQUIRES, Introduction to the Theory of Thermal Neutron Scattering, Cambridge University Press, Cambridge (1978).

CHAPTER 6

MAGNETIC EXCITATIONS

So far we have assumed that the thermal average value of the magnetic moment at a given site is well defined and we have neglected any fluctuations. In this model, magnetic ions are frozen in one fundamental quantum state. However, we know that there are excited states, crystal field levels, multiplets. Transitions between different quantum states can be induced by temperature and contribute to the thermal variation of thermodynamic properties of magnetic compounds such as specific heat, susceptibility, magnetization, lattice parameters, elastic constants,... This is a single–ion picture where the energy level, scheme is determined by the crystal field and spin–orbit interactions, for example.

But there are other types of interactions, namely exchange interactions which couple spin operators on different sites; those interactions which tie magnetic moments together are equivalent to the binding potential for the atomic displacements in solids: if one moment is tilted away from its equilibrium position, then, due to the restoring forces exerted by the surrounding moments, this will create a propagating oscillation of the moments. This is called a spin wave. The dispersion relation $\omega(\mathbf{q})$ of spin waves is determined by the different coupling interactions.

It is very valuable to obtain experimental results on the so–called single–ion excitations and the spin waves, which are collective excitations. Such excitations have been evidenced by inelastic neutron scattering experiments, which allow the determinations of both the single–ion energy levels and the dispersion relation of spin waves.

6.1 ELECTRON ENERGY LEVELS

In this section, we will first discuss energy levels of localized magnetic electrons ($4f$ electrons or $3d$ electrons in insulators). It has been seen that electrostatic interactions, which have the point symmetry of the magnetic ion site, remove the degeneracy of the free atom energy levels. Inelastic neutron scattering yields an experimental determination of those splittings: as shown in (5.1.23), the cross-section corresponding to a transition from $|\lambda\rangle$ to $|\lambda'\rangle$ is non–zero if those two single–ion states are coupled by a spin component operator; in the process, the neutrons exchange an energy amount $\hbar\omega = E_\lambda - E_{\lambda'}$ with the system, and this energy transfer can be determined by measuring the wavelength of the incident

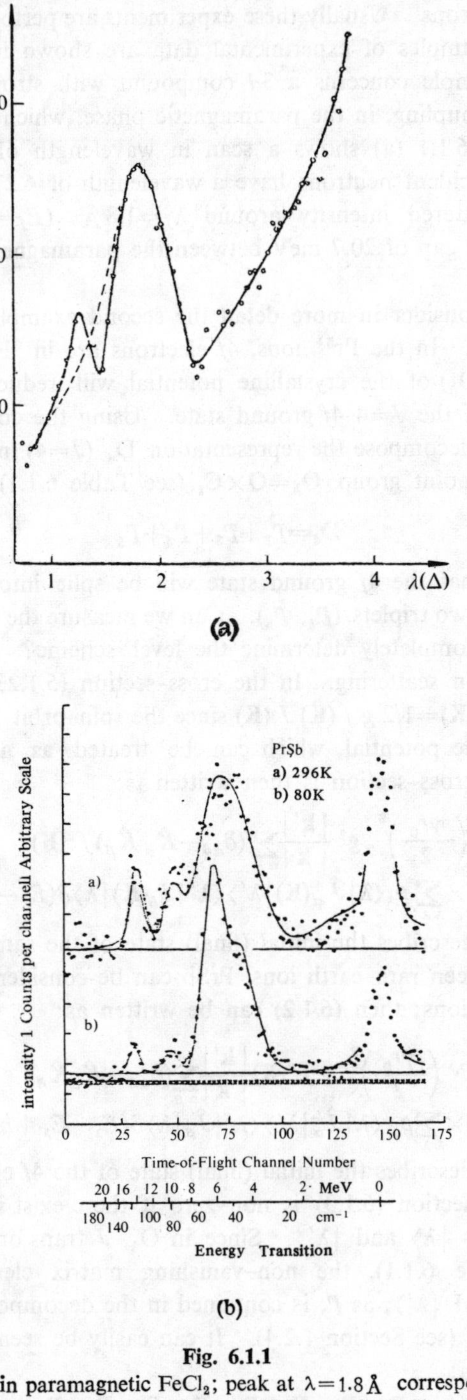

Fig. 6.1.1

(a) Inelastic scan in paramagnetic $FeCl_2$; peak at $\lambda = 1.8$ Å corresponds to a crystal field transition (from S. Hautecler 1962); (b) Time-of-flight scan in PrSb at different temperatures; the main peak at 6.3 meV corresponds to the Γ_1—Γ_4 transition; the other peaks can be attributed to transitions from excited states which are thermally populated (from K. C. Tuberfield 1971).

and scattered neutrons. Usually these experiments are performed on polycrystalline samples. Examples of experimental data are shown in Fig. 6.1.1.

The first example concerns a $3d$ compound with strong crystal field and weak spin–orbit coupling, in the paramagnetic phase, which will be discussed in Chapter 8. Fig. 6.1.1 (a) shows a scan in wavelength of scattered neutrons at $T=300\,^\circ$K. Incident neutrons have a wavelength of 4.27 Å ($E_i=4.48$ meV). We observed scattered intensity around $\lambda_f=1.8$ Å ($E_f=25.25$ meV) which leads to an energy gap of 20.7 meV between the paramagnetic ground state and an excited state.

Now let us consider in more detail the second example, PrSb. PrSb is a cubic paramagnet; In the Pr^{3+} ions, $4f$ electrons are in $^3H_4$ ground state; the cubic symmetry (O_h) of the crystalline potential will reduce the $2\times4+1=9$-fold degeneracy of the $J=4$ $4f$ ground state. Using the considerations of Section 1.2.4 we can decompose the representation D_4 ($J=4$) into irreducible representations of the point group $O_h=O\times C_i$ (see Table 6.1.1):

$$D_4=\Gamma_1+\Gamma_3+\Gamma_4+\Gamma_5 \tag{6.1.1}$$

Thus, we know that the $4f$ ground state will be split into a singlet (Γ_1), a doublet (Γ_3) and two triplets (Γ_4, Γ_5). Can we measure the energy gaps between these states and completely determine the level scheme? To get the answer, we turn to neutron scattering. In the cross–section (5.1.23) we can make use of the operator $\hat{Q}(\mathbf{K})=1/2\, g\, f(\hat{\mathbf{K}})\, \hat{J}(\mathbf{K})$ since the spin–orbit coupling is stronger than the crystalline potential, which can be treated as a perturbation. The inelastic neutron cross–section is then written as:

$$\begin{aligned}\frac{d^2\sigma}{d\Omega d\omega}&=\left(\frac{\gamma r_0}{2}\right)^2 g^2\frac{|\mathbf{k}'|}{|\mathbf{k}|}\sum_{\alpha\beta}(\delta_{\alpha\beta}-\hat{K}_\alpha\hat{K}_\beta)f^2(\mathbf{K})\\ &\times\sum_{\lambda\lambda'}p_\lambda\langle\lambda|\hat{J}_\alpha^+(\mathbf{K})|\lambda'\rangle\langle\lambda'|\hat{J}_\beta(\mathbf{K})|\lambda\rangle\delta(E_\lambda-E_{\lambda'}+\hbar\omega)\end{aligned} \tag{6.1.2}$$

where $|\lambda\rangle(|\lambda'\rangle)$ describes the initial (final) state of the sample. If we neglect any coupling between rare–earth ions, PrSb can be considered as the sum of N independent Pr^{3+} ions; then (6.1.2) can be written as:

$$\begin{aligned}\frac{d^2\sigma}{d\Omega d\omega}&=N\left(\frac{\gamma r_0}{2}\right)^2 g^2f^2(\mathbf{K})\frac{|\mathbf{k}'|}{|\mathbf{k}|}\sum_{\alpha\beta}(\delta_{\alpha\beta}-\hat{K}_\alpha\hat{K}_\beta)\\ &\times\sum_{\lambda\lambda'}p_\lambda\langle\lambda|\hat{J}_\alpha^+|\lambda'\rangle\langle\lambda'|\hat{J}_\beta|\lambda\rangle\delta(E_\lambda-E_{\lambda'}+\hbar\omega)\end{aligned} \tag{6.1.3}$$

where $|\lambda\rangle(|\lambda'\rangle)$ describes the initial (final) state of the $4f$ electrons in the Pr^{3+} ions. The cross–section (6.1.3) is non–zero if there exist matrix elements of $\hat{J}$ between the states $|\lambda\rangle$ and $|\lambda'\rangle$. Since in O_h, $\hat{J}$ transforms as Γ_4 (see basis functions in Table 6.1.1), the non–vanishing matrix elements are between the states $|\lambda\rangle$ and $|\lambda'\rangle$, as Γ_λ is contained in the decomposition of the direct product $\Gamma_4\times\Gamma_{\lambda'}$ (see Section 1.2.4). It can easily be seen that there are four allowed transitions:

$$\Gamma_1-\Gamma_4 \quad \Gamma_3-\Gamma_4 \quad \Gamma_3-\Gamma_5 \quad \Gamma_4-\Gamma_5$$

Thus an inelastic neutron experiment should evidence four transitions. The

Table 6.1.1
Character table of O

O	E	$8C_3$	$3C_{2x}$	$6C_{4x}$	$6C_{2xy}$	*bases*
Γ_1	1	1	1	1	1	$x^4+y^4+z^4$
Γ_2	1	1	1	−1	−1	
Γ_3	2	1	2	0	0	
Γ_4	3	0	−1	1	−1	$\hat{J}_\pm$, $\hat{J}_z$
Γ_5	3	0	−1	−1	1	
D_4	9	0	1	1	1	

probability factor p_λ is the Boltzmann factor

$$p_\lambda = \frac{n_\lambda}{e^{\beta E_\lambda} - 1} \tag{6.1.4}$$

where n_λ is a degeneracy weighting factor. At very low temperatures, only the ground state is populated and only transitions from the ground state to excited states can be observed. The single–ion level scheme obtained from the transitions (Fig. 6.1.1) is shown in Fig. 6.1.2. In this model, there is no **q**–dependence of the observed energies. However, experiments on single crystals (Fig. 6.1.3) have shown that there is a dispersion in energy, and, which is more important, a splitting of the Γ–point degeneracy. Even if the thermal average value of the magnetic moment operator is zero, there might still exist some exchange interactions between spin operators at different sites. Isotropic exchange between rare–earth ions would lead to dispersion but would not remove the degeneracies of the different branches. This shows that the coupling must be anisotropic.

Symmetry considerations show that the degeneracy of the Γ_4, Γ_3, Γ_5 states

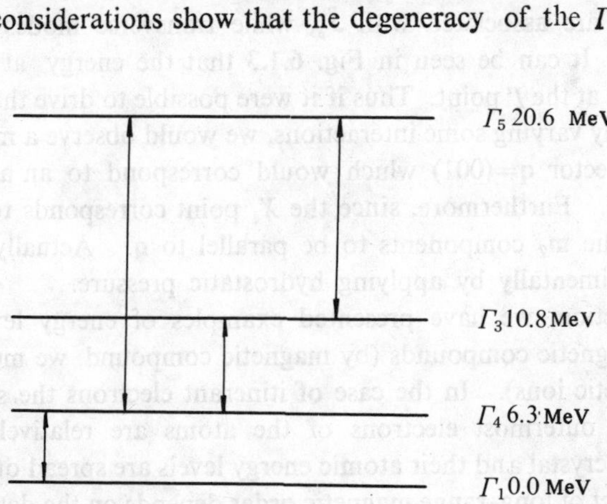

Fig. 6.1.2
Schematic crystal field levels scheme of Pr^{3+} in PrSb. The allowed dipole transitions are indicated as solid lines; energies of the levels were determined from time–of–flight experiments.

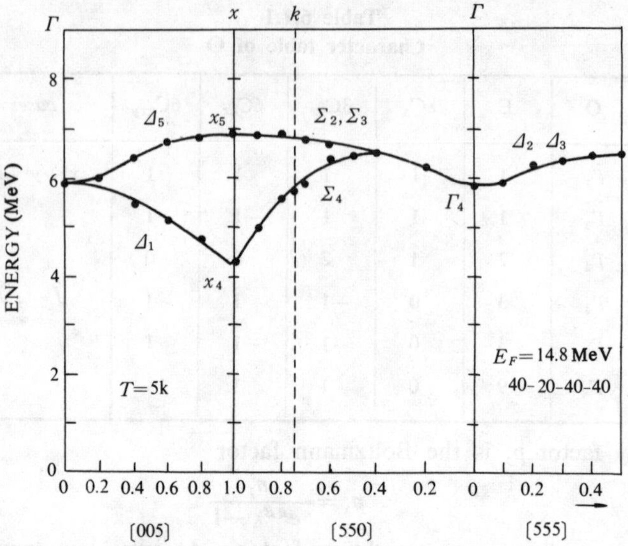

Fig. 6.1.3
The lifting of the triple degeneracy of the Γ_1—Γ_4 transition in PrSb.

may be lifted when going away from the Γ point: the little group G_q is less symmetric than O_h. Symmetry of adapted wave functions at **q** can be determined, in absence of inter–ion coupling, by projecting the Γ–point wave functions into the basis of the representations of G_q. This gives the maximum lifting of degeneracy that can be achieved. Again, matrix elements $\langle\lambda|\hat{J}_\alpha|\lambda'\rangle$ can be calculated and the cross–sections (6.1.3) have been obtained for some high–symmetry directions in Fig. 6.1.4. The allowed transitions are indicated as solid lines for the longitudinal magnetic excitons and dashed lines for the transverse excitations. Longitudinal modes are associated with $\hat{J}_z$, while transverse modes are induced by $\hat{J}_\pm$ operators. It can be seen in Fig. 6.1.3 that the energy at the X point is lower than that at the Γ point. Thus if it were possible to drive the X–point energy down to zero, by varying some interactions, we would observe a magnetic ordering with a wave vector **q**=(001) which would correspond to an antiferromagnetic order of type I. Furthermore, since the X_4 point corresponds to a $\hat{J}_z$ mode, we would expect the $\mathbf{m}_q$ components to be parallel to **q**. Actually, this has been observed experimentally by applying hydrostatic pressure.

In this section, we have presented examples of energy levels of localised electrons in magnetic compounds (by magnetic compound, we mean a compound made of magnetic ions). In the case of itinerant electrons the situation is more complex. The outermost electrons of the atoms are relatively free to move throughout the crystal and their atomic energy levels are spread out to form energy bands. The onset of long–range magnetic order depends on the details of the Fermi surface, and in turn, some modifications will occur when magnetic order sets in (see Chapter 9). Let us consider a schematic band diagram for a ferromagnet (most metals are ferromagnetic) as shown in Fig. 6.1.5; there are two bands

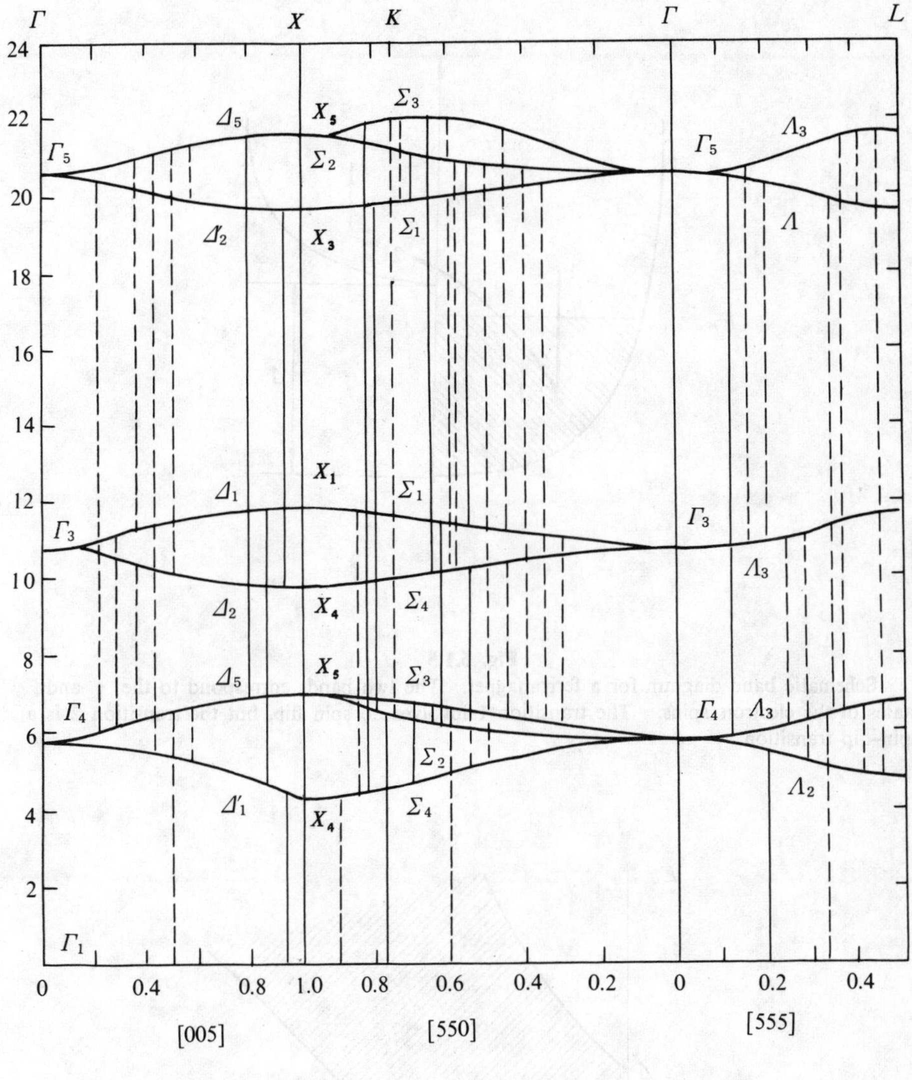

Fig. 6.1.4

The allowed dipole transitions along high-symmetry directions of the Brillouin zone in PrSb (see the text).

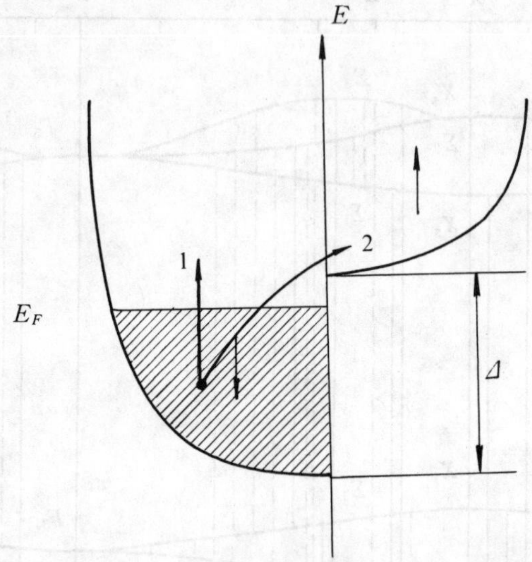

Fig. 6.1.5

Schematic band diagram for a ferromagnet. The two bands correspond to the ↑ and ↓ states of the electron spins. The transition 1 involves no spin flip, but the transition 2 is a spin-flip transition.

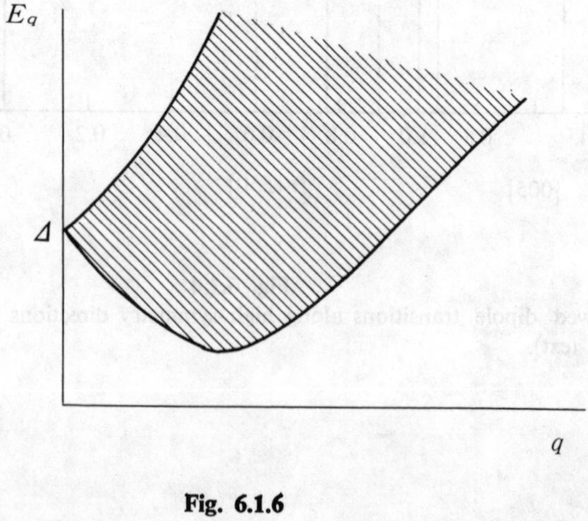

Fig. 6.1.6

Excitation spectrum in the case of type 2 transitions (Stoner excitations).

corresponding to the spin ↑ and spin ↓ states respectively. Due to the magnetic order, the two bands are separated by an energy $\Delta = \bar{U}\ (\langle n_\downarrow \rangle - \langle n^\uparrow \rangle)$. In this system, we can envisage two types of electronic transitions: one without change of the spin state of the electrons and another one which involves a spin flip (Fig. 6.1.5). The first transition moves an electron into a non-occupied state (due to the Pauli principle) and cannot be detected by neutron scattering (no spin flip). The second type of transition (Fig. 6.1.5) excites, for example, an electron from the down-spin band to the up-spin band. If the initial and final states of the electron are characterised by the same **q** vectors, then the energy of the excitation is $E\,(k=0)=\Delta$. An example of a spectrum for these so-called Stoner excitations is shown in Fig. 6.1.6. However, there are interactions between electrons, and if they are strong enough, those single electron excitations may transform into collective excitations.

6.2 COLLECTIVE EXCITATIONS — SPIN WAVES

Let us consider a magnetically ordered material. In our approach, we will first assume that the magnetic properties can be described by using an effective spin operator $\hat{S}$ together with a relevant g-factor. At zero temperature, each magnetic moment has its maximum value gS. However, at higher temperatures, there must be some deviations; some individual spin changes its $\langle \hat{S}_z \rangle_T$ (thermal average value of $\hat{S}_z$) from S to S–1. Due to the couplings between spins, this excitation propagates throughout the crystal and can be analysed in terms of normal modes called spin waves.

6.2.1 Linear spin-wave theory in ferromagnets

At zero temperature, the ferromagnetic ground state is defined by:

$$\langle \hat{S}_i^z \rangle_{T=0} = S$$

for all the N atoms i. Exchange interactions between those spins is represented by the usual isotropic Heisenberg Hamiltonian:

$$\hat{H} = -\sum_{i\ j} J(\mathbf{r}_i - \mathbf{r}_j)\hat{S}_i \hat{S}_j \tag{6.2.1}$$

where J depends only on $|\mathbf{r}_i - \mathbf{r}_j|$.

We describe by $|n\rangle$ the quantum state where n spin deviations occur

$$\hat{S}_i^z\,|n\rangle = (S-n)\,|n\rangle \tag{6.2.2}$$

From (1.1.25) we know that if $|m\rangle$ is an eigenstate of $\hat{S}_z$ with the eigenvalue m, then

$$\hat{S}^{\pm}\,|m\rangle = [(S \mp m)(S \pm m+1)]^{1/2}\,|m \pm 1\rangle$$

Thus in the basis $|n\rangle$, the matrix elements of $\hat{S}_i^{\pm}$ can be written as:

$$\hat{S}_i^{+}\,|n\rangle = (2Sn)^{1/2}\left(1 + \frac{1-n}{2S}\right)^{1/2}|n-1\rangle$$

$$\hat{S}_i^{-}\,|n\rangle = (2S(n+1))^{1/2}\left(1 - \frac{n}{2S}\right)^{1/2}|n+1\rangle \tag{6.2.3}$$

At low temperatures, we can assume that the number of spin deviations is small compared to $2S$. Then (6.2.3) can be simplified to:

$$\hat{S}_i^+|n\rangle \simeq (2S)^{1/2} n^{1/2} |n-1\rangle$$
$$\hat{S}_i^-|n\rangle \simeq (2S)^{1/2} (n+1)^{1/2} |n+1\rangle \qquad (6.2.4)$$

In this approximation, spin operators can be transformed into boson creation and annihilation operators $\hat{a}_i^+$ and $\hat{a}_i^-$ (Holstein–Primakoff transformation):

$$\hat{S}_i^\pm = (2S)^{1/2} \hat{a}_i^\mp \qquad (6.2.5)$$

such that

$$\hat{a}_i^-|n\rangle = n^{1/2}|n-1\rangle$$
$$\hat{a}_i^+|n\rangle = (n+1)^{1/2}|n+1\rangle \qquad (6.2.6)$$

Hence

$$\hat{a}_i^+\hat{a}_i^-|n\rangle = n|n\rangle$$
$$\hat{a}_i^-\hat{a}_i^+|n\rangle = (n+1)|n\rangle \qquad (6.2.7)$$

and

$$\hat{S}_i^z|n\rangle = (S - \hat{a}_i^+\hat{a}_i^-)|n\rangle \qquad (6.2.8)$$

By applying this transformation, the form of the Hamiltonian (6.2.1) is changed into a set of harmonic oscillators similar to those which are found in lattice dynamics:

$$\hat{H} = -NS^2 \sum_j J(\mathbf{r}_i - \mathbf{r}_j) + 2S \sum_i \hat{a}_i^+\hat{a}_i^- \sum_j J(\mathbf{r}_i - \mathbf{r}_j) - 2S \sum_{i,j} J(\mathbf{r}_i - \mathbf{r}_j) \hat{a}_i^- \hat{a}_j^+ \qquad (6.2.9)$$

As usual, Fourier transforms of $\hat{a}_i^\pm$ operators are introduced: they represent the propagating waves

$$\hat{b}_q^\pm = N^{-1/2} \sum_i \exp(\pm i\mathbf{q}\cdot\mathbf{r}_i) \hat{a}_i^\pm \qquad (6.2.10)$$

It can be shown that

$$\sum_{i,j} J(\mathbf{r}_i - \mathbf{r}_j) \hat{a}_i^- \hat{a}_j^+ = \sum_q J(\mathbf{q}) \hat{b}_q^- \hat{b}_q^+ = \sum_q J(\mathbf{q}) \hat{b}_q^+ \hat{b}_q^- \qquad (6.2.11)$$

where

$$J(\mathbf{q}) = \sum_j J(\mathbf{r}_i - \mathbf{r}_j) \exp(i\mathbf{q}\cdot(\mathbf{r}_i - \mathbf{r}_j))$$

Then the Hamiltonian (6.2.9) is written as:

$$\hat{H} = -S^2 N J(0) + \sum_q \hbar\omega_q \hat{b}_q^+ \hat{b}_q^- \qquad (6.2.12)$$

with

$$\hbar\omega_q = 2S(J(0) - J(\mathbf{q}))$$

The Hamiltonian contains a term $E_0 = -NS^2J(0)$ which is the ground state energy (in absence of any spin deviation) and a sum of harmonic oscillators which represent independent spin waves:

$$\hat{H} = E_0 + \sum_q \hat{H}_q$$

with

$$\hat{H}_q|n_q\rangle = \hbar\omega_q|n_q\rangle$$

where $|n_q\rangle$ is an eigenstate of $\hat{H}_q$.

The term $\hbar\omega_q$ represents the dispersion of the spin–wave modes; in this simple model, the dispersion of the branch is proportional to the Fourier transform of the exchange. This shows how important it is to determine the energy of these excitations in order to estimate the coupling constants.

However, we have seen that in metals there exist Stoner modes; at high $|\mathbf{q}|$

value (i.e. high energy) the collective modes will collapse into the continuum of the Stoner modes, so it is worth writing a dispersion relation which is valid at low $|\mathbf{q}|$.

If we assume a cubic lattice (a is the lattice constant) with only one exchange constant J between nearest neighbours, we have at low $|\mathbf{q}|$:

$$\hbar\omega_q \simeq Dq^2 \tag{6.2.13}$$

with

$$D = 2JSa$$

This parabolic dispersion has been observed in many ferromagnets even in metals such as iron; the stiffness constant D gives information about exchange interactions. However, in non-cubic materials, there might be deviations from parabolic behaviour or the appearance of an energy gap at $\mathbf{q}=0$ due to anisotropic interactions (terbium).

6.2.2 Thermodynamics of ferromagnets

It can be seen that spin waves are similar to phonons. (They are called magnons.) In the same way as phonons, they will be thermally excited and this will be reflected in thermodynamical properties such as magnetization or specific heat.

The number n of thermally excited spin waves at a given temperature is given by Bose statistics:

$$n = \frac{1}{N}\sum_{q\in BZ} n_q = \frac{1}{N}\sum_{q\in BZ} [\exp(\beta\hbar\omega_q) - 1]^{-1} \tag{6.2.14}$$

where $\mathbf{q}$ is a vector of the Brillouin zone (BZ). This summation can be turned into an integral

$$n = \frac{V_0}{(2\pi)^3}\int_{BZ} \{\exp(\beta\hbar\omega_q) - 1\}^{-1} d\mathbf{q} \tag{6.2.15}$$

At low temperatures, only the low-lying spin waves are excited; we can extend the integration to infinity because the integrand is small except when $\hbar\omega_q$ is small. Thus, assuming an isotropic dispersion law:

$$n = \frac{V_0}{(2\pi)^3}\int_0^\infty 4\pi q^2 dq \{\exp(\beta Dq^2) - 1\}^{-1} \tag{6.2.16}$$

If we set $x = \beta Dq^2$, then (6.2.16) turns into:

$$n = \frac{V_0}{4\pi^2}\frac{1}{(D\beta)^{3/2}}\int_0^\infty \frac{x^{1/2}}{e^x - 1}dx \tag{6.2.17}$$

$$n = \frac{V_0}{4\pi^2}\frac{1}{(D\beta)^{3/2}}\frac{\sqrt{\pi}}{2}\xi(3/2)$$

where $\xi(x)$ is the Riemann zeta function. Therefore, at low temperatures, n is proportional to $\beta^{-3/2} = (kT)^{3/2}$. Thus the decrease of saturation magnetization is given by:

$$\Delta m_s = S - \langle \hat{S}_z \rangle_T = n = V_0\, \xi(3/2)\left(\frac{kT}{4\pi D}\right)^{3/2} \tag{6.2.18}$$

This is the Bloch $T^{3/2}$ relation. It has been seen that the molecular field theory gives a different result. In this model, the departure from saturation is exponential:

$$\Delta m_s = \exp(-T/(S+1)T_c)$$

The internal energy $E = \sum_q n_q \hbar\omega_q$ can be evaluated in the same way:

$$E = \frac{V_0}{(2\pi)^3} \int_0^\infty 4\pi q^2 dq \frac{Dq^2}{\exp(\beta Dq^2) - 1} \tag{6.2.19}$$

which leads to

$$E \sim \left(\frac{kT}{D}\right)^{5/2} \tag{6.2.20}$$

thus the specific heat $c_v = \frac{\partial E}{\partial T}$ is given by:

$$c_v \sim \left(\frac{kT}{D}\right)^{3/2} \tag{6.2.21}$$

Of course, all these relations hold when the temperature is small compared to the ordering temperature (there must be only a few spin deviations). When the temperature gets higher, we must take into account interactions between spin waves, which introduce non–linear terms in the Hamiltonian (6.2.9).

In particular, this can be done by renormalising spin–wave excitations. For a cubic ferromagnet the energy $\hbar\omega_q(T)$ becomes

$$\hbar\omega_q(\beta) = \hbar\omega_q(T=0)\left\{1 - \frac{\sum_{q'} n_{q'} \hbar\omega_{q'}}{2J(0)NS^2}\right\} \tag{6.2.22}$$

with $n_q = [\exp(\beta\hbar\omega_q) - 1]^{-1}$.

These two equations can be solved numerically. Such a theory provides good results up to $T \simeq 0.90T_c$; however, it fails near T_c and a more sophisticated treatment must be used to account for excitations near T_c and eventually above T_c.

6.2.3 Magnetic anisotropy

So far, for simplicity, we have not mentioned the anisotropy effects. However, it will be shown that these effects are quite strong, depending on the local symmetry of the magnetic ion sites. The crystal field anisotropy leads to single–ion terms in the Hamiltonian which can be expressed in powers of spin operators. Treatment of such terms is beyond the scope of these lectures. High–order single–ion terms will be included in an anisotropy field $\mathbf{H}_{an}$ which will align all spins along a given direction.

Other possible terms are the dipolar interactions and anisotropic exchange coupling. Dipolar interactions can play an important role, but will be neglected here; anisotropic exchange can be dealt with by using an anisotropic g–tensor. For simplicity, we will represent the anisotropy by an anisotropy field $\mathbf{H}_{an}$; the dispersion relation (6.2.12) becomes for a ferromagnet:

$$\hbar\omega_q = g\mu_B \mathbf{H}_{an} + 2S(J(0) - J(\mathbf{q})) \tag{6.2.23}$$

6.2.4 Linear theory of spin waves in a two–sublattice antiferromagnet

As a starting point, we will use the Néel two–sublattice model: spin waves are generated from a fully ordered array of alternately pointing spins. Let N be the number of primitive cells which contain two types of atoms, one on the (up) a sublattice, the other on the (down) b sublattice. Spins are taken to be equivalent (the ferrimagnetic case is a generalisation of the antiferromagnetic case).

The anisotropy is handled as an effective field $\mathbf{H}_{an}$ which is assumed to be up at the a sites and down at the b sites and directed along the z-axis. The Hamiltonian can be written as:

$$\hat{H}=-g\mu_{\mathrm{B}}\mathbf{H}_{an}\left(\sum_l \hat{S}^z_{al}-\sum_m \hat{S}^z_{bm}\right)$$
$$-\sum_{l,l'} J_{ll'}\mathbf{S}_l\cdot\mathbf{S}_{l'}-\sum_{m,m'} J_{mm'}\hat{S}_m\cdot\hat{S}_{m'}-\sum_{l,m} J^{ab}_{lm}\hat{S}_l\cdot\hat{S}_m \tag{6.2.24}$$

where J (J^{ab}) is an intra (inter) sublattice coupling. As before, we introduce annihilation and creation operators:

$$\hat{S}^{\pm}_{al}=(2S)^{1/2}\hat{a}^{\mp}_l, \qquad \hat{S}^{\pm}_{bm}=(2S)^{1/2}\hat{b}^{\pm}_m$$
$$\hat{S}^z_{al}=S-\hat{a}^+_l\hat{a}^-_l, \qquad \hat{S}^z_{bm}=-S+\hat{b}^+_m\hat{b}^-_m$$

The calculations are similar to the ferromagnetic case, thus we only give the results.

The Hamiltonian (6.2.24) is written as the sum of two sets of harmonic oscillators, corresponding to the two sublattices:

$$\hat{H}=\sum_q \hbar\omega_q(\hat{\alpha}^+_q\hat{\alpha}^-_q+\hat{\beta}^+_q\hat{\beta}^-_q) \tag{6.2.25}$$

with

$$\hbar\omega_q=\{A^2-(2SJ^{ab}(\mathbf{q}))^2\}^{1/2} \tag{6.2.26}$$
$$A=-2SJ^{ab}(0)+2S(J(0)-J(\mathbf{q}))+g\mu_{\mathrm{B}}H_{an}$$

In the absence of an applied magnetic field, the two sublattices cannot be distinguished and the spin–wave spectrum is doubly degenerate.

Now, for simplicity, let us neglect the intrasublattice coefficient $J(\mathbf{q})$. The dispersion relation (6.2.26) reduces to:

$$\hbar\omega_q=2S[J^{ab}(0)^2(1+h_A)^2-J^{ab}(\mathbf{q})^2]^{1/2} \tag{6.2.27}$$

with

$$h_A=g\mu_{\mathrm{B}}H_{an}/2SJ^{ab}(0)$$

We can see that the dispersion is due to the exchange couplings, but the anisotropy induces an energy gap at $\mathbf{q}=0$

$$\hbar\omega(\mathbf{q}=0)=g\mu_{\mathrm{B}}[H^2_{an}+2H_{\mathrm{exch}}H_{an}]^{1/2} \tag{6.2.28}$$

where H_{exch} is the exchange field:

$$g\mu_{\mathrm{B}}H_{\mathrm{exch}}=2SJ^{ab}(0) \tag{6.2.29}$$

This energy gap can be large, even in the case of a weak anisotropy, because it is enhanced by the exchange. For example, in MnF_2, where the anisotropy is dipolar (Mn^{2+} is in an S state; there is no direct coupling of the magnetic moment to the lattice), the anisotropy field is evaluated to be H_{an}=9kOe, but the exchange is quite large H_{exch}=540 kOe, which leads to an energy gap of about 100 kOe (12.5 K).

Of course, the thermodynamical properties of the antiferromagnets would reflect the existence of this gap in the spin–wave dispersion. In particular, the sublattice magnetization is given by:

$$\langle S^z\rangle_T = S - \frac{1}{2N}\sum_{q\in BZ}\left\{\left[\frac{(1+h_A)^2}{(1+h_A)^2-\gamma_q^2}\right]^{1/2}\coth\left(\beta\frac{\hbar\omega_q}{2}\right)-1\right\} \quad (6.2.30)$$

with

$$J^{ab}(\mathbf{q}) = J^{ab}(0)\gamma_q$$

If we take the zero temperature limit ($\beta\to\infty$), it can be seen that $\langle S^z\rangle_T$ does not reduce to the value S expected from the assumption of the Néel ground state:

$$\langle S^z\rangle_{T=0} = S - \frac{1}{2N}\sum_{q\in BZ}\left\{\frac{1+h_A}{[(1+h_A)^2-\gamma_q^2]^{1/2}}-1\right\} \quad (6.2.31)$$

This departure can be related to the fact that the Néel state is not the real ground state of the system, it also involves zero point motions. The deviation from the Néel state depends on the crystalline structure (γ_q) and on the anisotropy. If we set $h_A=0$, it can be found that

$$\langle S^z\rangle_{T=0} = S - 0.06 \text{ for a body centred cubic lattice}$$

If we set up a large anisotropy ($h_A\to\infty$; Ising model) then the deviation vanishes.

At finite temperatures, it can be shown that the sublattice magnetization varies as T^2, which is to be compared to the $T^{3/2}$ law for a ferromagnet. The contribution of spin waves to the temperature dependence of the susceptibility and specific heat can be obtained in the same way as for a ferromagnet. Detailed calculations can be found in the review article of F. Keffer.

6.3 INELASTIC NEUTRON SCATTERING BY SPIN WAVES IN A FERROMAGNET

Let us consider a simple ferromagnet with one magnetic ion per unit cell with the moments aligned along the z-axis; again we will assume that the ground state multiplet of each ion can be represented by an effective spin $\hat{S}$. In this case the magnetic scattering cross-section for neutrons is written as:

$$\frac{d^2\sigma}{d\Omega d\omega} = \left(\frac{\gamma r_0}{2}\right)^2 (gf(\mathbf{K}))^2\frac{|\mathbf{k}'|}{|\mathbf{k}|}\sum_{\alpha\beta}(\delta_{\alpha\beta}-\hat{K}_\alpha\hat{K}_\beta)$$

$$\times\frac{1}{2\pi}\int_{-\infty}^{+\infty}\langle\hat{S}_\alpha(-\mathbf{K},0)\hat{S}_\beta(\mathbf{K},t)\rangle_T e^{-i\omega t}dt \quad (6.3.1)$$

We recall that:

$$\langle AB\rangle_T = \sum_\lambda p_\lambda\langle\lambda|AB|\lambda\rangle$$

where $|\lambda\rangle$ are the eigenstates of the system.

In the linear approximation (no interactions between spin waves in Section 6.2.1), the total Hamiltonian (6.2.1) can be expressed as

$$\hat{H} = E_0 + \sum_q \hat{H}_q$$

and the eigenstate $|\lambda\rangle$ is made of the products

$$|\lambda\rangle = |n_0\rangle\ldots|n_q\rangle\ldots \quad (6.3.2)$$

where $|n_q\rangle$ is an eigenstate of $\hat{H}_q$ (a spinwave of wave vector $\mathbf{q}$, energy $\hbar\omega_q$). Thus, in (6.3.1) we must calculate matrix elements of the form:

$$\langle n_q|\hat{S}_\alpha(-\mathbf{K},0)\hat{S}_\beta(\mathbf{K},t)|n_q\rangle \quad (6.3.3)$$

It can be shown that, in this approximation, the only non-zero matrix elements are

$$\begin{aligned}&\langle n_q|\hat{S}_z(-\mathbf{K},0)\hat{S}_z(\mathbf{K},t)|n_q\rangle\\&\langle n_q|\hat{S}_{\pm}(-\mathbf{K},0)\hat{S}_{\mp}(\mathbf{K},t)|n_q\rangle\end{aligned} \tag{6.3.4}$$

Calculation of these matrix elements requires some tedious algebra; we give the results:

$$\langle\lambda|\hat{S}_z(-\mathbf{K},0)\hat{S}_z(\mathbf{K},t)|\lambda\rangle= N\frac{(2\pi)^3}{\delta_0}\left\{S^2-\frac{2S}{N}\sum_{q'}n_{q'}\right\}\sum_{\tau}\delta(\mathbf{K}-\boldsymbol{\tau}) \tag{6.3.5}$$

$$\langle\lambda|\hat{S}_{\pm}(-\mathbf{K},0)\hat{S}_{\mp}(\mathbf{K},t)|\lambda\rangle= \frac{(2\pi)^3}{V_0}2S\sum_{q,\tau}\left(n_q+\frac{1}{2}\pm\frac{1}{2}\right)e^{\pm i\omega_q t}\delta(\mathbf{K}\mp\mathbf{q}-\boldsymbol{\tau}) \tag{6.3.6}$$

It can be seen that the longitudinal part (6.3.5) does not depend on time, in this model there is no fluctuation in the modulus of the magnetic moment and this term gives rise to elastic scattering (Bragg scattering). The transverse part (6.3.6) contains the phase factor $\exp(\pm i\omega_q t)$, which can be represented by a precession of the magnetic moments about the z-axis (classical picture of spin waves). Taking the thermal average and integrating over time leads to

$$N\frac{(2\pi)^3}{V_0}\{S^2-2S\langle n\rangle_T\}\delta(\omega)\sum_{\tau}\delta(\mathbf{K}-\boldsymbol{\tau}) \tag{6.3.7}$$

and

$$\frac{(2\pi)^3}{V_0}2S\sum_{q,\tau}\langle n_q+\tfrac{1}{2}\pm\tfrac{1}{2}\rangle_T\delta(\omega\mp\omega_q)\,\delta(\mathbf{K}\mp\mathbf{q}-\boldsymbol{\tau}) \tag{6.3.8}$$

With a little more algebra, we arrive at the final results for the magnetic scattering cross-section in the linear approximation:

$$\begin{aligned}\frac{d^2\sigma}{d\Omega d\omega}=&\frac{(\gamma r_0)^2}{2}(gf(\mathbf{K}))^2\frac{|\mathbf{k}'|}{|\mathbf{k}|}\frac{(2\pi)^3}{V_0}\\&\times\{(1-\hat{K}_z^2)N(S^2-2S\langle n\rangle_T)\sum_{\tau}\delta(\mathbf{K}-\boldsymbol{\tau})\delta(\omega)\\&+(1+\hat{K}_z^2)\frac{S}{2}\sum_{\tau,q}(\langle n_q+1\rangle_T\delta(\omega-\omega_q)\delta(\mathbf{K}-\mathbf{q}-\boldsymbol{\tau})\\&+\langle n_q\rangle_T\delta(\omega+\omega_q)\delta(\mathbf{K}+\mathbf{q}-\boldsymbol{\tau}))\}\end{aligned} \tag{6.3.9}$$

As already mentioned, the first part of (6.3.9) is purely elastic scattering (delta function of ω); the intensity is given by $(NS^2-2S\sum_q\langle n_q\rangle_T)$ which is the square of the magnetization in the linear spin wave theory (Section 6.2.2) in agreement with the elastic cross-section (5.1.32).

The second term corresponds to inelastic scattering, it contains the Bose population factor

$$\langle n_q\rangle_T=\frac{1}{e^{\beta\hbar\omega_q}-1} \tag{6.3.10}$$

At low temperatures ($\beta\to\infty$), for a finite ω_q, this term is very small; this corresponds to the fact that only a few spin waves are thermally excited. This means that spin waves can be observed only if they are created by the neutrons. In other words, when neutrons lose an energy $\hbar\omega_q$ then there is an emission of

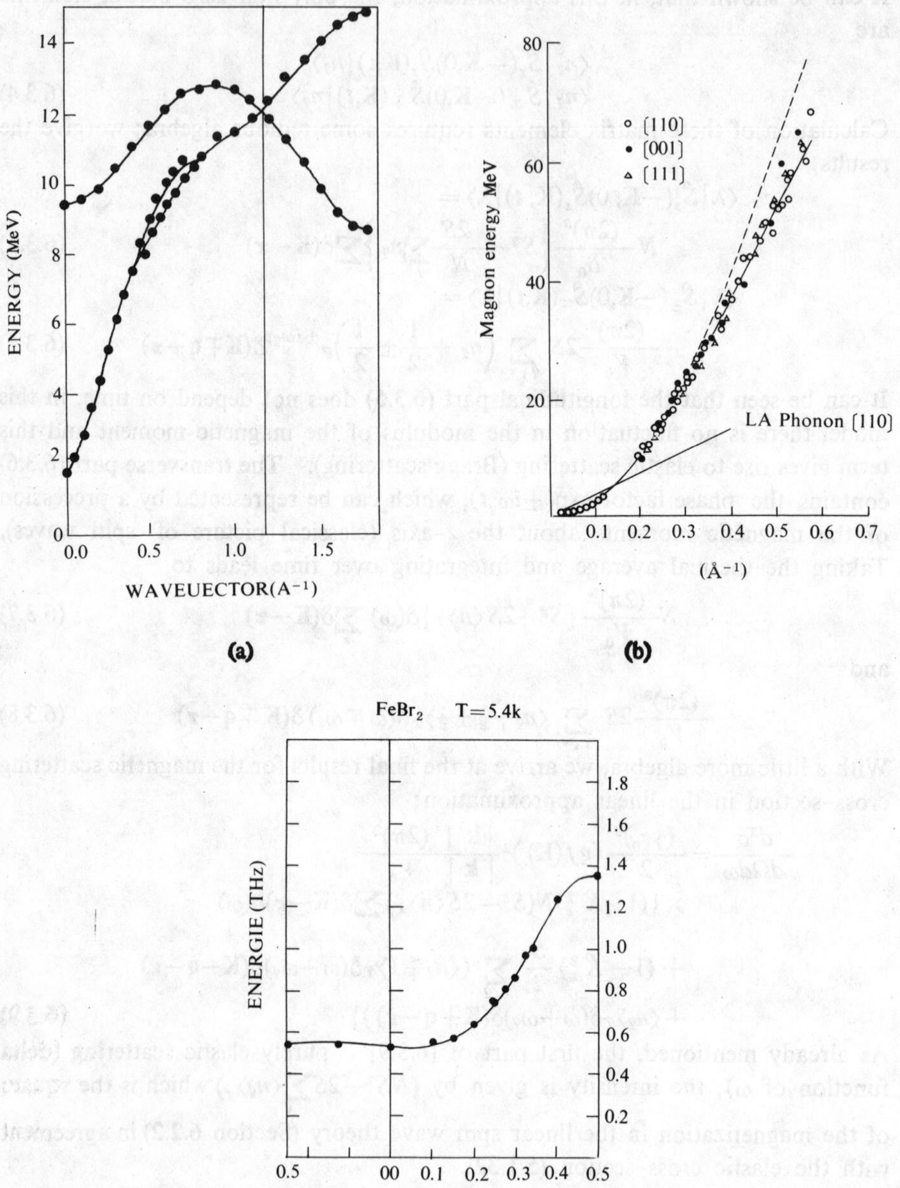

Fig. 6.3.1
Spin-wave spectra

(a) Spin-wave dispersion along the *a* direction in ferromagnetic terbium (T=4.2 K). Two branches (acoustic- and optic-like) are observed because of the two ions in the unit cell; (b) Spin-wave dispersion in iron along different directions. A dispersion relation Dq^2 is observed at low $|\mathbf{q}|$; (c) Spin-wave dispersion in $FeBr_2$. The very small dispersion along the c^* direction indicates a very weak inter-plane coupling.

a spin wave whose wave vector $\mathbf{q}$ is such that $\mathbf{K}-\mathbf{q}+\boldsymbol{\tau}=0$. The intensity for such a process is given by $\langle n_q+1\rangle_T$, which is greater than one. At higher temperatures, the neutrons can gain energy ($\omega=-\omega_q$) by absorbing a spin wave of wave vector $\mathbf{q}$ if $\mathbf{K}+\mathbf{q}+\boldsymbol{\tau}=0$. Thus the dispersion relation $\omega(\mathbf{q})$ can be measured in principle over the entire Brillouin zone. The experimental results allow a determination of the exchange $J(\mathbf{q})$ (cf. (6.2.12)). This formalism can be extended to non–Bravais lattices (more than one atom per cell: appearance of acoustic and optic spin waves) and to more complicated magnetic structures.

Many experimental determinations of spin–wave dispersion have been obtained by means of inelastic neutron scattering. Rare–earth metals, transition metals (Fe, Ni, Co) and many other compounds have been studied. As a general comment, we can say the Hamiltonian $\hat{H}$ (6.2.1) or (6.2.4) is too simple a model to account for experimental results. More sophisticated couplings (in particular anisotropic couplings) must be included. Nevertheless, $\hat{H}$ can be considered as a good starting point.

Inelastic neutron scattering is a powerful tool because it allows investigation over the entire Brillouin zone, but it must be kept in mind that magnetic excitations at $q=0$ can also be observed by resonance techniques.

REFERENCES

A.P. CRACKNELL, Magnetism in Crystalline Materials, Pergamon Press, Oxford (1975).

S. HAUTECLER, J. KONSTATINOVIC, D. CRIBIER, B. JACROT, *C. R. Acad. Sci.*, **254**, 1026 (1962).

F. KEFFER, Spin Waves, in Handbuch der Physik, Vol. XVIII 2, Springer, Berlin, Heidelberg, New York (1966).

W. MARSHALL, S.W. LOVESEY, Theory of Thermal Neutron Scattering, Clarendon Press, Oxford.

G. L. SQUIRES, Introduction to the Theory of Thermal Neutron Scattering, Cambridge University Press, Cambridge (1978).

K.C. TUBERFIELD, L. PASSELL, R. J. BIRGENEAU, E. BUCHER, *J. Appl. Phys.*, **42**, 1746 (1971).

CHAPTER 7

4f MAGNETISM

7.1 INTRODUCTION

As seen previously, the fourteen elements of the rare–earth group are characterised by the presence of $4f$ electrons in their normal electronic configurations. The number of $4f$ electrons varies from element to element and depends on the valency. In most chemical compounds the rare earths appear as tripositive ions; in these conditions the number of electrons increases from $4f^1$ in Ce to $4f^{14}$ in Lu along the series. Two other elements are normally considered as rare earths because of their chemical properties; La just before Ce in the same period, and Y which comes in the same position as La in the preceding period (fifth period).

In this chapter, we are dealing with the rare–earth elements in the condensed state: rare–earth metals and rare–earth compounds. The $4f$ electrons are closely bound inside the outer closed shells of the atom. Therefore, their wave functions are slightly modified when going from the free ion to the solid state. The $4f$ electrons are subject to two main types of forces from their environment. First, the array of charges in the crystal produces an electric field at any one ion called the Crystalline Electric Field, which causes a Stark splitting of the free–ion energy levels. By modifying the electronic orbits, it has an important influence on the magnetic properties. There are also forces which couple the $4f$ electrons of the different ions. These may take various forms, but the most important are of the exchange type, giving rise to cooperative magnetic properties.

7.2 MAGNETIC INTERACTIONS

7.2.1 The indirect exchange interaction

In metallic alloys, due to the strongly localized character of the $4f$ shell, the interactions can only occur through conduction electrons. As for the other types of exchange interactions (direct or superexchange), this indirect interaction is of electrostatic origin. A spin $\mathbf{S}_i$, localized on atom i, interacts with conduction electrons and leads to a spin polarization. Then, this polarization interacts with another spin $\mathbf{S}_j$ localized on atom j and therefore creates an indirect interaction between the spins $\mathbf{S}_j$ and $\mathbf{S}_i$. This interaction–which is well known–has been introduced by Ruderman and Kittel, and developed by Kasuya and Yosida; it is therefore called the RKKY interaction. In this hypothesis each conduction electron $\mathbf{s}(\mathbf{r})$ interacts with the spin $\mathbf{S}_n$ of the $4f$ electrons according to the Hamiltonian:

$$\hat{H}=-\sum_n \Gamma(\mathbf{r}-\mathbf{R}_n)\mathbf{s}(\mathbf{r})\cdot\mathbf{S}_n \tag{7.2.1}$$

where $\Gamma(\mathbf{r}-\mathbf{R}_n)$ is the constant of interaction.

Let us assume that $\Gamma(\mathbf{r})$ is a punctual interaction $\Gamma(\mathbf{r})=\Gamma\delta(\mathbf{r})$. For a given configuration of the $4f$ spins, we want to determine the state of the conduction electrons.

(a) ***Polarisation of the conduction band***

Let us assume that the conduction electrons are free, they can therefore be described by a wave function such as:

$$|k\sigma\rangle=\exp(i\mathbf{k}\cdot\mathbf{r})|\sigma\rangle \tag{7.2.2}$$

where $|\sigma\rangle$ characterises the spin ($|\sigma\rangle=|\pm 1/2\rangle$).

We introduce the usual second quantization operators $C^+_{k\sigma}$ and $C_{k\sigma}$. $C^+_{k\sigma}$ creates a conduction electron with wave vector $\mathbf{k}$ and spin σ; $C_{k\sigma}$ destroys it.

$$|k\sigma\rangle=C^+_{k\sigma}|0\rangle \tag{7.2.3}$$
$$C_{k\sigma}|k\sigma\rangle=|0\rangle$$

To find the Hamiltonian in second quantization, we expand in the complete basis of wave functions $|k\sigma\rangle$. Knowing that $\sum_{k,\sigma}|k\sigma\rangle\langle k\sigma|=1$, we obtain:

$$\hat{H}=\sum_{k\,k'\sigma\,\sigma'}|k\sigma\rangle\langle k\sigma|\hat{H}|k'\sigma'\rangle\langle k'\sigma'| \tag{7.2.4}$$

and since

$$|k\sigma\rangle=C^+_{k\sigma}C_{k'\sigma'}|k'\sigma'\rangle \tag{7.2.5}$$

and

$$C_{k'\sigma'}|k'\sigma'\rangle\langle k'\sigma'|=C_{k'\sigma'} \tag{7.2.6}$$

$$\hat{H}=\sum_{k\,k'\sigma\,\sigma'}C^+_{k\sigma}C_{k'\sigma'}\langle k\sigma|\hat{H}|k'\sigma'\rangle \tag{7.2.7}$$

taking into account that:

$$\iiint \exp[i(\mathbf{k}'-\mathbf{k})\cdot(\mathbf{r}-\mathbf{R}_n)][(\mathbf{r}-\mathbf{R}_n)]d^3\mathbf{r}=\Gamma$$

with

$$\langle k\sigma|\hat{H}|k'\sigma'\rangle=-\sum_n \exp[i(\mathbf{k}-\mathbf{k}')\cdot\mathbf{R}_n]\Gamma\langle\sigma|\mathbf{s}(\mathbf{r}_n)\cdot\langle\mathbf{S}_n\rangle|\sigma'\rangle \tag{7.2.8}$$

and

$$\mathbf{s}(\mathbf{r})\langle\mathbf{S}_n\rangle=s^z(\mathbf{r})\langle S^z_n\rangle+\frac{1}{2}\left[s^+(\mathbf{r})\langle S^-_n\rangle+s^-(\mathbf{r})\langle S^+_n\rangle\right] \tag{7.2.9}$$

At this stage, we take into account only the term $s^z(\mathbf{r})\langle S^z_n\rangle$, i.e. we assume that $\langle S^-_n\rangle$ and $\langle S^+_n\rangle$ are zero. Such a property holds for a collinear structure. More generally, it can be shown that in any case $\langle S^-_n\rangle$ and $\langle S^+_n\rangle$ do not participate in a spin polarisation.

$\hat{H}$ can then be written:

$$\hat{H}=-\frac{1}{2}\sum_{k\,k'n}\Gamma\exp[i(\mathbf{k}-\mathbf{k}')\cdot\mathbf{R}_n]\langle S^z_n\rangle(C^+_{k'\uparrow}C_{k\uparrow}-C^+_{k'\downarrow}C_{k\downarrow}) \tag{7.2.10}$$

(b) *First-order perturbation*

To first order, the energy change of the conduction electrons provided by the Hamiltonian is:

$$\Delta E=\sum_{k^0,\sigma}\langle k^0\sigma|\hat{H}|k^0\sigma\rangle \tag{7.2.11}$$

where $|k^0\sigma\rangle$ is the wave function of the conduction electrons without the perturbation.

Since:

$$\langle k\sigma|C^+_{k'\sigma'}C_{k''\sigma''}|k\sigma\rangle=\delta_{kk'}\delta_{kk''}\delta_{\sigma\sigma'}\delta_{\sigma\sigma''} \tag{7.2.12}$$

and

$$\sum_k\langle k\sigma|C^+_{k\sigma}C_{k\sigma}|k\sigma\rangle=N\sigma \tag{7.2.13}$$

we obtain:

$$\Delta E=-\tfrac{1}{2}\Gamma(N_+-N_-)\sum_n\langle S^z_n\rangle \tag{7.2.14}$$

The perturbing Hamiltonian yields a polarisation of the conduction band. However, the induced difference in the occupation of the bands of spin ↑ and ↓ provides a decrease of kinetic energy.

$$\Delta E_c=\frac{N_+-N_-}{2}\,\varepsilon=\frac{1}{4n(\varepsilon_F)}(N_+-N_-)^2 \tag{7.2.15}$$

Minimising the total difference in energy with respect to $N=N_+-N_-$ leads to:

$$N_+-N_-=\Gamma n(\varepsilon_F)\sum_n\langle S^z_n\rangle \tag{7.2.16}$$

Knowing that for a free electron: $n(\varepsilon_F)=\dfrac{3N}{2\varepsilon_F}$, (7.16) becomes:

$$N_+-N_-=\frac{3N}{2}\frac{\Gamma}{\varepsilon_F}\sum_n\langle S^z_n\rangle \tag{7.2.17}$$

For a ferromagnetic arrangement ($\sum_n\langle S^z_n\rangle\neq 0$), one then gets, to first order, a constant polarisation of the conduction band.

(c) *Second-order perturbation*

The second-order perturbation for the energy corresponds to first order for the wave functions. The perturbed wave functions of the conduction electrons are given by:

$$\Phi_{k\sigma}=\Phi^0_{k\sigma}+\sum_{\substack{k'\sigma'\\ k'\neq k}}\frac{\langle k^0\sigma|\hat{H}|k^{0\prime}\sigma'\rangle}{E_k-E_{k'}}\Phi^0_{k'\sigma'} \tag{7.2.18}$$

Knowing that for free electrons $E_k=\dfrac{\hbar^2k^2}{2m}$ and that:

$$\langle k^0\sigma|C^+_{k''\sigma''}C_{k'''\sigma'''}|k^{0\prime}\sigma'\rangle=\delta_{kk''}\delta_{k'k'''}\delta_{\sigma\sigma''}\delta_{\sigma'\sigma'''} \tag{7.2.19}$$

we obtain directly:

$$\Phi_{k\pm}=\Phi^0_{k\pm}-\frac{m}{\hbar^2}\sum_{k'\neq k}\frac{\Gamma}{k^2-k'^2}\sum_n\exp[i(\mathbf{k}-\mathbf{k}')\cdot\mathbf{R}_n][\pm\langle S^z_n\rangle\Phi^0_{k'\pm}] \tag{7.2.20}$$

The density of conduction electrons of spin σ is given by:

$$\rho_\sigma(\mathbf{r})=\sum_{k=0}^{k^\sigma_F}\langle\sigma||\Phi_{k\sigma}|^2|\sigma\rangle \tag{7.2.21}$$

k_F^σ designates the maximum wave vector of the conduction band for spin σ.

We retain in (7.2.21) only the first term corresponding to $|\Phi_{k\sigma}^0|^2$ and the second term corresponding to the double product of the first and second terms of (7.2.20). Then:

$$\rho_\pm(\mathbf{r}) = \sum_{k=0}^{k_F^+} \Big\{ \langle \pm |\Phi_{k\pm}^0|^2 \pm \rangle - \frac{m}{\hbar^2} \sum_{k' \neq k} \frac{\Gamma}{\mathbf{k}^2 - \mathbf{k}'^2} \sum_n \exp[-i(\mathbf{k}-\mathbf{k}')\cdot\mathbf{R}_n]$$
$$\times \langle \pm | \Phi_{k\pm}^0 (\pm \langle S_n^z \rangle \Phi_{k'\pm}^{0*}) | \pm \rangle \qquad (7.2.22)$$
$$- \frac{m}{\hbar^2} \sum_{k' \neq k} \frac{\Gamma}{k^2 - k'^2} \sum_n \exp[-i(\mathbf{k}-\mathbf{k}')\cdot\mathbf{R}_n] \langle \pm | \Phi_{k\pm}^{0*} (\pm \langle S_n^z \rangle \Phi_{k'\pm}^0) | \pm \rangle$$

We do not develop all the calculations which lead to:

$$\rho_\pm(\mathbf{r}) = N_\pm \frac{(3N)^2}{\varepsilon_F} \pi \Gamma \sum_n F(2k_F |\mathbf{r}-\mathbf{R}_n|) \langle S_n^z \rangle \qquad (7.2.23)$$

with:

$$F(x) = \frac{x \cos x - \sin x}{x^4} \qquad (7.2.24)$$

The variation of $F(x)$ is shown in Fig. 7.2.1.

Formula (7.2.23) includes the uniform polarisation which arises from first-order perturbation. Thus the present calculation takes into account the previously computed polarisation (7.2.16). In the case of 4f metals, Γ is positive. Consequently, the polarisation of the conduction electrons in the neighbourhood of an atom is parallel to its spin $\langle \mathbf{S}_n \rangle$.

The spin polarisation produced by the spin $\mathbf{S}_n$ interacts with the neighbouring spins and therefore creates an indirect interaction between the rare-earth spins. One can then write the energy interaction between spins as:

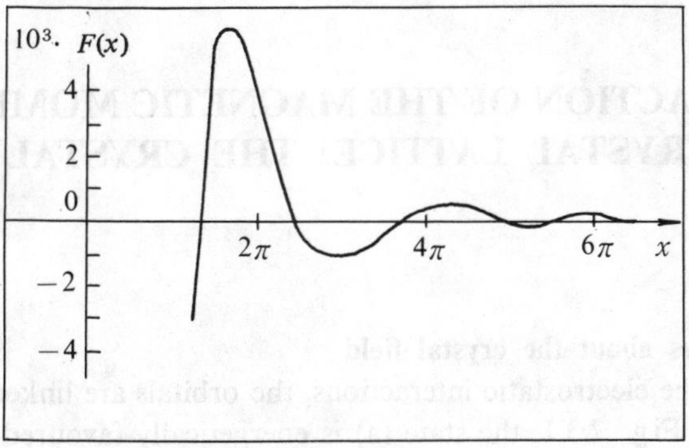

Fig. 7.2.1

$$E = \frac{(3N)^2}{2\varepsilon_F} \pi \Gamma^2 \sum_{\substack{n,m \\ m \neq n}} \mathbf{S}_n \cdot \mathbf{S}_m F(2k_F |\mathbf{R}_n - \mathbf{R}_m|) \qquad (7.2.25)$$

Replacing $\mathbf{S}$ by its projection on $\mathbf{J}$ ((g_J-1) $\mathbf{J}$):

$$E = \frac{(3N)^2}{3\varepsilon_F} \pi \Gamma^2 (g_J-1)^2 \sum_{n,m} \mathbf{J}_n \cdot \mathbf{J}_m F(2k_F |\mathbf{R}_n - \mathbf{R}_m|) \qquad (7.2.26)$$

Finally, this interaction energy is formally equivalent to a Heisenberg interaction energy:

$$\hat{H}_{ex} = -\sum_{n,m} J(R_{nm})\mathbf{J}_n \cdot \mathbf{J}_m \tag{7.2.27}$$

where:

$$J(R_{nm}) = -\frac{(3N)^2}{2\varepsilon_F}\pi\Gamma^2(g_J-1)^2F(2k_F|\mathbf{R}_n-\mathbf{R}_m|) \tag{7.2.28}$$

This interaction, which occurs only in the intermetallic compounds, can lead to magnetic ordering temperatures a little higher than 200K.

7.2.2 Other types of magnetic interactions

(a) In the multipole magnetic interaction the dipolar term is preponderant. It can be expressed by the classical interaction between two magnetic moments $\boldsymbol{\mu}_i$ and $\boldsymbol{\mu}_j$ and can be exactly calculated:

$$\mathscr{H}_{ij} = \frac{\boldsymbol{\mu}_i \cdot \boldsymbol{\mu}_j}{r_{ij}^3} - 3\,\frac{(\boldsymbol{\mu}_i \cdot \mathbf{r}_{ij})(\boldsymbol{\mu}_j \cdot \mathbf{r}_{ij})}{r_{ij}^5}$$

When the magnetic moment is high, which is the case for some rare-earth ions, this energy is a few Kelvins.

(b) In the ionic compounds the exchange interactions are of superexchange type. This indirect interaction takes place through the diamagnetic ions (O, S, Se, P,...). A more detailed description of this interaction is given in a later section. Its order of magnitude is a few Kelvins.

7.3 INTERACTION OF THE MAGNETIC MOMENTS WITH THE CRYSTAL LATTICE: THE CRYSTAL ELECTRIC FIELD

7.3.1 Generalities about the crystal field

Because of the electrostatic interactions, the orbitals are linked to the lattice. For instance, in Fig. 7.3.1, the state (a) is energetically favoured in comparison with state (b).

The interactions, by destroying the spherical symmetry of the ion, split the degeneracy of the ground multiplet of the free ion.

At this stage, two very different cases must be considered. As a matter of fact, in the transitional series 3*d* (Fe group) and 4*f* (rare-earth atoms) the relative importances of the spin-orbit coupling and of the crystal field are inverted (Fig. 7.3.2.). The L-S coupling is much larger in the 4*f* series than in the 3*d* one since the rare-earth elements are heavy. Conversely, the crystal field is

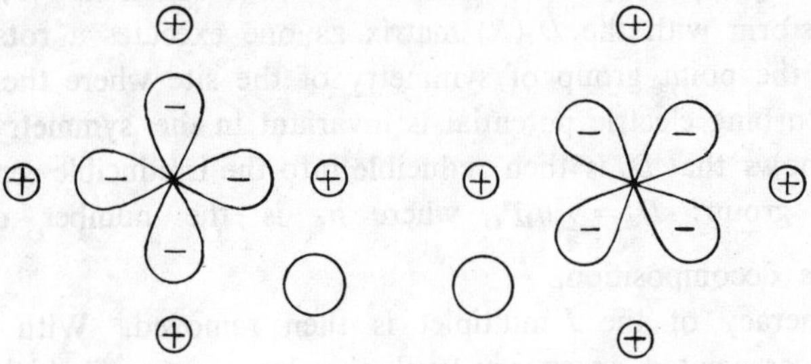

Fig. 7.3.1
d orbitals of *xy* type in the crystal field created by neighbouring ions considered as point charges.

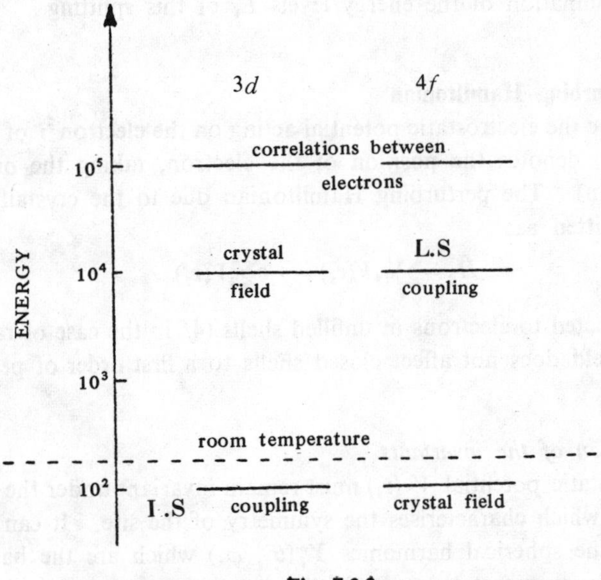

Fig. 7.3.2
Crystal field and spin-orbit coupling in 3*d* and 4*f* ions.

weaker in the 4*f* series, since the shell is screened by the outer 5*d* 6*s* shells.

As illustrated in Fig. 7.3.2, the origin of the crystal field results from the interaction between the non-spherical orbitals and the electrostatic field of the environment, which is also non-spherical. In the following we consider the case of a 4*f* ion, i.e. that the crystal field effects are one order of magnitude smaller than the spin-orbit coupling. The case of 3*d* ions will be discussed in the next chapter, but the way to treat the crystal field effect is the same for 4*f* and 3*d* ions.

7.3.2 Splitting of the free-ion multiplet by the crystalline electric field

Each multiplet of the free ion is characterised by the quantum number J. This state, $2J+1$ times degenerate, is associated with the D_J representation of the rotation group. This means that the wave functions $|J,M_J\rangle$ of the multiplet transform with the $D_J(R)$ matrix as one executes a rotation R.

Let G be the point group of symmetry of the site where the studied ion lies. The perturbing electric potential is invariant in the symmetry operations of G. One knows that D_J is then reducible into the irreducible representations Γ_i of the G group: $D_J=\sum_i n_i\Gamma_i$, where n_i is the number of times Γ_i appears in this decomposition.

The degeneracy of the J multiplet is then removed. With each representation Γ_i is associated an energy level, the degeneracy of which is equal to the order of Γ_i. As an example, the decomposition of the D_6 into the irreducible representations of the cubic point group O_h is shown in Section 7.3.3 (a).

As we have seen previously (Chapter 1), group theory allows one to predict the splitting of each multiplet by the crystalline electric field; however it does not allow the determination of the energy levels E_i of this splitting.

7.3.3 The perturbing Hamiltonian

Let $V(\mathbf{r}_i)$ be the electrostatic potential acting on the electron i of the studied magnetic ion ($\mathbf{r}_i$ denotes the position of the electron, taking the origin at the centre of the ion). The perturbing Hamiltonian due to the crystalline electric field can be written as:

$$\hat{H}_c=\sum_i q_i V(\mathbf{r}_i)=-e\sum_i V(\mathbf{r}_i) \tag{7.3.1}$$

The sum is restricted to electrons in unfilled shells (4f in the case of rare earths), as the crystal field does not affect closed shells to a first order of perturbation.

(a) *Determination of the invariants*

The electrostatic potential $V(\mathbf{r}_i)$ must remain invariant under the operations of the G group which characterises the symmetry of the site. It can always be expressed with the spherical harmonics $Y_l^m(\theta_i, \varphi_i)$ which are the basis vectors of the irreducible representations D_l of the rotation group:

$$V(\mathbf{r}_i)=\sum_l r_i^l \sum_{m=-l}^{+l} A_l^m\, Y_l^m(\theta_i, \varphi_i) \tag{7.3.2}$$

Then it is a matter of getting down to determine the A_l^m, i.e. the linear cominations of Y_l^m which remain invariant under the symmetry operations of G. We have seen that the D_l can be reduced to irreducible representations of G.

$$D_l=\sum_i n_i\Gamma_i$$

If the identity representation Γ_1 of G appears in this decomposition, this means that there exists a linear combination of the Y_l^m, the basis vectors of D_l, which remains invariant under the symmetry operations of G.

As an example, here is the decomposition of several D_l into the irreducible representation of the cubic group O_h.

$$D_0=\Gamma_1$$
$$D_1=\Gamma_4$$
$$D_2=\Gamma_3+\Gamma_5$$
$$D_3=\Gamma_2+\Gamma_4+\Gamma_5$$
$$D_4=\Gamma_1+\Gamma_3+\Gamma_4+\Gamma_5$$
$$D_5=\Gamma_3+2\Gamma_4+\Gamma_5$$
$$D_6=\Gamma_1+\Gamma_2+\Gamma_3+\Gamma_4+2\Gamma_5$$

The Γ_1 representation appears only in the decomposition of the representations D_0, D_4 and D_6. We do not take into account D_0 because it is associated with Y_0^0, i.e. with a constant term in $V(\mathbf{r}_i)$ the effect of which is only to shift the origin of the energy level scale. We do not consider the terms with $l>6$ because we shall see further that these terms do not appear in the perturbation. Thus one has to consider (in the case of the cubic group O_h) two invariants: one of fourth order and the other of sixth order:

$$\sum_{m=-4}^{+4} A_4^m Y_4^m(\theta_i, \varphi_i) \text{ and } \sum_{m=-6}^{+6} A_6^m Y_6^m(\theta_i, \varphi_i)$$

In the Appendix to this chapter we report the general expressions of the Y_l^m's and the expressions of the most usual spherical harmonics.

In order to get these two invariants it is possible to use the projection operator: let ψ be a function which transforms following an irreducible representation of the rotation group. It is possible to find a function $\psi_i^{(\alpha)}$ which transforms following the $\Gamma^{(\alpha)}$ of G by using the formula:

$$\psi_i^{(\alpha)}=\frac{f_\alpha}{g}\sum_G \Gamma_{i\,i}^{(\alpha)}\hat{G}\psi \tag{7.3.3}$$

(f_α=dimension of the representation $\Gamma^{(\alpha)}$, g=order of the group G, $\hat{G}$=operation $\hat{G}$ of the group G). However, in the case of the cubic group, due to the great number of elements of G, it is easier to look directly for the invariant by applying some symmetry operations.

Let us choose the x–, y– and z–axes parallel to the fourfold axes. Let us consider the spherical harmonic Y_4^m and let us execute a rotation of angle $2\pi/4$ around z. (φ is replaced by $\varphi+2\pi/4$). The Y_l^m being proportional to $e^{im\varphi}$, only the Y_4^0, Y_4^4 and Y_4^{-4} are not modified. One shows then easily that the invariant is:

$$Y_4^0+A(Y_4^4+Y_4^{-4})=\frac{3}{16\sqrt{\pi}}[35\cos^4\theta-30\cos^2\theta+3+A\sqrt{70}\sin^4\theta\cos4\varphi] \tag{7.3.4}$$

In order to determine A, multiplying this expression by r^4 one can write the invariant in cartesian coordinates (x, y, z) and one executes a rotation of angle $2\pi/3$ around the [111] axis: by replacing x by y, y by z and z by x, the polynomial must remain invariant whatever x, y and z are. One obtains then $A=\sqrt{5/14}$.

In the same way, one determines the sixth-order invariant. The electrostatic potential in a cubic symmetry site can finally be written:

$$V(\mathbf{r}_i)=A_4 r_i^4\left\{Y_4^0(\theta_i,\varphi_i)+\sqrt{\frac{5}{14}}\left[Y_4^4(\theta_i,\varphi_i)+Y_4^{-4}(\theta_i,\varphi_i)\right]\right\}$$
$$+A_6 r^6\left\{Y_6^0(\theta_i,\varphi_i)-\sqrt{\frac{7}{2}}\left[Y_6^4(\theta_i,\varphi_i)+Y_6^{-4}(\theta_i,\varphi_i)\right]\right\} \quad (7.3.5)$$

For the other point groups the number of Y_l^m used to describe $V(\mathbf{r}_i)$ is not the same, but $V(\mathbf{r}_i)$ can be obtained in the same way. For one ion lying in a hexagonal site one obtains for example:

$$V(\mathbf{r}_i)=A_2^0 r_i^2 Y_2^0+A_4^0 r_i^4 Y_4^0+A_6^0 r_i^6 Y_6^0+A_6^6 r_i^6(Y_6^6+Y_6^{-6}) \quad (7.3.6)$$

In this last case the number of A_l^m parameters is four, while it was two in the cubic case. In general the number of parameters required to describe $V(\mathbf{r}_i)$ is more important when the symmetry is low.

(b) *The point charge model*

In this oversimplified model, one considers that the electrostatic potential of the surroundings arises from point electric charges located at the centre of the atoms of the crystal. At a point **r** the electrostatic potential can then be written:

$$V(r,\theta,\varphi)=\sum_j \frac{q_j}{|\mathbf{R}_j-\mathbf{r}|} \quad (7.3.7)$$

where q_j is the charge of the ion j of the surroundings and $\mathbf{R}_j$ its position.

If one knows the charge q_j, this potential can be calculated precisely. Although this model gives sometimes the correct sign of the A_l^m coefficients, it is shown to fail in most cases. As a matter of fact, it neglects the finite extent of charges on the ions, the overlap of the magnetic ions' wave functions with those of neighbouring ions, and the complex effects of "screening" of the magnetic electrons by the outer electron shells of the magnetic ion. Moreover, in metallic compounds, this model does not take into account the conduction electrons which give rise to a strong contribution to the crystal field Hamiltonian.

7.3.4 Calculation of the matrix elements of the perturbing Hamiltonian $\hat{H}_c$

In the basis $|J, M_J\rangle$ of the considered multiplet, the elements of the matrix which must be diagonalised are of the type:

$$\langle J,M_J|\hat{H}_c|J,M'_J\rangle=\langle J,M_J|-e\sum_i V(\mathbf{r}_i)|J,M'_J\rangle \quad (7.3.8)$$

(a) *Direct integration*

The free-ion wave functions $|J, M_J\rangle$ are obtained from determinental product states involving single-electron wave functions $\phi_i=\psi_i(\mathbf{r}_i)\,\chi_i(\mathbf{s}_i)$ (ψ_i=orbital state, χ_i=spin state) on which the corresponding terms $V(\mathbf{r}_i)$ in the $\hat{H}_c$ act. The matrix elements, expressed in polar coordinates, therefore, reduce to sums of terms of the form:

$$\int \psi_i^*(\mathbf{r}_i) r_i^l\, Y_l^m(\theta_i,\varphi_i)\psi_i(\mathbf{r}_i)d^3\mathbf{r}_i \quad (7.3.9)$$

Because $\psi_i(\mathbf{r}_i)=R_{nl'}(r_i)\,Y_{l'}^{m'}(\theta_i,\varphi_i)$ (see Chapter 1) this integral is the product of two parts:

a radial part:

$$\langle r^l \rangle = \int [R_{nl'}(r_i)]^2 r_i^l r_i^2 dr_i \tag{7.3.10}$$

an orbital part:

$$\int Y_{l'}^{m'}(\theta_i, \varphi_i) Y_l^m(\theta_i, \varphi_i) Y_{l'}^{m''}(\theta_i, \varphi_i) \sin\theta_i \, d\theta_i d\varphi_i \tag{7.3.11}$$

For rare-earth ions the $\langle r^l \rangle$'s were calculated and are tabulated.

We will now see the selection rules limiting the number of non-zero matrix elements.

In the case of rare-earth ions $l'=3$ ($l'=2$ for the $3d$ ions). We will use the three representation theorem.

(i) $Y_{l'}^{m'}$ and $Y_{l'}^{m''}$ transform according to the $D_{l'}$ representation of the rotation group. In order that the D_0 appear in the decomposition of the direct product $D_{l'} \times D_l \times D_{l'}$ it is necessary that $l \leqslant 2l'$. Thus $l \leqslant 6$ in the case of rare earths and $l \leqslant 4$ in the case of the $3d$ transition elements. This is the reason why we did not write terms of an order higher than six in the expansion of the electrostatic potential $V(\mathbf{r}_i)$.

(ii) Let us consider the group of inversion through the origin ($\mathbf{r} \to -\mathbf{r}$). This group contains two elements and hence two one-dimensional irreducible representations (Table). One easily shows that the Y_l^m with $l=2n$ ($n=$ integer) transform according to the identity representation Γ_1, while the Y_l^m with $l=2n+1$ transform according to Γ_2. Applying the three representation theorem one sees that in formula (7.3.11) l must be even; that is to say, in the expansion of $V(\mathbf{r}_i)$ one only takes into account the Y_l^m terms with $l=2n$.

	E	i	Basis functions
Γ_1	1	1	Y_l^m, $l=2n$
Γ_2	1	$\bar{1}$	Y_l^m, $l=2n+1$

(iii) In this case we apply the three representation theorem for the two-dimensional rotation group C_∞. This Abelian group has representations of the type $\Gamma_m = e^{im\phi}$ (ϕ=rotation angle). A Y_l^m spherical harmonic is a basis function of the Γ_m representation. The three representation theorem leads to:

$$e^{-im'\phi} e^{im\phi} e^{im''\phi} = e^{i[m-(m'-m'')]\phi} = 1$$

this must be verified whatever ϕ is. Thus one has $m=m'-m''$.

(b) *The Stevens' "Operator Equivalents" method*

This is by far the most convenient method for evaluating the matrix elements of the crystalline potential between coupled wave functions specified by J (or L).

It eliminates the need to go back to single electron wave functions by the use of an "operator equivalent" to $\hat{H}_c$ consisting of angular momentum operators which act on the angular part of the wave function. This is an application for the Wigner–Eckart theorem (Section 1.2.4). Due to the fact that the angular momentum **J** and the position of an electron **r** are both vectors, to find the operator equivalents to such terms as $\sum_i f(x_i, y_i, z_i)$ occurring in $\hat{H}_c$, one replaces x, y and z by J_x, J_y and J_z respectively, always allowing for the non-commutation of J_x, J_y and J_z. This is done by replacing products of x, y and z by an expression consisting of all the possible different combinations of J_x, J_y and J_z, divided by the total number of combinations.

Some simple examples are:

$$\sum_i 3z_i^2 - r_i^2 \equiv \alpha_J \langle r^2 \rangle [3J_z^2 - J(J+1)] = \alpha_J \langle r^2 \rangle O_2^0 \quad (7.3.12)$$

$$\sum_i x_i y_i \equiv \alpha_J \langle r^2 \rangle [(J_x J_y - J_y J_x)/2] \quad (7.3.13)$$

In this way one will write:

$$\langle J, M_J | \sum_i (3z_i^2 - r_i^2) | J, M'_J \rangle \equiv \alpha_J \langle r^2 \rangle \langle J, M_J | [3J_z^2 - J(J+1)] | J, M'_J \rangle \quad (7.3.14)$$

The multiplicative factor α_J is a constant depending on l of the electron (3 in the case of rare earths), and J of the considered rare–earth element. The constants are β_J and γ_J for fourth– and sixth–order terms respectively. Their values are tabulated for all rare–earth elements. So instead of $\langle r^2 \rangle$, one uses $\langle r^4 \rangle$ and $\langle r^6 \rangle$ for the fourth– and sixth–order terms respectively. All these quantities are tabulated. For the values and the expressions of the equivalent operators O_l^m see the contribution of Hutchings in Solid States Physics Vol. 16.

We give below some equivalent operators which are often used:

$$\sum 35z^4 - 30r^2z^2 + 3r^4 \equiv \beta_J \langle r^4 \rangle [35J_z^4 - 30J(J+1)J_z^2 + 25J_z^2 - 6J(J+1) + 3J^2(J+1)^2] = \beta_J \langle r^4 \rangle O_4^0$$

$$\sum x^4 - 6x^2y^2 + y^4 \equiv \beta_J \langle r^4 \rangle \frac{1}{2} [J_+^4 + J_-^4]$$

$$\sum 231z^6 - 315z^4r^2 + 105z^2r^4 - 5r^6 \equiv \gamma_J \langle r^6 \rangle [231J_z^6 - 315J(J+1)J_z^4 + 735J_z^4 + 105J^2(J+1)^2J_z^2 - 525J(J+1)J_z^2 + 294J_z^2 - 5J^3(J+1)^3 + 40J^2(J+1)^2 - 60J(J+1)] = \gamma_J \langle r^6 \rangle O_6^0$$

$$\sum (11z^2 - r^2)(x^4 - 6x^2y^2 + y^4) \equiv \gamma_J \langle r^6 \rangle \frac{1}{4} [(11J_z^2 - J(J+1) - 38)(J_+^4 + J_-^4) + (J_+^4 + J_-^4)(11J_z^2 - J(J+1) - 38)] = \gamma_J \langle r^6 \rangle O_6^4$$

$$\sum (x^6 - 15x^4y^2 + 15x^2y^4 - y^6) \equiv \gamma_J \langle r^6 \rangle \frac{1}{2} [J_+^6 + J_-^6]$$

As an example, the crystal field perturbing Hamiltonian in cubic symmetry can be written as (the x– and z–axes are taken parallel to fourfold rotation axes):

$$\hat{H}_c = A_4 \beta_J \langle r^4 \rangle [O_4^0 + 5O_4^4] + A_6 \gamma_J \langle r^6 \rangle [O_6^0 - 21O_6^4] \quad (7.3.15)$$

For all the rare earths the $\langle J, M_J | O_l^m | J, M'_J \rangle$ matrix elements are tabulated in the paper of Hutchings.

(c) ***Kramers, non-Kramers ions***

As already seen in Section 1.1.4, depending on the number of electrons, even or odd, the degeneracy of the free–ion ground multiplet is respectively odd (non–Kramers ion) or even (Kramers ion). According to Kramers theorem, in the latter case, without a magnetic field, all the levels are at least doublets. Conversely, for non–Kramers ions under the same conditions, the degeneracy can be totally split.

7.3.5 Crystal field in rare–earth ions (4*f* elements)

In the 4*f* series, the crystal field is two orders of magnitude smaller than the spin–orbit coupling. Consequently, the crystal field removes the degeneracy of the ground multiplet determined by the spin–orbit coupling. Then, it is generally observed that crystal field effects are of the same order of magnitude as the molecular field or a very intense applied field. The nature of each level (wave function, magnetic moment) will depend on the conjugate actions of these different contributions. We will illustrate these effects, in what follows, by two examples: one where the crystal field is preponderant compared to exchange, and a second where the situation is reversed.

(a) *Strong crystal field*: TmSb

TmSb crystallises in the cubic structure of NaCl structure type. The crystal field acting on the ground multiplet $^3H_6$ (S=1, L=5, J=6) of the Tm^{3+} ion can be written as:

$$\hat{H}_c = B_4(O_4^0 + 5O_4^4) + B_6(O_6^0 - 21O_6^6) \tag{7.3.16}$$

where the O_l^m are operators, linear combinations of J_x, J_y, J_z, for example:

$$O_4^0 = 35J_z^4 - 30J(J+1)J_z^2 + 25J_z^2 - 6J(J+1) + 3J^2(J+1)^2 \tag{7.3.17}$$

The D_6 representation of the rotation group associated with J=6 can be decomposed into the Γ_i representations of the cubic group which define the

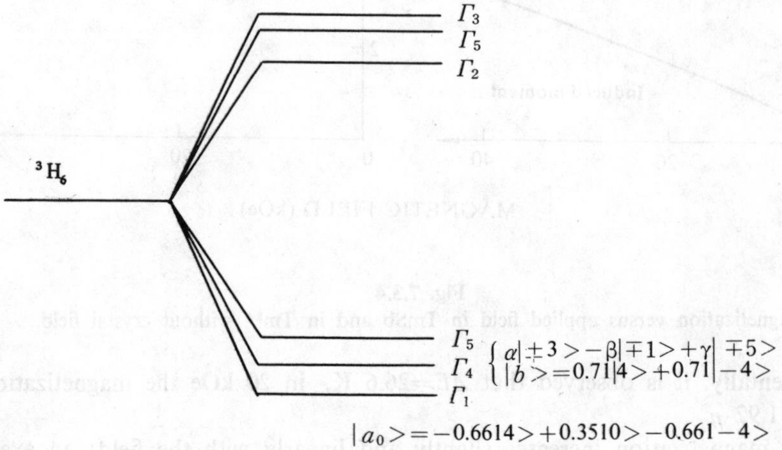

Fig. 7.3.3
Crystal field level scheme for Tm^{3+} ion in TmSb.

sub–space associated with each level of the ion for this symmetry.

$$D_6=\Gamma_1\text{ (singlet)}+\Gamma_2\text{(singlet)}+\Gamma_3\text{(doublet)}+\Gamma_4\text{(triplet)}+2\Gamma_5\text{(triplet)}.$$

The splitting of the ground state multiplet is schematized in Fig. 7.3.3. One notices that some levels are singlet since Tm is a non–Kramers ion, especially, the ground level is a non–magnetic singlet. In order to determine the effect of a magnetic field on the magnetization of TmSb, one has to introduce the perturbation $\hat{H}_{ze}=-g_J\mu_B\ HJ_z$.

To the first order in calculation, the energy of the ground level is not modified since $\langle a_0|J_z|a_0\rangle=0$. But, the ground multiplet becomes:

$$|a_1\rangle=|a_0\rangle+g_J\mu_B H\sum_i|b_i\rangle\frac{\langle b_i|J_z|a_0\rangle}{E_i-E_0} \tag{7.3.18}$$

J_z being associated with Γ_4: Γ_i must be contained in $\Gamma_4\otimes\Gamma_1=\Gamma_4$.

$$|a_1\rangle=-0.66|4\rangle+0.35|0\rangle-0.66|-4\rangle+\frac{8\times0.71\times0.66g_J\mu_B H}{\Delta E}(-0.71|4\rangle+0.71|-4\rangle)$$

To first order the magnetization will be:

$$\sigma=\langle a_1|g_J\mu_B J_z|a_1\rangle=\frac{2\times16\times(0.71\times0.66)^2\,g_J\,\mu_B H_z}{\Delta E}\times4$$

$$\sigma=\frac{1.1\times H(\text{kOe})}{\Delta E(\text{K})}\mu_B \tag{7.3.19}$$

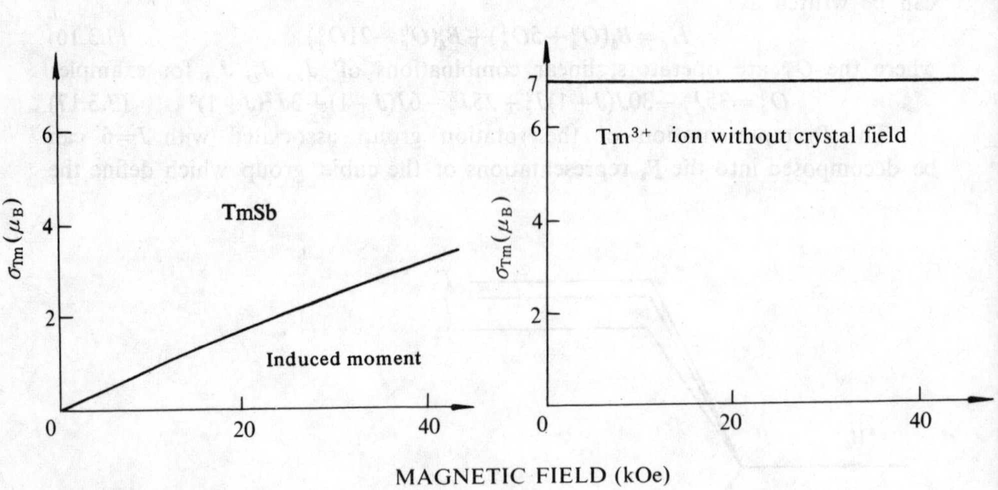

Fig. 7.3.4

Magnetization versus applied field in TmSb and in Tm^{3+} without crystal field.

Experimentally, it is observed that $\Delta E=26.6$ K, in 20 kOe the magnetization reaches 1.92 μ_B.

The magnetization increases slightly and linearly with the field; an exact calculation, in agreement with experimental values, gives the variation shown Fig. 7.3.4. Without the crystal field, applying a field, even very weak, will lead to the maximum magnetization.

(b) *Strong molecular field*

The molecular field splits the ground multiplet into $2J+1$ equally separated levels. The crystal field, weaker, acts as a perturbation (Fig. 7.3.5). Let us assume that the symmetry is uniaxial: the preponderant term of the crystal field is of 2nd order (quadrupolar term) and can be written:

$$\hat{H}_c = B_2^0 O_2^0 = B_2^0 (3J_z^2 - J(J+1)) \qquad (7.3.20)$$

In the case of Tb, the modification of the energy of the ground level $|J_z=6\rangle$ is:

$$\langle 6|\hat{H}_c|6\rangle = 66 B_2^0 \qquad (7.3.21)$$

This is the energy in the case where the magnetization (i.e. the molecular field) is parallel to the z-axis of the uniaxial symmetry. Let us examine what the energy becomes if the magnetization is parallel to x, i.e. perpendicular to z.

Such a situation is equivalent to a magnetization parallel to z and a crystal field parallel to x. The rotation of the crystal field by 90° leads to:

$$\hat{H}'_c = -\frac{B_2^0}{2}\left[3J_z^2 - J(J+1) - \frac{3}{2}(J_+^2 + J_-^2)\right] \qquad (7.3.22)$$

The modification of the energy of the ground level $|J_z=6\rangle$ is then:

$$\langle 6|\hat{H}'_c|6\rangle = -33 B_2^0 \qquad (7.3.23)$$

In the case where $B_2^0 > 0$, such a case is energetically favourable. The magnetization tends to be along x. The energy difference between the direction of easy magnetization (x) and that of hard magnetization (z) is called the anisotropy energy. In this example. it is 99 B_2^0. It is possible to overcome the anisotropy energy by applying a magnetic field perpendicular to the direction of easy magnetization. The experimental situation described above is encountered in Tb metal ($J=6$). The magnetization process when the field is applied parallel or perpendicular to the easy direction of magnetization is illustrated in Fig. 7.3.6.

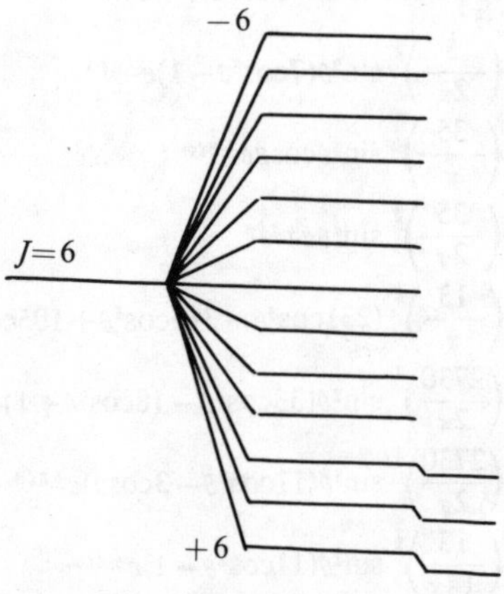

Fig. 7.3.5

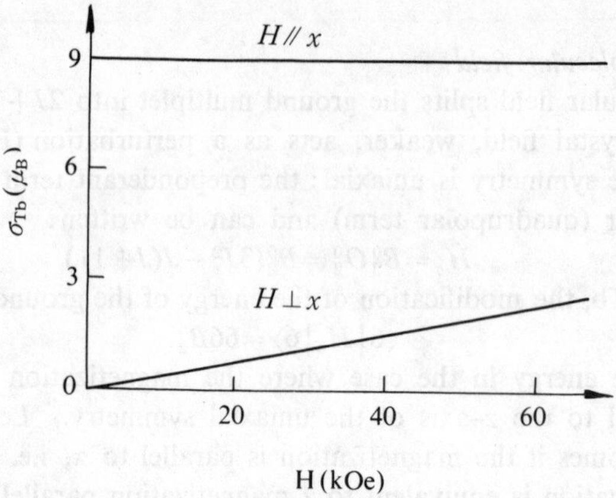

Fig. 7.3.6
Magnetization versus applied field in Tb metal at 4.2 K.

REFERENCES

B. COOPER, O. VOGT, *Phys. Rev.*, **B1**, 1211 (1970).

B. COQBLIN, The Electronic Structure of Rare-earth Metals and Alloys, Academic Press New York (1977).

M. T. HUTCHINGS, *Sol. Stat. Phys.*, **16**, 227 (1964).

Appendix

Some of the More Commonly Occurring Spherical Harmonics

$$Y_2^0 = \frac{1}{4}\left(\frac{5}{\pi}\right)^{\frac{1}{2}}(3\cos^2\theta - 1)$$

$$Y_2^{\pm 2} = \frac{1}{4}\left(\frac{15}{2\pi}\right)^{\frac{1}{2}}\sin^2\theta e^{\pm 2i\phi}$$

$$Y_4^0 = \frac{3}{16}\frac{1}{\pi^{\frac{1}{2}}}(35\cos^4\theta - 30\cos^2\theta + 3)$$

$$Y_4^{\pm 2} = \frac{3}{8}\left(\frac{5}{2\pi}\right)^{\frac{1}{2}}\sin^2\theta(7\cos^2\theta - 1)e^{\pm 2i\phi}$$

$$Y_4^{\pm 3} = \mp\frac{3}{8}\left(\frac{35}{\pi}\right)^{\frac{1}{2}}\sin^3\theta\cos\theta e^{\pm 3i\phi}$$

$$Y_4^{\pm 4} = \frac{3}{16}\left(\frac{35}{2\pi}\right)^{\frac{1}{2}}\sin^4\theta e^{\pm 4i\phi}$$

$$Y_6^0 = \frac{1}{32}\left(\frac{13}{\pi}\right)^{\frac{1}{2}}(231\cos^6\theta - 315\cos^4\theta + 105\cos^2\theta - 5)$$

$$Y_6^{\pm 2} = \frac{1}{64}\left(\frac{2730}{2\pi}\right)^{\frac{1}{2}}\sin^2\theta(33\cos^4\theta - 18\cos^2\theta + 1)e^{\pm 2i\phi}$$

$$Y_6^{\pm 3} = \mp\frac{1}{32}\left(\frac{2730}{2\pi}\right)^{\frac{1}{2}}\sin^3\theta(11\cos^3\theta - 3\cos\theta)e^{\pm 3i\phi}$$

$$Y_6^{\pm 4} = \frac{21}{32}\left(\frac{13}{14\pi}\right)^{\frac{1}{2}}\sin^4\theta(11\cos^2\theta - 1)e^{\pm 4i\phi}$$

$$Y_6^{\pm 6} = \frac{231}{64}\left(\frac{13}{231\pi}\right)^{\frac{1}{2}}\sin^6\theta e^{\pm 6i\phi}$$

CHAPTER 8

IONIC 3*d* COMPOUNDS

Transition metal (3*d*) ions are characterised by unpaired 3*d* electrons in the 3*d* electronic shell. The number of these 3*d* electrons around the ions depends upon the nature of the chemical bonding with anions in non–metallic materials However, 3*d* electrons can be considered as almost localized electrons, but they are very sensitive to any surrounding potentials, in particular to crystal electric fields which originate from the distribution of electrical charges and dipoles of the neighbouring ions. We first describe these effects, and then present exchange mechanisms which account for the magnetic ordering of 3*d* insulators. Finally we discuss an example, $FeCl_2$.

8.1 CRYSTAL FIELD EFFECTS—ANISOTROPY

As we have seen in Section 1.3.2, the 3*d* electronic shells of the 3*d* series compounds are not shielded by other outmost shells. This explains why 3*d* electrons are, here, more sensitive to the surrounding potentials than 4*f* electrons in rare earths.

In the 4*d* and 5*d* series (palladium and platinum groups), the crystal field energy V_c is larger than the separation between atomic terms ($V_c \sim 10^5$ K, see Section 1.3.2); thus V_c must be treated as a perturbation of the $(4d)^x$ or $(5d)^x$ configuration. The individual electronic wave functions are not $R_{n2}(r)\ Y_2^m(\theta,\varphi)$ anymore as in a free–ion picture; they have the point symmetry of the *d* ion site. This is called the strong field scheme, which will shortly be described in an example (see Section 8.1.2).

In the 3*d* compounds, V_c is typically of the order of 10^4 K, which is less than the separation between atomic terms (see Fig. 7.3.2.), V_c is a perturbation on the atomic term (*L, S*) which is given by Hund's rules. This is called the weak field scheme, which is similar to the crystal field theory described in Section 7.3.3. However, in 3*d* compounds, V_c is larger than spin–orbit coupling (~100K), and V_c couples to the orbital part of the wave functions only.

An isolated 3*d* ion can be described by a Hamiltonian which has a spherical symmetry. When this ion is embedded in a crystal, the total Hamiltonian has the point symmetry of the ion's site, which is lower than spherical symmetry. As discussed in Section 1.1.9, the symmetry reduction will lead to a lifting of the degeneracy of the 3*d* orbital wave functions; if the crystal field perturbation is strong enough(and the symmetry low enough), the orbital degeneracy is completely removed and the orbital groundstate is a singlet: the angular momentum $\hat{\mathbf{L}}$ of the ion is quenched (L is reduced to $L=0$) and we observe "spin-only" magnetic properties. To a first-order approximation, there is no coupling between the crystal and the magnetic moment of the ion; there is no single-ion anisotropy. However, in many cases, $\hat{\mathbf{L}}$ is not completely quenched. Then the orbital groundstate can be represented by an effective $\hat{\mathbf{l}}$ operator ($L>l$); because of the spin-orbit coupling, the residual angular moment induces single-ion anisotropy.

Most 3*d* ions have an environment whose local symmetry is approximately cubic (either octahedral or tetrahedral). Deviations from this high symmetry can be treated as perturbations and are dealt with as will be indicated in a few examples.

8.1.1 3*d* electron in a cubic electric field

Let us consider a cubic site (the point symmetry is T_d or O_h—Fig. 8.1.1) An independent 3*d* electronic orbital state (symmetry D_2) is split into a doublet and a triplet: (see Table 8.1.1):

$$D_2 \rightarrow \Gamma_3 + \Gamma_5 \text{ for } O_h \text{ point symmetry}$$

and

$$D_2 \rightarrow (\Gamma_2 + \Gamma_3) + \Gamma_4 \text{ for } T_d \text{ point symmetry}$$

Table 8.1.1
Character table of T and O point groups

T	E	$4C_3$	$4C_3^2$	$3C_2$
Γ_1	1	1	1	1
Γ_2	1	ω	ω^2	1
Γ_3	1	ω^2	ω	1
Γ_4	3	0	0	-1

O	E	$8C_3$	$6C_2$	$6C_4$	$3C_4^2$
Γ_1	1	1	1	1	1
Γ_2	1	1	-1	-1	1
Γ_3	2	-1	0	0	2
Γ_4	3	0	-1	1	-1
Γ_5	3	0	1	-1	-1
D_2	5	-1	1	-1	1

This group theoretical result does not tell us anything about the position of the new states.

However, we can find the form of the wave functions by making use of the projection operators (1.2.12). Let us take the z-axis along one of the 4-fold axis of the cubic site. Single $3d$ electron wave functions are written as $|d, m\rangle \equiv \psi_{2m}(\theta, \varphi)R_{3d}(r)$ where m takes the values $-2, \ -1, 0, +1, \ +2$, $\psi_{2m}(\theta, \varphi)$ is a spherical harmonic function. Under the operations of point symmetry, $R_{3d}(r)$ is invariant, and the angular part transforms into linear combinations of $\psi_{2m}(\theta, \varphi)$. It is more convenient to use linear combinations of $\psi_{2m}(\theta, \varphi)$ (basis functions of D_2) and project them into Γ_3 and Γ_5 to obtain wave functions describing the states of a $3d$ electron in the crystal field.

We will use:

$$\varphi_x = \frac{i}{\sqrt{2}}(|d,1\rangle + |d,-1\rangle) = \left(\frac{15}{4\pi}\right)^{1/2} \frac{yz}{r^2} R_{3d}(r)$$

$$\varphi_y = \frac{-1}{\sqrt{2}}(|d,1\rangle - |d,-1\rangle) = \left(\frac{15}{4\pi}\right)^{1/2} \frac{zx}{r^2} R_{3d}(r)$$

$$\varphi_z = \frac{-i}{\sqrt{2}}(|d,2\rangle - |d,-2\rangle) = \left(\frac{15}{4\pi}\right)^{1/2} \frac{xy}{r^2} R_{3d}(r) \tag{8.1.1}$$

$$\varphi_u = |d,0\rangle = \left(\frac{5}{16\pi}\right)^{1/2} \frac{3z^2 - r^2}{r^2} R_{3d}(r)$$

$$\varphi_v = \frac{1}{\sqrt{2}}(|d,2\rangle + |d,-2\rangle) = \left(\frac{15}{16\pi}\right)^{1/2} \frac{x^2 - y^2}{r^2} R_{3d}(r)$$

Transformation matrices of the φ_i are given in Table 8.1.2.

It can be seen that $\varphi_x, \varphi_y, \varphi_z$ transform into each other, and that φ_u and φ_v transform also into each other; the matrices in Table 8.1.2. are in a block form as in (1.2.3): the $\varphi_x, \varphi_y, \varphi_z, \varphi_u, \varphi_v$ induce the representation D_2 which is reducible into Γ_3 and Γ_5 whose basis functions can be taken as φ_u, φ_v and φ_x, φ_y, φ_z respectively. Linear combinations of these functions would lead to equivalent representations. Thus it is not worth using the projection operator.

The energies of the two states associated with the Γ_3 and Γ_5 representations must be calculated by using a Hamiltonian similar to (7.3.2):

$$V_c(\mathbf{r}) = \sum_{l,m} a_l^m r^l Y_l^m(\theta, \varphi) \tag{8.1.2}$$

The expansion in l can be limited to the fourth-order terms: in perturbation theory, we calculate matrix elements:

$$\langle R_{3d}(r) Y_{l'}^{m'}(\theta,\varphi) | V_c(\mathbf{r}) | R_{3d}(r) Y_{l''}^{m''}(\theta,\varphi)\rangle \tag{8.1.3}$$

which are non-vanishing only if the representation $D_{l'}$ is found in the decomposition of the direct product $D_l \otimes D_{l''}$. (cf. Section 1.2.4). It is known that

$$D_l \otimes D_{l''} = \sum_{J=|l'-l''|}^{J=l'+l''} D_J$$

Thus (8.1.3) is non-zero if l is such that

$$|l - l''| \leqslant l' \leqslant l + l'' \tag{8.1.4}$$

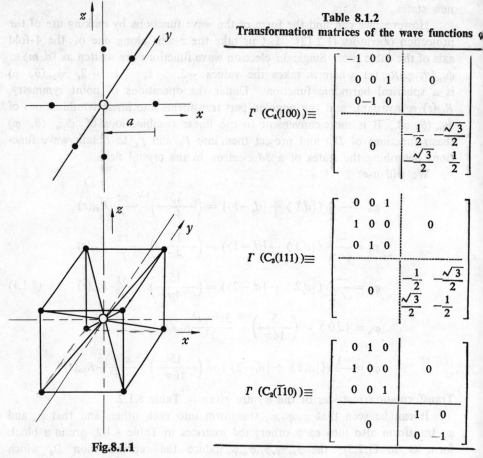

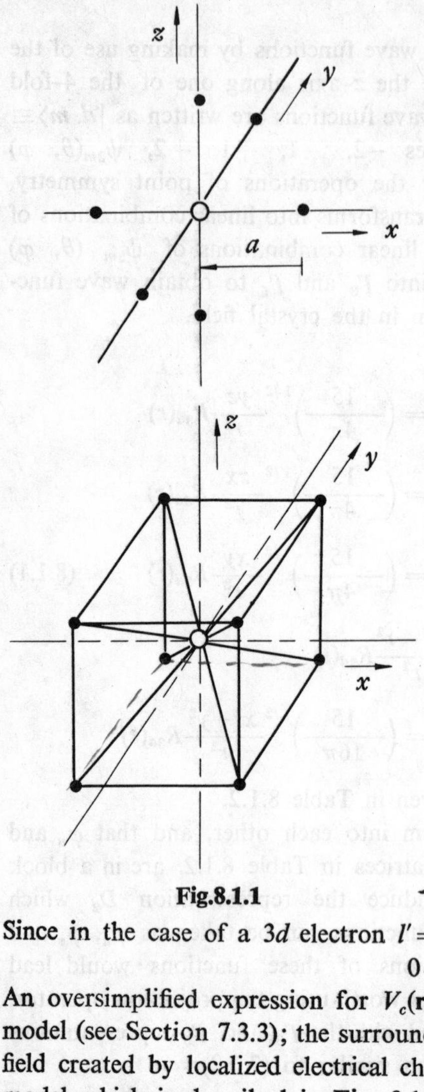

Fig.8.1.1

Table 8.1.2

Transformation matrices of the wave functions φ

$\Gamma\,(C_4(100)) \equiv$	$\left[\begin{array}{ccc\|cc} -1 & 0 & 0 & & \\ 0 & 0 & 1 & & 0 \\ 0 & -1 & 0 & & \\ \hline & 0 & & -\frac{1}{2} & -\frac{\sqrt{3}}{2} \\ & & & -\frac{\sqrt{3}}{2} & \frac{1}{2} \end{array}\right]$
$\Gamma\,(C_3(111)) \equiv$	$\left[\begin{array}{ccc\|cc} 0 & 0 & 1 & & \\ 1 & 0 & 0 & & 0 \\ 0 & 1 & 0 & & \\ \hline & 0 & & -\frac{1}{2} & -\frac{\sqrt{3}}{2} \\ & & & \frac{\sqrt{3}}{2} & -\frac{1}{2} \end{array}\right]$
$\Gamma\,(C_2(\bar{1}10)) \equiv$	$\left[\begin{array}{ccc\|cc} 0 & 1 & 0 & & \\ 1 & 0 & 0 & & 0 \\ 0 & 0 & 1 & & \\ \hline & 0 & & 1 & 0 \\ & & & 0 & -1 \end{array}\right]$

Since in the case of a $3d$ electron $l'=l''=2$, we have

$$0 \leqslant l \leqslant 4$$

An oversimplified expression for $V_c(\mathbf{r})$ can be found by using a point charge model (see Section 7.3.3); the surrounding potential is represented by an electric field created by localized electrical charges. In a cubic site, we can use the model which is described in Fig. 8.1.1. We have

$$V_c^{\mathrm{pcm}}(\mathbf{r}) = \sum_{i=1}^{i=6} \frac{Ze^2}{|\mathbf{R}_i - \mathbf{r}|} \tag{8.1.5}$$

where $\mathbf{r}$ is the position of the $3d$ electron. The quantity $\dfrac{1}{|\mathbf{R}_i-\mathbf{r}|}$ can be expanded as a series of Legendre polynomials. If the distance a is much larger than the mean radius $\sqrt{\langle r^2\rangle_{3d}}$ then

$$V_c^{\mathrm{pcm}}(\mathbf{r}) = Ze^2 \sum_{i=1}^{6} \sum_{l=0}^{\infty} \frac{1}{a}\left(\frac{r}{a}\right) P_l(\cos\omega_i) \tag{8.1.6}$$

where ω_i is the angle between $\mathbf{R}_i$ and $\mathbf{r}$. It can be shown (see any text book) that

$$P_l(\cos\omega_i)=\frac{4\pi}{2l+1}\sum_{m=-l}^{l}Y_l^m(\theta,\varphi)Y_l^{*m}(\theta_i,\varphi_i) \tag{8.1.7}$$

Thus

$$V_c^{\mathrm{pcm}}(\mathbf{r})=\sum_{l,m}a_l^m r^l Y_l{}^m(\theta,\varphi)$$

with

$$a_l^m=\frac{4\pi}{2l+1}\frac{Ze^2}{a^{2l+1}}\sum_{i=1}^{6}Y_l^{*m}(\theta_i,\varphi_i) \tag{8.1.8}$$

The a_l^m can be easily calculated. Limiting ourselves to the fourth order, we find for the cubic case that:

$$V_c^{\mathrm{pcm}}(\mathbf{r})=\frac{6Ze^2}{a}+\frac{\sqrt{4\pi}}{3}\frac{7}{2}\frac{Ze^2}{a^5}r^4\Big\{Y_4^0,(\theta,\varphi)$$

$$+\left(\frac{5}{14}\right)^{1/2}[Y_4^4(\theta,\varphi)+Y^{-4}_4(\theta,\varphi)]\Big\}+\cdots \tag{8.1.9}$$

Using the wave functions φ_x, φ_y, φ_z and φ_u, φ_v we can determine the energy of the two states Γ_5 and Γ_3. The operator $V_c^{\mathrm{pcm}}(\mathbf{r})$ is found to be diagonal in this basis (as expected since the φ_i induce the two representations Γ_3 and Γ_5). We arrive at:

$$E(\Gamma_5)=E_0+6\frac{Ze^2}{a}-4Dq$$

$$E(\Gamma_3)=E_0+6\frac{Ze^2}{a}+6Dq \tag{8.1.10}$$

with

$$D_q=\frac{35Ze^2}{4a^5}\frac{5}{105}\langle r^4\rangle_{3d}$$

The triplet Γ_5 has the lowest energy in this approximation of a cubic crystal field In the case of a tetrahedral field (Fig. 8.1.1.(b)), $V_c^{\mathrm{prm}}(\mathbf{r})$ can be written as:

$$V_c^{\mathrm{pcm}}(\mathbf{r})=\frac{8Ze^2}{a}-\frac{\sqrt{4\pi}}{3}\frac{28}{9}\frac{Ze^2}{a^5}r^4$$

$$\times\Big\{Y_4^0(\theta,\varphi)+\left(\frac{5}{14}\right)^{1/2}[Y_4^4(\theta,\varphi)+Y^{-4}_4(\theta,\varphi)]\Big\} \tag{8.1.11}$$

In this case, the sequence of the two states Γ_4 and $(\Gamma_2+\Gamma_3)$ is inverted: the ground state is the doublet $(\Gamma_2+\Gamma_3)$.

The splitting of an electronic d state by a cubic crystalline electric field is given by10 Dq. Now, let us assume that we have several d electrons at the same site. If 10 Dq is larger than the electrostatic interactions (strong field scheme), then we fill the cubic orbital states φ_x, φ_y, φ_z, φ_u, φ_v while trying to obtain the maximum spin value (first Hund rule). On the other hand, if $10Dq$ is less than the term separation (weak field scheme), then V_c lifts the degeneracy of the groundstate term $\psi_{L,s}(r,\theta,\varphi)$. The two schemes are applied to the d^2 configuration.

8.1.2 d^2 configuration in a cubic field

The Hamiltonian of this two-electron system is written as

$$\hat{H}=\hat{h}_1+\hat{h}_2+\hat{g}_{12} \tag{8.1.12}$$

where $\hat{h}_i=-\frac{\hbar^2}{2m}\Delta_i+V(\mathbf{r}_i)$ is a one-electron operator, whereas $\hat{g}_{12}$ is the two-electron interaction operator. $V(\mathbf{r}_i)$ is the sum of two parts:

$$V(\mathbf{r}_i)=V_0(\mathbf{r}_i)+V_c(\mathbf{r}_i)$$

where $V_0(\mathbf{r}_i)$ is the atomic potential and $V_c(\mathbf{r}_i)$ is the crystalline electric field potential with O_h point symmetry.

Thus

$$\hat{H}=\hat{H}_0+\hat{H}_1+\hat{g}_{12} \tag{8.1.13}$$

where

$$\hat{H}_0=\sum_{i=1}^{2}\left(-\frac{\hbar^2}{2m}\Delta_i+V_0(\mathbf{r}_i)\right)$$

$$\hat{H}_1=\sum_{i=1}^{2}V_c(\mathbf{r}_i)$$

$\hat{H}_1$ and $\hat{g}_{12}$ are assumed to be smaller than $\hat{H}_0$. In the strong field scheme, $\hat{H}_1$ is larger than $\hat{g}_{12}$. The atomic d levels are split into a triplet Γ_5 (φ_x, φ_y, φ_z) and a doublet $\Gamma_3(\varphi_u, \varphi_v)$. The two-electron system will be described by the direct products of those representations, if we assume that the interaction between d electrons is much smaller than $\hat{H}_1$. We will have 3 cubic terms: $(\Gamma_5)^2$, (Γ_3, Γ_5) and $(\Gamma_3)^2$.

Each cubic term will be split, due to correlation between electrons:

$$\Gamma_5\otimes\Gamma_5=\Gamma_1+\Gamma_3+\{\Gamma_4\}+\Gamma_5$$

$$\Gamma_3\otimes\Gamma_5=\Gamma_4+\Gamma_5$$

$$\Gamma_3\otimes\Gamma_3=\Gamma_1+\{\Gamma_2\}+\Gamma_3$$

where { } denotes the antisymmetric part of the product. According to the Pauli principle, if the orbital (spin) part is symmetric, then the spin (orbital) part must be antisymmetric. In the case of a two-electron system, a symmetric spin part corresponds to a total spin $S=1$, and antisymmetric spin state to $S=0$.

Thus the Γ_4 and Γ_2 representations in the $(\Gamma_5)^2$ and $(\Gamma_3)^2$ configurations are associated with $S=1$; all the others have $S=0$. In the case of the (Γ_3, Γ_5) cubic configuration, the Γ_4, Γ_5 representation can have $S=0$ or $S=1$. Wave functions of the various terms can be obtained from two-electron wave functions (Slater determinants); term energies are evaluated by using those wave functions (see Sugano et al.). The level scheme is described in Fig. 8.1.2.

Now, we consider the weak coupling scheme; in this picture, the electronic correlations, $\hat{g}_{12}$, are stronger than the crystal field potential $\hat{H}_1$, which can be considered as a perturbation from the free-ion terms. The terms arising from the d^2 configuration (see 1.3.2) are: ^{3}F, ^{3}P, ^{1}G, ^{1}D, ^{1}S, they correspond to ($S=1$, $L=3$), ($S=1$, $L=1$), ($S=0$, $L=4$),($S=0$, $L=2$) and ($S=0$, $L=0$) states respectively. According to Hund's rules, ^{3}F is the ground state.

The perturbation $\hat{H}_1$ will lift the orbital degeneracy of these terms, see (1.1.29). The reduction of the D_L representations into the irreducible representations of O_h leads to:

$$^3\mathrm{F}\longrightarrow {}^3\Gamma_2+{}^3\Gamma_4+{}^3\Gamma_5$$

$$^3\mathrm{P}\longrightarrow {}^3\Gamma_4$$

$$^1G \longrightarrow {}^1\Gamma_1 + {}^1\Gamma_3 + {}^1\Gamma_4 + {}^1\Gamma_5$$
$$^1D \longrightarrow {}^1\Gamma_3 + {}^1\Gamma_5$$
$$^1S \longrightarrow {}^1\Gamma_1$$

Wave functions and energies for these crystal field levels can be calculated. The level scheme is shown in Fig. 8.1.2.

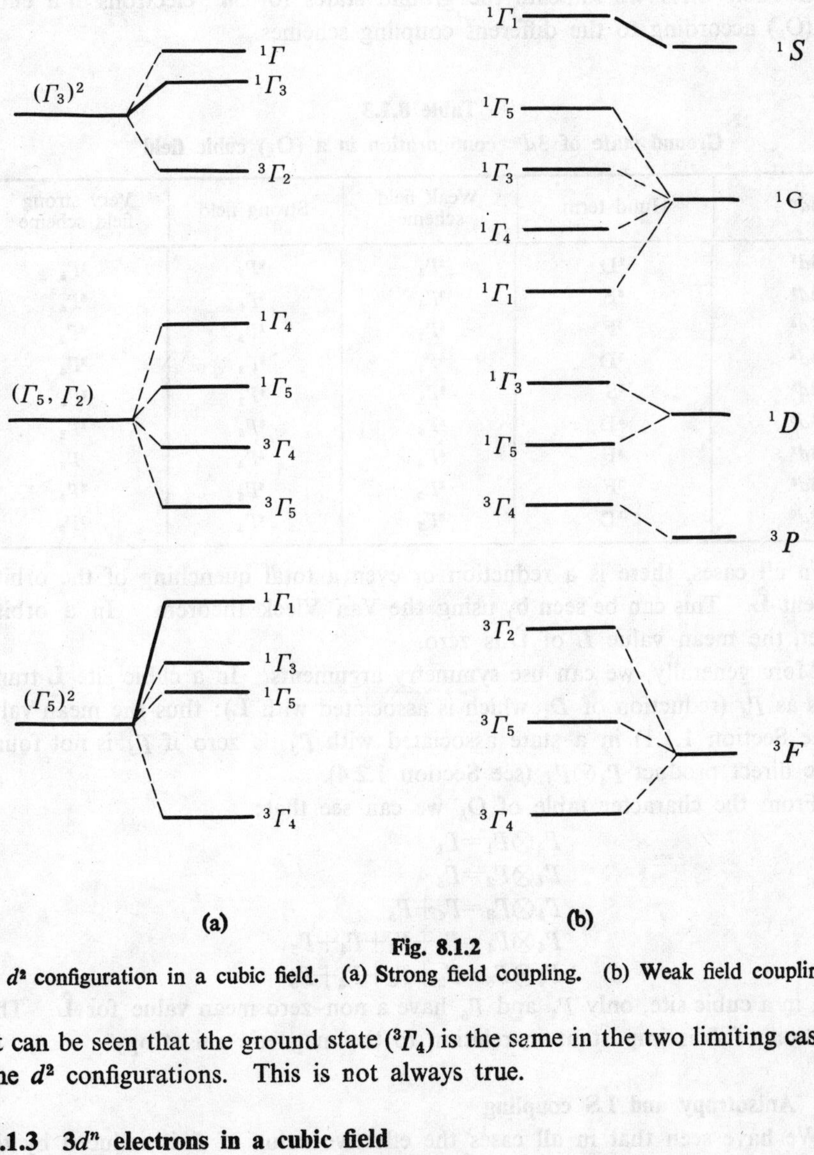

Fig. 8.1.2

d^2 configuration in a cubic field. (a) Strong field coupling. (b) Weak field coupling.

It can be seen that the ground state ($^3\Gamma_4$) is the same in the two limiting cases for the d^2 configurations. This is not always true.

8.1.3 $3d^n$ electrons in a cubic field

In the case of $3d$ ions, both weak field and strong field schemes can apply.

It is difficult to determine all the resulting energy levels but it is important to know the symmetry of the ground state.

In the strong field picture, the crystal field interaction, which couples to orbital motion of electrons, can modify the total spin S; in the case of very strong field coupling, the splitting 10 Dq becomes very large and can get larger than the electron spin coupling leading to the first Hund rule; instead of filling the triplet Γ_5 and then doublet Γ_3, while keeping spins parallel, we fill Γ_5 with up and down electrons, and then we go to Γ_3.

In Table 8.1.3 we indicate the ground states for $3d^n$ electrons in a cubic field (O_h) according to the different coupling schemes.

Table 8.1.3

Ground state of $3d^n$ configuration in a (O_h) cubic field

$3d^n$	Hund term	Weak field scheme	Strong field	Very strong field scheme
$3d^1$	${}^2D$	${}^2\Gamma_5$	${}^2\Gamma_5$	${}^2\Gamma_5$
$3d^2$	${}^3F$	${}^3\Gamma_4$	${}^3\Gamma_4$	${}^3\Gamma_4$
$3d^3$	${}^4F$	${}^4\Gamma_2$	${}^4\Gamma_2$	${}^4\Gamma_2$
$3d^4$	${}^5D$	${}^5\Gamma_3$	${}^5\Gamma_3$	${}^3\Gamma_4$
$3d^5$	${}^6S$	${}^6\Gamma_1$	${}^6\Gamma_1$	${}^2\Gamma_5$
$3d^6$	${}^5D$	${}^5\Gamma_5$	${}^5\Gamma_5$	${}^1\Gamma_1$
$3d^7$	${}^4F$	${}^4\Gamma_4$	${}^4\Gamma_4$	${}^2\Gamma_3$
$3d^8$	${}^3F$	${}^3\Gamma_2$	${}^3\Gamma_2$	${}^3\Gamma_2$
$3d^9$	${}^1D$	${}^2\Gamma_3$	${}^2\Gamma_3$	${}^2\Gamma_3$

In all cases, there is a reduction or even a total quenching of the orbital moment $\hat{\mathbf{L}}$. This can be seen by using the Van Vleck theorem: In a orbital singlet, the mean value $\bar{L}$ of $\hat{\mathbf{L}}$ is zero.

More generally, we can use symmetry arguments. In a cubic site $\hat{\mathbf{L}}$ transforms as Γ_4 (reduction of D_1 which is associated with $\hat{\mathbf{L}}$); thus the mean value $\bar{L}$ (see Section 1.1.1) in a state associated with Γ_j, is zero if Γ_j is not found in the direct product $\Gamma_4 \otimes \Gamma_j$ (see Section 1.2.4).

From the character table of O_h we can see that:

$$\Gamma_4 \otimes \Gamma_1 = \Gamma_1$$
$$\Gamma_4 \otimes \Gamma_2 = \Gamma_5$$
$$\Gamma_4 \otimes \Gamma_3 = \Gamma_4 + \Gamma_5$$
$$\Gamma_4 \otimes \Gamma_4 = \Gamma_1 + \Gamma_3 + \Gamma_4 + \Gamma_5$$
$$\Gamma_4 \otimes \Gamma_5 = \Gamma_2 + \Gamma_3 + \Gamma_4 + \Gamma_5$$

Thus, in a cubic site, only Γ_4 and Γ_5 have a non-zero mean value for $\hat{\mathbf{L}}$. This reduction of L is important in relation to the magnetic anisotropy.

8.1.4 Anisotropy and LS coupling

We have seen that in all cases the effective value of L is reduced by the crystal field. Let us consider the spin–orbit coupling, $\lambda\, \hat{\mathbf{L}} \cdot \hat{\mathbf{S}}$. In 3$d$ ions,

λ is of the order of 10^2K; therefore this coupling can be considered as a perturbation compared to cubic crystal field splittings (10 $Dq \simeq 10^4$K). A first-order perturbation ($\lambda/10\ Dq \simeq 10^{-2}$) would involve the effective value of $\hat{\mathbf{L}}$ in the ground state, which is zero for the $3d^3$, $3d^4$, $3d^5$, $3d^8$, $3d^9$ configurations in the weak and strong coupling schemes. Thus, for those configurations, up to first order, there would not be any spin–orbit coupling; there would be spin-only magnetism and no single–ion anisotropy.

However, $\lambda\hat{\mathbf{L}}\cdot\hat{\mathbf{S}}$ couples to the excited states (not for the d^5 configuration where $L=0$) and there is a little mixing which induces magnetic anisotropy; this will be shown in an example.

The $3d^1$, $3d^2$, $3d^6$, $3d^7$ configurations have an effective L value of $L=1$. The **LS** coupling induces intermediate g–values and single–ion anisotropy. It must be kept in mind that very often the local symmetry is not cubic; departures from this high symmetry introduce new terms into the Hamiltonian which remove the degeneracy of the cubic ground state; those terms must be treated on the same level as the spin–orbit coupling.

8.1.5 Ion Cu^{2+}–$3d^9$ configuration

Let us consider a Cu^{2+} ion (9 electrons in the d shell) in a cubic field. The free–ion ground state is easily obtained by replacing the missing electron in the d shell by a hole, which leads to the ^{2}D free–ion ground state ($S=1/2$, $L=2$).

The cubic field will remove the 5-fold orbital degeneracy, according to the reduction:

$$D_2 = \Gamma_3 + \Gamma_5 \qquad \text{(see Section 8.1.1.)}$$

The crystal field Hamiltonian can be written by using the equivalent operators (see Section 7.3.4) or, in a simpler way, by considering the missing electron of the d^9 configuration as a hole. We arrive at an Hamiltonian similar to (8.1.2), but we must change the sign of the electronic charge. In a point charge model, we arrive at the conclusion that Γ_3 is the ground state of the $3d^9$ configuration in a cubic field (O_h).

We have just seen that in first-order perturbation theory, there is no spin–orbit coupling and that we arrive at isotropic spin-only magnetic properties. However, the spin–orbit coupling and a tetragonal distortion of the cubic site must be taken into account. The spin–orbit coupling has been discussed in Chapter 1. The tetragonal lattice distortion arises from symmetry–lowering effects: this might be due to the structure of the compound or some spontaneous distortion (static Jahn–Teller effect) which can be explained as follows: let us consider the hole of Cu^{2+} in the Γ_3 ground state; the wave functions (8.1.1) φ_u and φ_v of Γ_3 are non-isotropic; if the hole is set into φ_u, the electronic density is reduced along the Oz axis; therefore the two ligands along Oz can get closer to the Cu^{2+} ion (reduction of the screening). On the other hand, if the hole is set into φ_v, then the electronic reduction occurs along Ox and Oy; therefore we observe 4 shorter bonds in the (Oxy) plane and 2 longer bonds along Oz. Of course, such bond length modifications occur only if the electrostatic energy gain overcomes the loss in elastic energy.

Now let us turn back to Cu^{2+}. The cubic states Γ_3 and Γ_5 (Fig. 8.1.3) will be split by this type of tetragonal distortion. First we assume that the temperature is low enough, so the distortion occurs along a given cubic axis Oz. The irreducible representations of point group O_h are listed in Table 8.1.1. The character table of D_4 is given below.

Character table for D_4

D_4	E	$2C_{4z}$	C_{2z}	C_{2x} C_{2y}	C_{2xy} $C_{2x\bar{y}}$
X_1	1	1	1	1	1
X_2	1	−1	1	1	−1
X_3	1	−1	1	−1	1
X_4	1	1	1	−1	−1
X_5	2	0	−2	0	0

From these tables, we can see that

$$\Gamma_3 \longrightarrow X_1 + X_2$$
$$\Gamma_5 \longrightarrow X_3 + X_5$$

It should be noted that the wave functions (8.1.1) can be associated with the X's by looking at their transformation properties under the operation of D_4 (cf. the projection operator in Section 1.2.1). We can see that:

$$\begin{aligned} \varphi_u &\sim X_1 \\ \varphi_v &\sim X_2 \\ \varphi_z &\sim X_3 \\ \varphi_x, \varphi_y &\sim X_5 \end{aligned} \tag{8.1.14}$$

Now, the nature of the ground state arising from Γ_3 will depend upon the sign of the distortion. We will consider the case of a contraction along the Oz axis: the ground state is φ_u, i.e. it has the symmetry of X_1; Γ_5 will be split into X_3 and X_5, X_5 having a lower energy. The reverse would hold in the case of an elongation along Oz. The level scheme is thus described in Fig. 8.1.4.

If we apply a magnetic field **H**, we introduce a Hamiltonian:

$$\hat{H}_m = \mu_B(\hat{\mathbf{L}} + g_s\hat{\mathbf{S}}) \cdot \mathbf{H} \tag{8.1.15}$$

At low temperatures, only the ground state X_1 is populated. The effect of the small magnetic field **H**, is thus limited to X_1; however, X_1 is an orbital singlet, the effective value of L is zero and we should have spin-only susceptibility, i.e. an isotropic g value, $g_s \simeq 2.002$. However, at low temperatures, there is experimental evidence for anisotropic g-values in some Cu^{2+} paramagnetic salts ($CuSo_4 \cdot 6H_2O$, $CuSiF_6 \cdot 6H_2O$). This anisotropy is due to a mixing of the ground

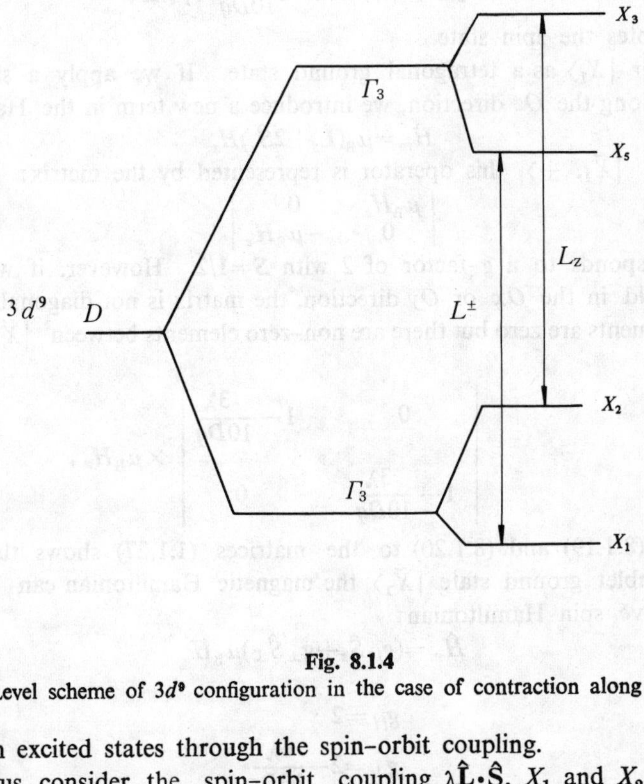

Fig. 8.1.4
Level scheme of $3d^9$ configuration in the case of contraction along Oz.

state with excited states through the spin–orbit coupling.

Let us consider the spin–orbit coupling $\lambda\hat{\mathbf{L}}\cdot\hat{\mathbf{S}}$. X_1 and X_2 are orbital singlets: up to first order their energies are unaffected by $\hat{H}_{so}$. However, there are matrix elements of $\hat{\mathbf{L}}$ between X_1 and X_5 and between X_2 and X_3 ($\hat{\mathbf{L}}$ transforms as X_4+X_5 in D_4). Due to second–order perturbation, the wave functions are modified but we will neglect the shifts in energy ($(\lambda/10Dq)^2 \simeq 10^{-4}$).

According to (1.1.32), the new wave functions $|\tilde{X}_1\rangle$ and $|\tilde{X}_2\rangle$ are given by

$$|\tilde{X}_1\rangle = |X_1\rangle - \lambda\sum_{\alpha}\frac{\langle X_{5,\alpha}|\hat{\mathbf{L}}\cdot\hat{\mathbf{S}}|X_1\rangle}{E_{x_5}-E_{x_1}}|X_{5,\alpha}\rangle \tag{8.1.16}$$

$$|\tilde{X}_2\rangle = |X_2\rangle - \lambda\sum_{\alpha}\frac{\langle X_{3,\alpha}|\hat{\mathbf{L}}\cdot\hat{\mathbf{S}}|X_2\rangle}{E_{x_3}-E_{x_2}}|X_{3,\alpha}\rangle \tag{8.1.17}$$

The energy differences $E_{X_3}-E_{X_2}$ and $E_{X_5}-E_{X_1}$ are taken to be equal to $10\,Dq$.

The dot product $\hat{\mathbf{L}}\cdot\hat{\mathbf{S}}$ is written as:

$$\hat{\mathbf{L}}\cdot\hat{\mathbf{S}}=\hat{L}_z\cdot\hat{S}_z+\frac{1}{2}(\hat{L}_+\hat{S}_-+\hat{L}_-\hat{S}_+)$$

$\hat{L}_z$ transforms as X_4 in D_4, whereas $\hat{L}_\pm$ transform as X_5; thus there is no spin flip in $|\tilde{X}_2\rangle$, but there is a mixture of up and down spin states in $|\tilde{X}_1\rangle$. Using the Equations (8.1.1) and (1.1.25) we arrive at:

$$|\tilde{X}_1,\pm\rangle=|\varphi_u,\ \pm\rangle-\frac{\lambda}{10Dq}\frac{\sqrt{3}}{\sqrt{2}}|(d,\pm1),\mp\rangle$$

$$|\tilde{X}_2,\pm\rangle=|\varphi_v,\pm\rangle\pm\frac{\lambda}{10Dq}i|\varphi_z,\pm\rangle \tag{8.1.18}$$

where $\pm$ denotes the spin state.

Consider $|X_1\rangle$ as a tetragonal ground state. If we apply a small magnetic field along the Oz direction, we introduce a new term in the Hamiltonian:

$$\hat{H}_m=\mu_B(\hat{L}_z+2\hat{S}_z)H_z$$

In the basis $|\tilde{X}_1,\ \pm\rangle$, this operator is represented by the matrix:

$$\begin{vmatrix} \mu_B H_z & 0 \\ 0 & -\mu_B H_z \end{vmatrix} \tag{8.1.19}$$

which corresponds to a g–factor of 2 with $S=1/2$. However, if we apply a magnetic field in the Ox or Oy direction, the matrix is not diagonal anymore; diagonal elements are zero but there are non–zero elements between $|\tilde{X}_1,\ +\rangle$ and $|\tilde{X}_1,-\rangle$:

$$\begin{vmatrix} 0 & 1-\dfrac{3\lambda}{10Dq} \\ 1-\dfrac{3\lambda}{10Dq} & 0 \end{vmatrix}\times\mu_B H_x\,. \tag{8.1.20}$$

Comparing (8.1.19) and (8.1.20) to the matrices (1.1.27) shows that, within the spin doublet ground state $|\tilde{X}_1\rangle$ the magnetic Hamiltonian can be written as an effective spin Hamiltonian:

$$\hat{H}_m=(g_{//}\hat{S}_z+g_\perp\hat{S}_\perp)\mu_B H \tag{8.1.21}$$

with

$$g_{//}=2$$

$$g_\perp=2-\frac{6\lambda}{10Dq} \tag{8.1.22}$$

In the case of elongation along Oz (i.e. X_2 is ground state) we would obtain:

$$g_{//}=2-\frac{8\lambda}{10Dq}$$

$$g_\perp=2-\frac{2\lambda}{10Dq} \tag{8.1.23}$$

For Cu^{2+}, λ is negative, therefore g–values will be strictly greater than 2. In $CuSO_4.6H_2O$, resonance measurements yield $g=2.4$ and $g=2.08$ which corresponds to a elongation of a cubic environment along a cubic axis. Of course, if the temperature is raised, the two lowest states $|\tilde{X}_1\rangle$ and $|\tilde{X}_2\rangle$ will be equally populated; this will lead to an isotropic g–factor, which is an average of (8.1.22) and (8.1.23)

$$g_{iso}=2-\frac{4\lambda}{10Dq}$$

which is observed experimentally, $g \simeq 2.24$.

In conclusion, the admixture of states modifies the value of the ground state magnetic moment. Without spin–orbit coupling, the magnetic moment of Cu^{2+} would be isotropic and equal to $1\mu_B$ ($g=2$). However, the spin–orbit coupling introduces an orbital contribution to the wave functions, which in turn modifies the magnetic moment, and this orbital contribution to the moment depends on the magnetic field direction.

8.2 EXCHANGE INTERACTIONS IN IONIC COMPOUNDS

In the previous example, Cu^{2+} ions were considered as isolated entities experiencing a local crystal electric field. However, electrons are coupled by exchange interactions among which we can distinguish direct exchange, indirect exchange, itinerant exchange and superexchange. Indirect exchange and itinerant exchange occur in metallic systems. Direct exchange and superexchange are important mechanisms in non-metallic systems.

8.2.1 Direct exchange

Direct exchange originates from ordinary Coulomb interactions together with the Pauli principle (see Section 1.1.8). If we consider two electrons in two orthogonal orbitals i and j, the exchange interaction can be written as:

$$E_{ij}(\uparrow\uparrow)-E_{ij}(\uparrow\downarrow)=2J_{ij}$$

with

$$J_{ij}=\iint d\mathbf{r}_1 d\mathbf{r}_2\, \varphi_i^*(\mathbf{r}_1)\varphi_j(\mathbf{r}_1)\frac{e^2}{r_{12}}\varphi_j^*(\mathbf{r}_2)\varphi_i(\mathbf{r}_2) \tag{8.2.1}$$

J_{ij} is a positive quantity, thus this mechanism leads to ferromagnetism. However, if we consider non-orthogonal orbitals in an attractive potential V (nuclei) then the exchange coupling J_{ij} can be written as:

$$J_{ij}=J_{ij}^0-2S_{ij}V_{ij} \tag{8.2.2}$$

where J_{ij}^0 is a Dirac exchange integral similar to (8.2.1). S_{ij} represents the overlap of the two wave functions and V_{ij} describes the interaction of the nuclei and the charge density $\varphi_i(\mathbf{r})\varphi_j^*(\mathbf{r})$:

$$V_{ij}=\int d\mathbf{r}\varphi_i(\mathbf{r})V\varphi_j^*(\mathbf{r})$$

As mentioned by Anderson, most of the chemical bonds (overlap) involve electrons of opposite spins; this means that in most cases (where there is overlap) J_{ij} is negative and leads to antiferromagnetism. It is well known that most of the insulators that order magnetically are antiferromagnetic; it is also known that, in these substances, magnetic ions are far apart (3—4 Å) which makes the overlap integral S_{ij} vanishingly small. In conclusion, in insulating magnetic compounds, direct exchange is ferromagnetic and does not account for the almost universal antiferromagnetism.

8.2.2 Superexchange–Anderson's theory

In Section 8.1, we have mentioned the coupling between ligands and the *d* electrons of the magnetic ion: there is an admixture of the localized *d* wave function and the ligand wave function. This modification of the ligand wave functions is transmitted to the other magnetic ions and this is the origin of the superexchange mechanism which can be transmitted over large distances.

In this model, we must consider the crystal (ligands+magnetic ions) as a whole; this is a task presenting considerable difficulties. Anderson proposed solving this problem in a two–step procedure: (a) we solve the problem of a *d* electron of a magnetic ion surrounded by the other ions, without taking into account any *d-d* interaction; (b) turning on interactions between *d* electrons, what are the different magnetic interactions between the ions?

The first part is achieved by using Hartree–Fock equations, which lead to bands of *d* electrons in the form of Bloch. waves:

$$E_m(\mathbf{k})=a_m+\sum_{\boldsymbol{\tau}} b_m(\boldsymbol{\tau})\exp(i\,\mathbf{k}\cdot\boldsymbol{\tau}) \tag{8.2.3}$$

k is a vector of the reciprocal lattice and the $\boldsymbol{\tau}$ vectors are translations of the Bravais lattice.

The a_m represent the crystal field splittings in the very strong field coupling; the $b_m(\boldsymbol{\tau})$ are transfer integrals: they represent the kinetic energy of *d* electrons, as can be seen by using Wannier functions instead of Bloch functions. The Hartree–Fock self-consistent field, H_{sc}, has solutions

$$\hat{H}_{sc}\varphi_{m,k}(\mathbf{r})=E_m(\mathbf{k})\varphi_{m,k}(\mathbf{r}) \tag{8.2.4}$$

Localised Wannier ψ_m $(\mathbf{r}-\mathbf{n})$ functions are made up of Bloch functions:

$$\psi_m(\mathbf{r}-\mathbf{n})=\frac{1}{\sqrt{N}}\sum_q \exp(i\,\mathbf{q}\cdot\mathbf{n})\varphi_{m,q}(\mathbf{r}) \tag{8.2.5}$$

The $\psi_m(\mathbf{r}-\mathbf{n})$ are transformed by H_{sc}:

$$\hat{H}_{sc}\psi_m(\mathbf{r}-\mathbf{n})=a_m\psi(\mathbf{r}-\mathbf{n})+\sum_{\boldsymbol{\tau}} b_m(\boldsymbol{\tau})\psi(\mathbf{r}-\mathbf{n}-\boldsymbol{\tau}) \tag{8.2.6}$$

The $b_m(\boldsymbol{\tau})$ represent the transfer from site $(\mathbf{n})$ to site $(\mathbf{n}+\boldsymbol{\tau})$. Turning to the second part of the problem, we must put together the *d* electrons belonging to different cores: we introduce a repulsive electrostatic energy U ($U\sim 10$ eV for *d* electrons) which keeps each electron on its core at a zero–order approximation (we are dealing with insulators). Thus the effect of $(H_{sc}+U)$ on the ψ_m $(\mathbf{r}-\mathbf{n})$ is given by:

$$(\hat{H}_{sc}+U)\psi_m(\mathbf{r}-\mathbf{n})\approx a_m\psi_m(\mathbf{r}-\mathbf{n}) \tag{8.2.7}$$

But there are other terms, which can be considered as perturbations and which are exchange terms: (i) Coulomb interaction+Pauli principle; (ii) virtual excited states involving transfer of *d* electrons.

Let us consider the first effects. Wannier wave functions are orthogonal, and Dirac theory of direct exchange can apply, leading to a ferromagnetic coupling between *d* electrons on the same site (first Hund rule)

$$\hat{V}^{\,\mathrm{n,n}}_{\mathrm{exch}}=-\sum_{m,m'} J_{mm'}(0)\hat{s}^m_{\mathrm{n}}\hat{s}^{m'}_{\mathrm{n}} \tag{8.2.8}$$

(all $\hat{s}^m_{\mathrm{n}}$ combine to form $\hat{S}_{\mathrm{n}}$) and also to a ferromagnetic coupling between different ions

$$\hat{V}^{\mathbf{n},\mathbf{n}+\boldsymbol{\tau}}_{\text{exch}} = -\sum_{m,m'} J_{mm'}(\boldsymbol{\tau}) \hat{s}^{m}_{\mathbf{n}} \hat{s}^{m'}_{\mathbf{n}+\boldsymbol{\tau}} \tag{8.2.9}$$

with

$$J_{mm'}(\boldsymbol{\tau}) = \int \psi^{*}_{m}(\mathbf{r}-\mathbf{n})\psi_{m'}(\mathbf{r}-\mathbf{n}-\boldsymbol{\tau}) \frac{e^2}{|\mathbf{r}-\mathbf{r}'|} \psi^{*}_{m'}(\mathbf{r}'-\mathbf{n}-\boldsymbol{\tau})\psi_{m}(\mathbf{r}'-\mathbf{n}) d\mathbf{r} d\mathbf{r}' \tag{8.2.10}$$

Superexchange theory contains direct exchange mechanisms which are ferromagnetic. Superexchange itself arises from the second type of perturbations induced by the non-diagonal part of $\hat{H}_{sc}$, $\hat{H}_{\text{off}}$:

$$\hat{H}_{\text{off}}\psi_m(\mathbf{r}-\mathbf{n}) = \sum_{\boldsymbol{\tau}} b_m(\boldsymbol{\tau})\psi_m(\mathbf{r}-\mathbf{n}-\boldsymbol{\tau})$$

Of course, such an excited state where a d–electron is moved from its own core to another one is elevated by the electrostatic repulsion U; if spin states of the electrons at site $\mathbf{n}$ and site $\mathbf{n}+\boldsymbol{\tau}$ are identical, such a transfer is impossible due to the Pauli principle if the orbital wave functions are non–orthogonal.

Let us consider a transfer for a given $\boldsymbol{\tau}$. The two electrons at $\mathbf{n}$ and $\mathbf{n}+\boldsymbol{\tau}$ can be parallel or anti–parallel: this leads to a degeneracy of 4 of the ground state (one electron on each site):

$$\begin{aligned} \chi_1 &= |\psi^{+}_{m}(\mathbf{r}-\mathbf{n})\psi^{+}_{m}(\mathbf{r}-\mathbf{n}-\boldsymbol{\tau})| \\ \chi_2 &= |\psi^{-}_{m}(\mathbf{r}-\mathbf{n})\psi^{-}_{m}(\mathbf{r}-\mathbf{n}-\boldsymbol{\tau})| \\ \chi_3 &= |\psi^{+}_{m}(\mathbf{r}-\mathbf{n})\psi^{-}_{m}(\mathbf{r}-\mathbf{n}-\boldsymbol{\tau})| \\ \chi_4 &= |\psi^{-}_{m}(\mathbf{r}-\mathbf{n})\psi^{+}_{m}(\mathbf{r}-\mathbf{n}-\boldsymbol{\tau})| \end{aligned} \tag{8.2.11}$$

We have two excited states

$$\begin{aligned} \chi^{e}_{1} &= |\psi^{+}_{m}(\mathbf{r}-\mathbf{n})\psi^{-}_{m}(\mathbf{r}-\mathbf{n})| \\ \chi^{e}_{2} &= |\psi^{+}_{m}(\mathbf{r}-\mathbf{n}-\boldsymbol{\tau})\psi^{-}_{m}(\mathbf{r}-\mathbf{n}-\boldsymbol{\tau})| \end{aligned} \tag{8.2.12}$$

The effect of $\hat{H}_{\text{off}}$ will remove the 4–fold degeneracy of the ground state; according to (1.1.32), the second–order correction to the energy is given by the eigenvalues of the matrix $E^{(2)}$:

$$E^{(2)}_{pp'} = \sum_{q} \frac{\langle p|\hat{H}_{\text{off}}|q\rangle \langle q|\hat{H}_{\text{off}}|p'\rangle}{E^{0}_{p} - E^{0}_{q}}$$

which takes the form

$$\begin{bmatrix} 0 & 0 & 0 & 0 \\ 0 & 0 & 0 & 0 \\ 0 & 0 & -\dfrac{2b^2(\boldsymbol{\tau})}{U} & -\dfrac{2b^2(\boldsymbol{\tau})}{U} \\ 0 & 0 & -\dfrac{2b^2(\boldsymbol{\tau})}{U} & -\dfrac{2b^2(\boldsymbol{\tau})}{U} \end{bmatrix} \tag{8.2.13}$$

in the bases χ_1, χ_2, χ_3, χ_4. It can be seen that the new singlet ground state has an energy $E = -\dfrac{4b^2(\boldsymbol{\tau})}{U}$, and its wave function is

$$\frac{1}{\sqrt{2}}\{|\psi^{+}(\mathbf{r}-\mathbf{n})\psi^{-}(\mathbf{r}-\mathbf{n}-\boldsymbol{\tau})| - |\psi^{-}(\mathbf{r}-\mathbf{n})\psi^{+}(\mathbf{r}-\mathbf{n}-\boldsymbol{\tau})|\} \tag{8.2.14}$$

It is even under particle permutation: this is an antiferromagnetic state (S=0).

The triplet excited state ($E=0$) is a ferromagnetic state ($S=1$). The transfer integral $b(\boldsymbol{\tau})$ always favours the antiferromagnetic state: this is the superexchange coupling. In a more general way, it can be represented by the operator:

$$\hat{V}_{\text{sup}}^{\text{n,n}+\boldsymbol{\tau}}=\sum_{m,m'} 4\,\frac{|b_{mm'}(\boldsymbol{\tau})|^2}{U}\hat{s}_{\text{n}}^{m}\hat{s}_{\text{n}+\tau}^{m'} \tag{8.2.15}$$

Perturbation theory can be carried on further, but we restrict ourselves to this degree of expansion. To summarise, exchange interactions can be written as the sum of an antiferromagnetic coupling and a ferromagnetic coupling:

$$\hat{H}_{\text{exch}}^{\text{n,n}+\boldsymbol{\tau}}=\sum_{m,m'}\left[\frac{4|b_{mm'}(\boldsymbol{\tau})|^2}{U}-J_{mm'}(\boldsymbol{\tau})\right]\hat{s}_{\text{n}}^{m}\hat{s}_{\text{n}+\tau}^{m'} \tag{8.2.16}$$

Since Hund's rule applies, $\mathbf{s}_{\text{n}}^{m}=\frac{1}{Z}\mathbf{S}_{\text{n}}$ where Z is the number of d-electrons and $\mathbf{S}_{\text{n}}$ the total spin; we can write:

$$\hat{H}_{\text{exch}}^{\text{n,n}+\tau}=-J_{\text{n,n}+\tau}\hat{S}_{\text{n}}\cdot\hat{S}_{\text{n}+\tau} \tag{8.2.17}$$

with

$$J_{\text{n,n}+\tau}=\frac{1}{Z^2}\sum_{m,m'}\left[\frac{-4|b_{mm'}(\boldsymbol{\tau})|^2}{U}+J_{mm'}(\boldsymbol{\tau})\right]$$

There is competition between superexchange (antiferromagnetic) and direct exchange (ferromagnetic). Accurate ab initio calculations are difficult to perform. However, some estimations can be made (superexchange ranges from 50 K to 1000 K in oxides and fluorides), also semi-empirical laws have been established by Goodenough and Kanamori which show that a crucial parameter is the bonding angle at the ligand.

8.2.3 Conclusion

We have shown that exchange interactions in insulators can be represented by a Heisenberg Hamiltonian

$$\hat{H}_{ex}=-\sum J_{ij}\hat{\mathbf{S}}_i\cdot\hat{\mathbf{S}}_j$$

where the coupling constant J_{ij} can be positive (ferromagnetism) or negative (antiferromagnetism). In many cases, the dominant exchange is antiferromagnetic.

Higher order terms such as $(\hat{\mathbf{S}}_1\times\hat{\mathbf{S}}_2)^2$ can be obtained by perturbation theory. Anisotropic exchange terms may also be present; they have the form $E_{an}=\mathbf{D}\cdot(\hat{\mathbf{S}}_1\times\hat{\mathbf{S}}_2)$ which was introduced by Dzialoshinsky (*Soviet Physics JETP*, **6**, 821 and 1259 (1957)). Such anisotropic terms were introduced by Moriya (*Phys. Rev.*, **120**, 91 (1960)) on the basis of the effects of spin-orbit coupling in the theory of superexchange.

8.3 $FeCl_2$: A HIGHLY ANISOTROPIC ANTIFERROMAGNETIC COMPOUND

Many ionic compounds exhibit antiferromagnetic long range order at low temperatures. However, it is worth looking at one of the famous iron halide compounds: $FeCl_2$ (or $FeBr_2$).

The crystallographic structure is rhombohedral (cf. Fig. 8.3.1.): it consists of sandwiches of Cl–Fe–Cl planes which are stacked on top of each other. Obviously, this is an anisotropic crystallographic structure; the magnetic properties will reflect this anisotropy.

In $FeCl_2$, Fe^{2+} has a ^5D ($L=2$; $S=2$) ground state. The symmetry of the Fe^{2+} site is almost cubic with a small trigonal distortion along the c–axis of the structure. The electrical field potential created by the Z diamagnetic Cl^- ions can be written in terms of spherical harmonics

$$\hat{V}_c = \sum_{i=1}^{Z} \sum_{l=0}^{\infty} \sum_{m=-l}^{+l} A_l^m r_i^l Y_l^m(\theta_i, \varphi_i) \tag{8.3.1}$$

where r_i, θ_i,φ_i are coordinates of the ith electron of one Fe^{2+} ion. The c-axis is taken as the z coordinate.

The A_l^m can be obtained by a point charge model; however, very often, this model leads to incorrect values for the A_l^m (even the sign being wrong!). We are only interested in the form (symmetry) of this potential.

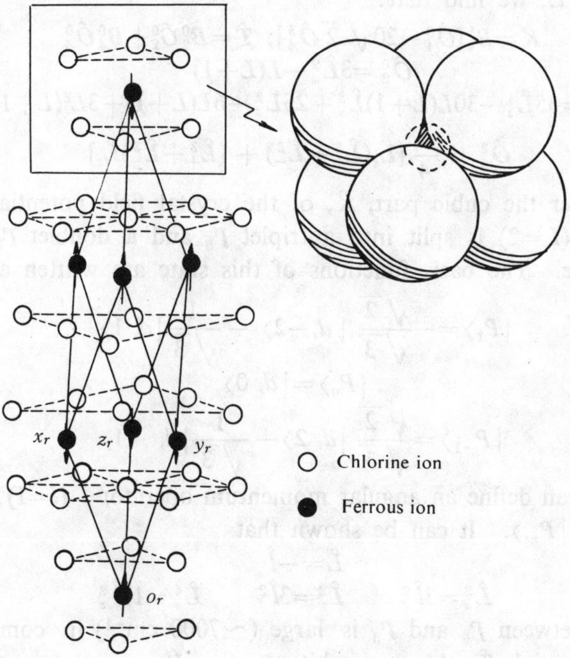

Fig. 8.3.1
Crystal and magnetic structure of $FeCl_2$. O_r,X_r,Y_r,Z_r, define the rhombohedral primitive axes.

We will restrict ourselves to first–order perturbation within the ^5D ground state of the Fe^{2+} ion. We have to evaluate matrix elements within the $L=2$ manifold. As we have seen in Section 1.2.4, matrix elements of V_c between $|j\rangle$ and $|j'\rangle$ are non–zero if the representation $\Gamma^{j'}$ is found in the decomposition of the direct product $\Gamma_{Vc} \otimes \Gamma^j$.

In our case:

$$\Gamma^{j'} \equiv D_2 \equiv \Gamma^{i}$$
$$\Gamma_{V_c} \equiv D_l \qquad l\text{: integer.} \tag{8.3.2}$$

Thus if D_2 has to be found in $D_l \otimes D_2$ we can assume $l < 4$ with l even. The other terms in $\hat{V}_c$ would not contribute.

The cubic part of $\hat{V}_c$, $\hat{K}$, can be expressed as:

$$\hat{K} = \sum_{i=1}^{Z} A_4^1 r_i^4 \left\{ Y_4^0(\theta_i, \varphi_i) + \sqrt{\frac{10}{7}} (Y_4^3(\theta_i, \varphi_i) - Y^{-3}_4(\theta_i, \varphi_i)) \right\} \tag{8.3.3}$$

and the trigonal $\hat{T}$ part:

$$\hat{T} = \sum_{i=1}^{Z} A_2^0 r_i^2 Y_2^0(\theta_i, \varphi_i) + \sum_{i=1}^{Z} A_4^0 r_i^4 Y_4^0(\theta_i, \varphi_i) \tag{8.3.4}$$

$\hat{K}$ is a fourth-order tensor which is invariant in the cubic symmetry $O_h = m3m$; $\hat{K} + \hat{T}$ is invariant in a trigonal symmetry ($D_{3d} = \overline{3}\,m$). Since we restrict ourselves to a given L manifold, the matrix elements of $\hat{K}$ and $\hat{T}$ are proportional to a basis function of 4th order of the Γ_1 representation of O_h and D_{3d} respectively. Such a basis function can be obtained by projecting the representation associated with $\mathbf{L} \times \mathbf{L} \times \mathbf{L} \times \mathbf{L}$; we find that:

$$\hat{K} = B_4^1[\hat{O}_4^0 - 20\sqrt{2}\,\hat{O}_4^3]; \quad \hat{T} = B_2^0 \hat{O}_2^0 + B_4^0 \hat{O}_4^0 \tag{8.3.5}$$

$$\hat{O}_2^0 = 3\hat{L}_z^2 - L(L+1)$$
$$\hat{O}_4^0 = 35\hat{L}_z^4 - 30L(L+1)\hat{L}_z^2 + 25\hat{L}_z^2 - 6L(L+1) + 3L^2(L+1)^2 \tag{8.3.6}$$

$$\hat{O}_4^3 = \frac{1}{4}[\hat{L}_z(\hat{L}_+^3 + \hat{L}_-^3) + (\hat{L}_+^3 + \hat{L}_-^3)\hat{L}_z] \tag{8.3.7}$$

First we consider the cubic part, $\hat{K}$, of the crystal field potential. We know that a D state ($L=2$) is split into a triplet Γ_5 and a doublet Γ_3. The Γ_5 is the ground state. The basis functions of this state are written as:

$$|P_1\rangle = -\frac{\sqrt{2}}{\sqrt{3}}\,|d, -2\rangle - \frac{1}{\sqrt{3}}|d, 1\rangle$$
$$|P_0\rangle = |d, 0\rangle \tag{8.3.8}$$
$$|P_{-1}\rangle = \frac{\sqrt{2}}{\sqrt{3}}\,|d, 2\rangle - \frac{1}{\sqrt{3}}|d, -1\rangle$$

Within Γ_5, we can define an angular momentum operator $\hat{l}$ ($l=1$) whose eigenvectors are the $|P_m\rangle$. It can be shown that

$$\hat{L} = -\hat{l}$$
$$\hat{L}_z^2 = 3\hat{l}_z^2 \qquad \hat{L}^2 = 3\hat{l}^2 \qquad \hat{L}_z^4 = 11\hat{l}_z^2 \tag{8.3.9}$$

The splitting between Γ_5 and Γ_3 is large ($\simeq 7000\ \text{cm}^{-1}$) in comparison with the trigonal potential, $\hat{T}$, the spin-orbit coupling $\hat{V}_{LS}$ or exchange interactions. Thus we will confine the influence of these interactions to a first-order approximation.

Within Γ_5, $\hat{T}$ and $\hat{V}_{LS}$ can be written as:

$$\hat{T} = -\Delta(\hat{l}_z^2 - 2/3) \qquad \Delta = -9B_2^0 + 80B_4^0$$
$$\hat{V}_{LS} = \lambda' \hat{l} \cdot \hat{s} \tag{8.3.10}$$

The energy level scheme can be determined as a function of $a = \Delta/\lambda'$. The energy differences between eigenstates can be measured by spectroscopy techniques; those yield the values $\lambda' \approx 65$ cm^{-1} (63K), $\Delta \approx 88$ cm^{-1} (84K). The level scheme is given in Fig. 8.3.2. It can be easily seen that at low temperatures, we can restrict ourselves to a fundamental triplet, which, again, can be handled by using an effective spin $S=1$.

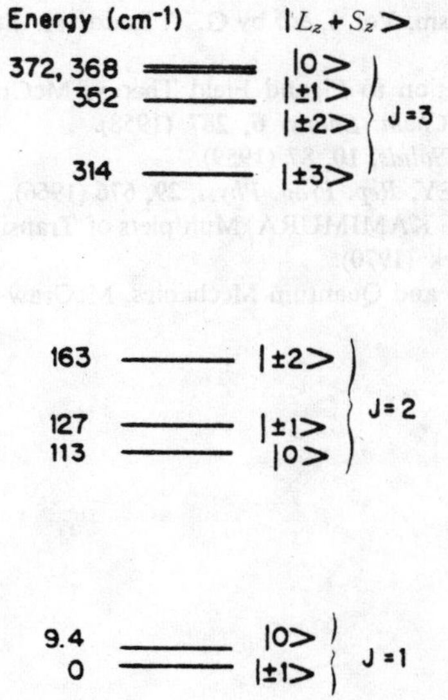

Fig. 8.3.2
Single-ion energy leve diagram for the $^5T_5$ state of the Fe^{2+} ion in $FeCl_2$.

Exchange interactions between real spins are assumed to have the form:

$$J_{ij}\hat{\mathbf{S}}_i \cdot \hat{\mathbf{S}}_j$$

Real spin $\hat{S}$ operators are expressed in terms of effective spin operators:

$$\hat{S}_z = g_z \hat{s}_z$$
$$\hat{S}_\pm = g_\pm \hat{s}_\pm \tag{8.3.11}$$

Here we can see the anisotropy induced by the crystal field $\hat{T}$ $(a=\Delta/\lambda)$. Also in Fig. 8.3.2 it is shown that the ground state is a $S^z = \pm 1$ state: the spins tend to align along the c-axis.

Thus, within the fundamental triplet, the Hamiltonian can be written as:

$$\hat{H} = -D\sum_i (\hat{s}^2_{i,z} - 2/3) - \sum_{ij} \tilde{J}_{ij} \left\{ \hat{s}_{iz}\hat{s}_{jz} + \frac{\eta}{2} (\hat{s}_{i+}\hat{s}_{j-} + \hat{s}_{i-}\hat{s}_{j+}) \right\}$$

$$D \simeq \frac{\Delta}{10}, \quad \tilde{J}_{ij} = g_z^2 J_{ij}, \quad \eta = (g_\pm / g_z)^2 \tag{8.3.12}$$

Let us discuss the exchange interactions J_{ij}. From the structure of $FeCl_2$ (Fig. 8.3.1) we may expect the intralayer coupling to be ferromagnetic (direct exchange); the interlayer coupling would be weaker and antiferromagnetic (super exchange). This turns out to be true. The magnetic structure is shown in Fig. 8.3.1: we have ferromagnetic layers stacked antiferromagnetically along the *c*-axis.

REFERENCES

P.W. ANDERSON, in Solid State Physics: Advances in Research and Applications, Vol. 14, ed. by H. Ehrenreich, Academic Press, New York (1963).

P.W. ANDERSON, in Magnetism, Vol. I, ed. by G. T. Rado, H. Suhl, Academic Press, New York, (1963).

C.J. BALLHAUSEN, Introduction to Ligand Field Theory, McGraw–Hill, New York.

J.B. GOODENOUGH, *Phys. Chem. Solids*, **6**, 287 (1958).

J. KANAMORI, *Phys. Chem. Solids*, **10**, 87 (1959).

J. OWEN, J. H. M. THORNLEY, *Rep. Prog. Phys.*, **29**, 676 (1966).

S. SUGANO, Y. TANABE, M. KAMIMURA, Multiplets of Transition-Metal Ions in Crystals Academic Press, New York (1970).

M. TINKHAM, Group Theory and Quantum Mechanics, McGraw–Hill, New York (1964).

CHAPTER 9

3d METALLIC MAGNETISM

9.1 THE d BAND

The coexistence in the periodic table of three well-defined long periods, ending with Ni, Pd and Pt and corresponding to the filling of respectively the 3d, 4d and 5d shells, strongly suggests that the peculiar properties of these metals correspond to a strong d character in their valency states (i.e. the conduction band).

The problem is to choose for the d electrons between a localized "atomic orbitals" description, as usually taken for the more localized 4f shells of rare-earth metals, and an extended "molecular orbital" approach, as for the others (sp). This choice has raised a classical controversy but it seems now that a band picture (molecular approach) is a reasonable starting point when describing the transition metals.

The band calculation described here is performed in the Hartree approximation: we study the wave functions and the energies of an electron in the electrostatic potential of the metal. This electrostatic potential is taken as a sum of atomic potentials V_i centered on the various lattice sites i:

$$V \simeq \sum_i V_i \tag{9.1.1}$$

For each site, in the metal, there are 5 atomic functions of d type, written as $|i,m\rangle$ where m is the projection of the orbital moment which can take 5 different values, 2, 1, 0, −1 and −2. The wave functions $|\psi\rangle$ in the metal are then taken as linear combinations of such atomic orbitals. This so-called LCAO Linear Combination of Atomic Orbitals method is valid since the s and d bands are distinct, and also, the interactions responsible for cohesion in the metal are weak compared to the electrostatic potential on each site (tight-binding approximation).

The matrix elements of the Hamiltonian are then:

$$\langle\psi|(T+\sum_i V_i)|\psi\rangle \tag{9.1.2}$$

where T is the kinetic energy and

$$|\psi\rangle = \sum_{i,m} a_{im}|im\rangle \tag{9.1.3}$$

Furthermore:

$$(T+V_i)|im\rangle = E_0|im\rangle \tag{9.1.4}$$

$$\langle im|jm'\rangle \simeq \delta_{ij}\delta_{mm'} \tag{9.1.5}$$

and

$$\sum_{i,m} |a_{im}|^2 = 1 \tag{9.1.6}$$

Among the matrix elements $\langle im|V_1|jm'\rangle$, only the two-centre integrals between first (or second) neighbours are retained.

The potential energy $\langle\psi|\sum_i V_i|\psi\rangle$ is then the sum of atomic terms:

$$\langle im|V_i|im\rangle \tag{9.1.7}$$

and of supplementary terms written as:

$$\alpha_{im} = \langle im|\sum_{j\neq i} V_j|im\rangle \tag{9.1.8}$$

$$\beta_{im}^{jm'} = \langle im|V_j|jm'\rangle \tag{9.1.9}$$

The atomic states $|im\rangle$ are not modified by the α_{im} terms, the effect of which is only to shift the energies of the atomic levels. The terms $\beta_{im}^{jm'}$, "transfer integrals", mix the atomic states into molecular states extending over the whole solid.

Going from the atomic state to the metal, the energy change can be written:

$$E = \sum_{i,m} |a_{im}|^2 \alpha_{im} + \sum_{\substack{i,m\\ j\neq i,m'}} a_{im}^* a_{jm'} \beta_{im}^{jm'} \tag{9.1.10}$$

The α_{im} and $\beta_{im}^{jm'}$ integrals, corresponding to an attractive potential for the electrons, are negative. We see that the contribution of the β integrals to the energy E varies with the values of the coefficients a_{im}, from a minimum value where most (or all) of the β terms are negative to a maximum value where most (or all) of these terms are positive. These two states of energies E_b and E_a correspond to the formation of bonding states and antibonding states respectively (Figs. 9.1.1 and 9.1.2).

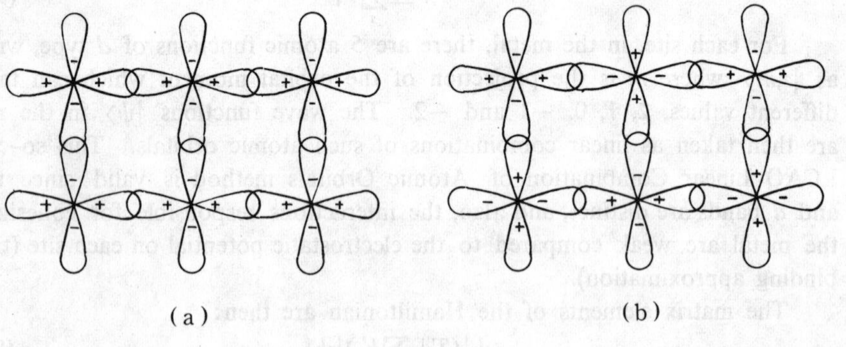

Fig. 9.1.1
(a) Bonding, (b) antibonding states in the *d* band: Schematic representation of the wave functions.

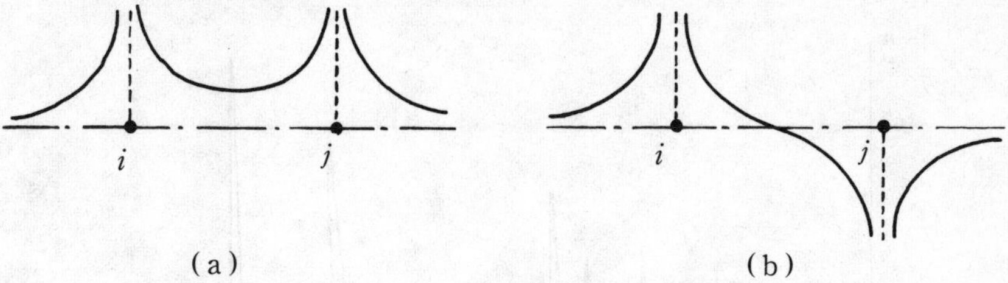

Fig. 9.1.2
Wave functions of bonding and antibonding states.

In the bonding state the electronic density is increased along the bonds, as compared with the atomic density; in the antibonding state the density is decreased. The $5N$ atomic d states $|im\rangle$ give rise to a band of $5N$ levels which are distributed quasi-continuously between these two extremes in energy: the β integrals give rise to the width w of the band and the α integrals give rise to the shift s of the atomic levels (Fig. 9.1.3).

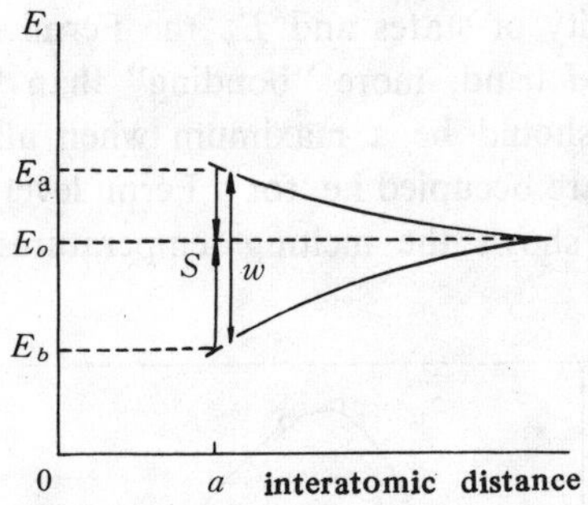

Fig. 9.1.3
Energy shift (s) and width (w) of a narrow band.

The shape of the d band obtained in this way clearly depends on the values taken for the α and β integrals. These are difficult to compute accurately. The main difficulty arises from the definition of the atomic potentials V_i. In principle, the lattice potential $\sum_i V_i$ should be computed in a self-consistent way. In fact, the V_i are usually taken as those of the positive ions. Typical values computed are 5—10 eV for the width w of the band and 1 — 2 eV for the shift s. These values are in agreement with experimental results. As an example, the density of states of Ni metal is shown in Fig. 9.1.4.

The total energy of the d electrons is obtained by summing the energies of the occupied one-electron states. Neglecting the contribution of the s electrons, the cohesive energy per atom E_s is the difference between this energy per atom

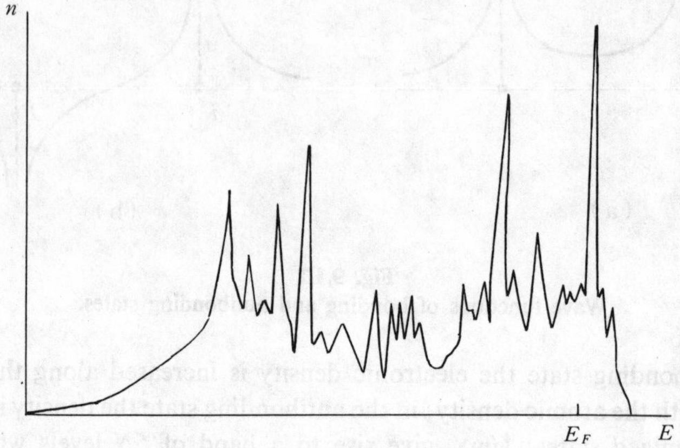

Fig. 9.1.4
Density of states $n(E)$ for the d band in Ni f.c.c. metal.

and the energy of one d electron in the atomic state:

$$E_s = 2\int_0^{E_F} (E_0 - E)n(E)dE \tag{9.1.11}$$

where $n(E)$ is the density of states and E_F the Fermi level. It is clear that in an incompletely filled d band, more "bonding" than "antibonding" states are occupied. The effect should be a maximum when all the bonding states, and no antibonding states, are occupied i.e. for a Fermi level E_F equal to the atomic energy E_0. Fig. 9.1.5 shows the melting temperatures of the 3d metals which

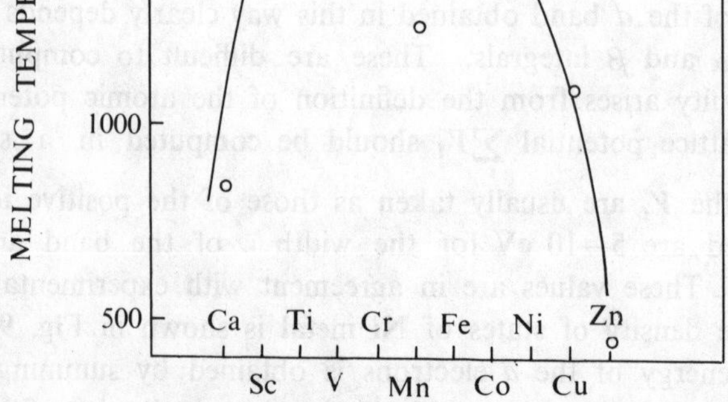

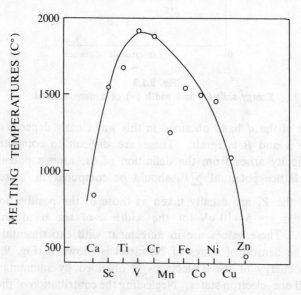

Fig. 9.1.5

are proportional to the cohesive energy: a peak of cohesion occurs near the middle of the transition series. This is consistent with a d band moderately symmetrical in energy with respect to E_0, and hence with α integrals small compared with the β ones; the shift s of the band is small compared with its width w.

Crystal field effects on the band structure

If the α integrals had values differing by amounts large compared with the values of the β integrals, each type of α integral could give rise to a separate d sub-band. For instance, in a lattice where each atomic site has a cubic environment, one would expect the $e_g(x^2-y^2,\ 2z^2-x^2-y^2)$ and t_{2g} $(xy,\ yz,\ zx)$ sub-bands. The smallness of the computed values of the α integrals points on the contrary to a situation where $|\alpha| \ll |\beta|$, and hence no crystal field splitting. Indeed, tight-binding computations suggest that, in cubic crystals, the e_g and t_{2g} parts of the density of states $n(E)$ are fairly uniformly distributed over most of the bandwidth; only the top and the bottom of the band have definite (e_g or t_{2g}) character. The situation for such pure metals seems therefore to be quite the opposite from that sometimes suggested for some cubic transition compounds with metallic conductivity but largely ionic character (oxides, sulfides).

9.2 ORIGIN OF MAGNETISM: ELECTRON-ELECTRON CORRELATION

In the Hartree approximation the total wave function $\psi(1,2,\cdots i,\cdots N)$ can be written as the product of one-electron functions: $\psi \simeq \prod_{i=1}^{N} \psi_i(i)$, each wave function corresponding either to a "molecular orbital" or to an "atomic orbital". This wave function does not obey the Pauli principle which implies the full antisymmetry of the total wave function (space and spin) when permuting 2 electrons: $\psi(1,\ \cdots i,\ j,\ \cdots N) = -\psi(1,\cdots j,i,\cdots N)$. On the contrary the wave function built in the Hartree-Fock model obeys the Pauli principle. This wave function is the determinant obtained from the matrix:

$$\psi = \begin{vmatrix} \varphi_1(1)\chi_1(1) & \varphi_1(2)\chi_1(2) \cdots\cdots & \varphi_1(N)\chi_1(N) \\ \varphi_2(1)\chi_2(1) & \cdots\cdots\cdots\cdots & \varphi_2(N)\chi_2(N) \\ \cdots\cdots & \cdots\cdots\cdots\cdots & \cdots\cdots \\ \varphi_N(1)\chi_N(1) & \cdots\cdots\cdots\cdots & \varphi_N(N)\chi_N(N) \end{vmatrix}$$

where the $\varphi_i(j)\ \chi_i(j) = \psi_i(j)$ are one-electron wave functions: $\varphi_i(j)$=space functions and $\chi_i(j)$=spin functions χ_+ and χ_- which are eigenfunctions of $\hat{s}_z$ with eigenvalues 1/2 and $-1/2$, respectively.

For example, in the case of two electrons 1 and 2, an antisymmetric space wave function, associated with a symmetrical spin function (spin state s=1), is written as:

$$\varphi_A = \frac{1}{\sqrt{2}}(\varphi_{im}(1)\varphi_{jm'}(2) - \varphi_{im}(2)\varphi_{jm'}(1)) \qquad (9.2.1)$$

Similarly, with an antisymmetrical spin wave function (spin state S=0) is associated a symmetrical space function:

$$\varphi_S = \frac{1}{\sqrt{2}}(\varphi_{im}(1)\varphi_{jm'}(2) + \varphi_{im}(2)\varphi_{jm'}(1)) \tag{9.2.2}$$

The electrostatic interaction energy between electrons splits the energy of these two states. The energy gap then corresponds to the energy difference between the antiparallel and parallel spin states.

Introducing the perturbing Hamiltonian:

$$\begin{aligned}\langle\varphi_A|\frac{1}{r_{12}}|\varphi_A\rangle = \frac{1}{2}\Big[&\langle\varphi_{im}(1)\varphi_{jm'}(2)|\frac{1}{r_{12}}|\varphi_{im}(1)\varphi_{jm'}(2)\rangle \\ &+\langle\varphi_{im}(2)\varphi_{jm'}(1)|\frac{1}{r_{12}}|\varphi_{im}(2)\varphi_{jm'}(1)\rangle \\ &-\langle\varphi_{im}(1)\varphi_{jm'}(2)|\frac{1}{r_{12}}|\varphi_{im}(2)\varphi_{jm'}(1)\rangle \\ &-\langle\varphi_{im}(2)\varphi_{jm'}(1)|\frac{1}{r_{12}}|\varphi_{im}(1)\varphi_{jm'}(2)\rangle\Big] \\ = &U_{ij} - J_{ij}\end{aligned} \tag{9.2.3}$$

and similarly for the symmetrical space wave function:

$$\langle\varphi_S|\frac{1}{r_{12}}|\varphi_S\rangle = U_{ij} + J_{ij}. \tag{9.2.4}$$

The J_{ij} are called the exchange terms and the U_{ij} are called the Coulomb correlations.

Due to the strongly localized character of the wave functions, it is obvious that the interatomic terms U_{ij} or J_{ij} $(i \neq j)$ are much weaker than the intraatomic terms U_{ii} and J_{ii}. Taking into account only the intraatomic terms, one then obtains

$$-\langle\varphi_S|\frac{1}{r_{12}}|\varphi_S\rangle = 2J^{mm}_{ii} = 2U^{mm}_{ii} = 2U$$

for 2 electrons in the same orbital, and

$$\langle\varphi_A|\frac{1}{r_{12}}|\varphi_A\rangle - \langle\varphi_S|\frac{1}{r_{12}}|\varphi_S\rangle = 2J^{mm'}_{ii}$$

for 2 electrons in different orbitals.

Since the number of *d* orbitals is 5, the probability for 2 electrons to be in the same orbital is 4 times less than to be in different orbitals. As a result, one defines a mean difference in energy between the antisymmetrical and the symmetrical states (i.e. between ↑↓ and ↑↑ states) which is 1/5 $(2J^{mm}_{ii} + 8J^{mm'}_{ii})$. The *U* terms tend to avoid two electrons with antiparallel spins sitting in the same orbital; the *J* terms, "exchange" terms, favour electrons in two different orbitals that have parallel spins. The first of these two terms is an order of magnitude larger than the second.

One then defines an average exchange energy per pair of electrons per atom $\bar{U}$ which represents the interactions favouring the creation of magnetic moments. The transfer integrals $\beta^{mm'}_{ij}$ associated with the bandwidth work in the opposite direction, since creating a magnetic moment implies the occupation of states of higher energies in the band. There is a competition between $\bar{U}$ and β. The balance is in favour of the creation of magnetic moments only for elements at the end of the 3*d* series: Cr, Mn, Fe, Co and Ni.

For these elements, the $\beta_{ij}^{mm'}$ terms which favour bonding states, i.e. delocalized states, tend to transfer magnetism from one atom to its neighbours, i.e. to create magnetic ordering. If the *d* band is nearly filled up, the structure is ferromagnetic in order to favour intraatomic exchange. This is the case for Fe, Co and Ni metals.

For ferromagnetism two cases have to be considered:

— If the two subbands with opposite spin are not filled up, the compound is a weak ferromagnet: this is the case of Fe metal (Fig. 9.2.1);

— If the subband with up spin is filled up, the compound is a strong ferromagnet: this is the case of Ni and Co metals (Fig. 9.2.1).

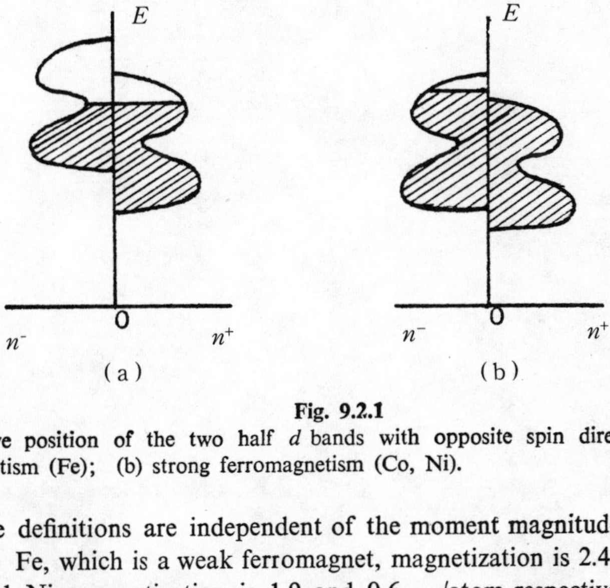

Fig. 9.2.1
Relative position of the two half *d* bands with opposite spin directions: (a) weak ferromagnetism (Fe); (b) strong ferromagnetism (Co, Ni).

These definitions are independent of the moment magnitude. As a matter of fact, in Fe, which is a weak ferromagnet, magnetization is 2.4 μ_B/Fe, whereas in Co and Ni, magnetization is 1.9 and 0.6 μ_B/atom respectively.

For a half-filled band, ferromagnetism is not observed. Let us consider two orbitals 1 and 2 in two different atoms, each of which is occupied by one electron.

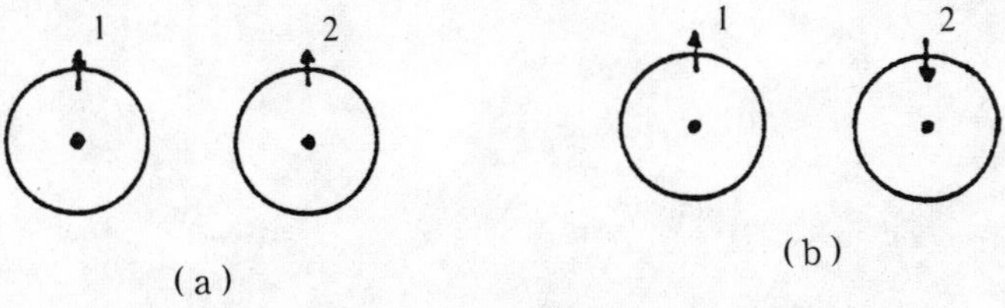

Fig. 9.2.2

If the spins are parallel (Fig. 9.2.2 (a)), each electron is attached to an atom and cannot jump from one site to another. Such an antibonding state is not energetically favoured. Actually, in such a case, the structure of lowest energy is antiferromagnetic (Fig. 9.2.2 (b)). Such a configuration favours the β integrals in comparison with $\bar{U}$.

Indeed in Cr and Mn metals, the *d* bands of which are nearly half-filled, negative interactions are present:

— Mn has a collinear antiferromagnetic structure,

— Cr has a sinusoidal antiferromagnetic structure.

REFERENCES

J. FRIEDEL, in The Physics of Metals, Vol. 1: Electrons, Chap. 8, ed. by J.M. Ziman, Cambridge University Press, Cambridge (1971).

G.T. RADO, H. SUHL (eds,.) Magnetism, Vol. IV, Academic Press, New York.

CHAPTER 10

STONER MODEL—ONSET OF 3*d* MAGNETISM

10.1 THE STONER MODEL

This is a simple model which accounts for the existence of ferromagnetism in a band model. If one assumes no orbital degeneracy, the interaction Hamiltonian can be written as:

$$\hat{H}_i = \bar{U} n_\uparrow n_\downarrow \tag{10.1.1}$$

where $n_\uparrow$ and $n_\downarrow$ represent the number of electrons per atom for each spin state ($n = n_\uparrow + n_\downarrow$). In this model, the existence of a magnetic moment is related to the onset of magnetic order.

(a) *Conditions for the stability of a ferromagnetic state* (Fig. 10.1.1)

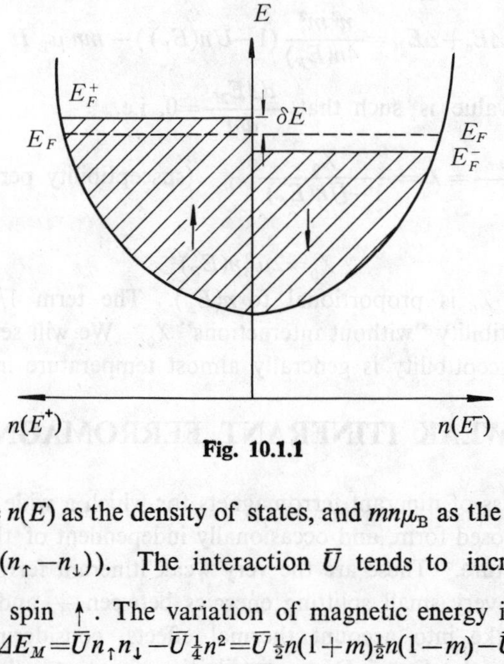

Fig. 10.1.1

Let us define $n(E)$ as the density of states, and $mn\mu_B$ as the magnetization per atom ($m = \frac{1}{n}(n_\uparrow - n_\downarrow)$). The interaction $\bar{U}$ tends to increase the number of electrons with spin $\uparrow$. The variation of magnetic energy is then:

$$\Delta E_M = \bar{U} n_\uparrow n_\downarrow - \bar{U}\tfrac{1}{4}n^2 = \bar{U}\tfrac{1}{2}n(1+m)\tfrac{1}{2}n(1-m) - \bar{U}\tfrac{1}{4}n^2 \tag{10.1.2}$$

$$\Delta E_M = -\bar{U}\tfrac{1}{4}n^2 m^2 \tag{10.1.3}$$

To this energy gain ΔE_M, is opposed the variation of energy ΔE_c due to the occupation of states of higher energies in the band. To first order, for a small displacement δE, ΔE_c is written as:

$$\Delta E_c = \frac{1}{2}\delta E(n_\uparrow - n_\downarrow) = \frac{1}{2}\delta Enm \qquad (10.1.4)$$

Therefore, the total variation in energy is:

$$\Delta E_c + \Delta E_M = -\bar{U}\tfrac{1}{4}n^2m^2 + \delta E\tfrac{1}{2}nm \qquad (10.1.5)$$

since:

$$n(E_F)\,\delta E = \frac{n_\uparrow - n_\downarrow}{2} \qquad (10.1.6)$$

hence

$$\Delta E_c + \Delta E_M = \frac{n^2m^2}{4n(E_F)}(1 - \bar{U}n(E_F)) \qquad (10.1.7)$$

If $(1-\bar{U}n(E_F))>0$, the state of lowest energy is obtained for $m=0$, i.e. the system is not magnetic.

If $(1-\bar{U}n(E_F))<0$, a splitting of the band appears leading to ferromagnetism. This is the classical Stoner condition. The conditions favoring a magnetic ordering are obviously a large value for $\bar{U}$, but also a large value for $n(E_F)$, the density of states at the Fermi level. This last condition explains why magnetism can occur only in a 3*d* band.

(b) *Paramagnetic susceptibility*

At the same order of approximation, let us calculate the magnetic susceptibility at zero Kelvin in a field H when the magnetic state is non–stable

$$\Delta E_c + \Delta E_M = \frac{n^2 m^2}{4n(E_F)}(1 - \bar{U}n(E_F)) - mn\,\mu_B\,H \qquad (10.1.8)$$

The equilibrium value is such that $\dfrac{d\Delta E_M}{dm}=0$, i.e.

$$\frac{mn\mu_B}{H} = \chi = \frac{\chi_0}{1-\bar{U}n(E_F)} \quad \text{(susceptibility per atom)} \qquad (10.1.9)$$

with

$$\chi_0 = 2\mu_B^2 n(E_F) \qquad (10.1.10)$$

The susceptibility χ_0 is proportional to $n(E_F)$. The term $1/(1-\bar{U}n(E_F))$ enhances the susceptibility "without interactions" χ_0. We will see later that when $T \ll T_F$, this susceptibility is generally almost temperature independent.

10.2 VERY WEAK ITINERANT FERROMAGNETISM

There is a class of itinerant ferromagnets for which a wide variety of results is obtainable in closed form, and occasionally independent of the single–particle energy band structure. These are the very weak itinerant ferromagnets, defined as materials with very small splitting energies between + and − spins.

In order to take into account thermal effects, considering single–particle excitations, we use the Fermi–Dirac distribution function, which gives the probability that a state at energy E will be occupied in an ideal electron gas in thermal equilibrium:

$$f(E)=1/\{\exp[(E-\eta)/kT]+1\} \tag{10.2.1}$$

The quantity η called the chemical potential, is a function of temperature; it is chosen for the particular problem in such a way that the total number of particles in the system is equal to n. This function $f(E)$ is plotted in Fig. 10.2.1 versus E/η for $kT=0$ and $kT=\frac{1}{5}\eta$.

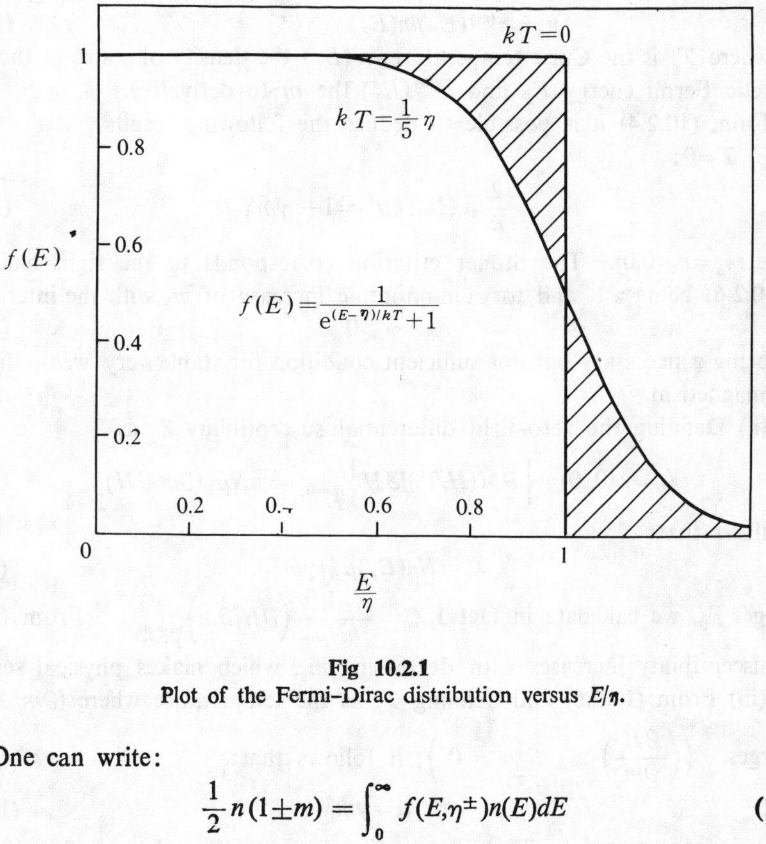

Fig 10.2.1
Plot of the Fermi–Dirac distribution versus E/η.

One can write:

$$\frac{1}{2}n(1\pm m)=\int_0^\infty f(E,\eta^\pm)n(E)dE \tag{10.2.2}$$

where

$$\eta^\pm=\mu\pm k\theta'_m\pm\mu_B H \tag{10.2.3}$$

$m=m\,(H, T)=M\,(H, T)/nN\mu_B$ is the relative magnetization, $M\,(H, T)$ is the magnetization associated with N atoms per unit volume and n particles per atom, μ is the chemical potential of the theory, $n(E)$ the density of single particle states per atom per spin and $k\theta'=\frac{n\bar{U}}{2}$ the interaction parameter (at $T=0$, $\eta^+=E_F{}^+$ and $\eta^-=E_F{}^-$). A very weak itinerant ferromagnet is then one for which $m_0=m(0,0)\ll 1$. In fields H which are not excessively strong, it is reasonable to assume that at the same time $m\,(H, T)\ll 1$. In that case, Equation (10.2.2) may be expanded over the temperature range $T/T_F \ll 1$ $(kT_F=E_F)$ to give the following result:

$$\frac{2}{n}n(E_F)(k\theta' m+\mu_B H)=m\left[1+\alpha\left(\frac{T}{T_c}\right)^2\right]+\gamma m^3\ldots \tag{10.2.4}$$

where

$$\alpha=\frac{1}{6}\pi^2(kT_c)^2(\nu_1^2-\nu_2)=\left(\frac{T_c}{T_F}\right)^2$$

$$\gamma=\frac{1}{8}\left[\frac{n}{n(E_F)}\right]^2\left(\nu_1^2-\frac{\nu_2}{3}\right)$$

$$\nu_n=n^{(m)}(E_F)/n(E_F) \tag{10.2.5}$$

and where T_c is the Curie temperature, $n(E_F)$ the density of states at the paramagnetic Fermi energy E_F and $n^{(m)}(E_F)$ the m–th derivative.

From (10.2.4) it is possible to deduce the following results:

(i) $T=0$:

$$\frac{2}{n}n(E_F)k\theta'=1+\gamma m_0^2 \tag{10.2.6}$$

where $m_0=m(0,0)$. The Stoner criterion corresponds to the right–hand side of (10.2.6) being$\geqslant 1$, and for a monotonic increase of m_0 with the interaction:

$$\gamma>0 \tag{10.2.7}$$

this being a necessary but not sufficient condition for stable very weak itinerant ferromagnetism.

(ii) Defining the zero–field differential susceptibility χ_0 as

$$\chi_0=\chi(0,0)=\left\{\partial M(H,T)/\partial H\right\}_{\substack{H=0\\T=0}}=nN\mu_B(\partial m/\partial H)_{\substack{H=0\\T=0}} \tag{10.2.8}$$

it follows that:

$$\chi_0=Nn(E_F)\mu_B^2/\gamma m_0^2 \tag{10.2.9}$$

(To get χ_0, we calculate in fact $1/\chi_0=\frac{1}{nN\mu_B}\left(\partial H/\partial m\right)_{\substack{m=m_0\\T=0}}$). From (10.2.9) the susceptibility increases with decreasing m_0, which makes physical sense.

(iii) From (10.2.6) and defining T_c as the temperature where $(\partial m/\partial H)_{H=0}$ diverges, $\left(\left(\frac{\partial H}{\partial m}\right)_{m=m(0,\,T)}=0\right)$; it follows that:

$$\alpha=\gamma m_0^2 \tag{10.2.10}$$

α being proportional to T_c^2, this equation leads to the value of T_c.

(iv) From (10.2.6), (10.2.8), (10.2.9) and (10.2.10), relation (10.2.4) may be rewritten:

$$\left[\frac{M(H,T)}{M(0,0)}\right]^3-\frac{M(H,T)}{M(0,0)}\left[1-\left(\frac{T}{T_c}\right)^2\right]=\frac{2\chi_0 H}{M(0,0)} \tag{10.2.11}$$

which leads to:

$$M(H,T)^2=M(0,0)^2[1-(T/T_c)^2+2\chi_0 H/M(H,T)] \tag{10.2.12}$$

Hence the theory predicts that plots of M^2 versus H/M at various temperatures give a series of parallel straight lines, that at T_c pass through the origin. Plots of this type are called "Arrott plots". In Fig. 10.2.2 such variations are

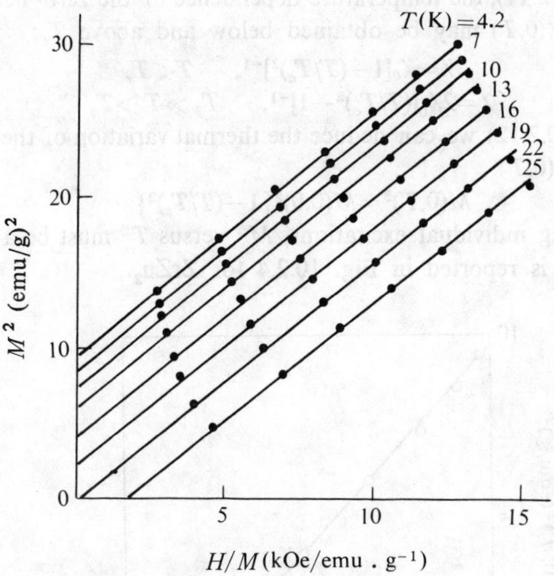

Fig. 10.2.2

The square of magnetization $M(H, T)^2$ is plotted against H/M (H,T) for the magnetizations given in Fig. 10.2.3.

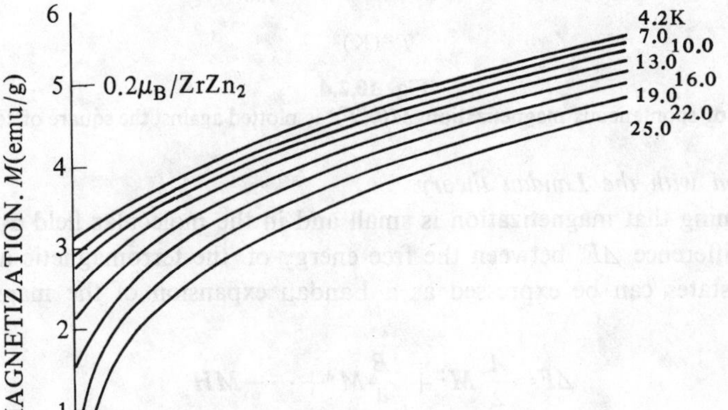

Fig. 10.2.3

High field magnetization curves of pure $ZrZn_2$.

drawn for the compound $ZrZn_2$ which is one of the best examples of very weak itinerant ferromagnet. As shown in Fig. 10.2.3, even at low temperatures there is a strong dependence of magnetization on the field.

(v) From (10.2.11), the temperature dependence of the zero–field differential susceptibility $\chi=\chi(0,T)$ may be obtained below and above T_c:

$$\chi=\chi_0[1-(T/T_c)^2]^{-1}, \qquad T<T_c$$
$$\chi=2\chi_0[(T/T_c)^2-1]^{-1}, \qquad T_F\gg T>T_c \tag{10.2.13}$$

(vi) From (10.2.12) we can deduce the thermal variation of the spontaneous magnetization $M(0,T)$

$$M(0,T)^2=M(0,0)^2\{1-(T/T_c)^2\} \tag{10.2.14}$$

Hence, considering individual excitations, M^2 versus T^2 must be a straight line. Such a variation is reported in Fig. 10.2.4 for $ZrZn_2$.

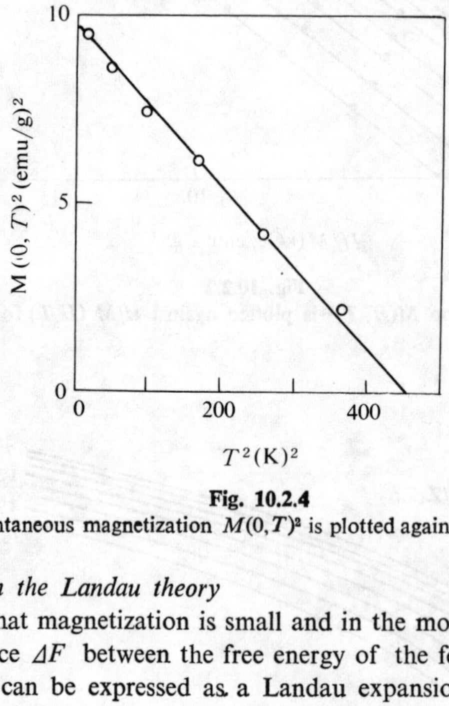

Fig. 10.2.4
The square of spontaneous magnetization $M(0,T)^2$ is plotted against the square of temperature.

Comparison with the Landau theory

Assuming that magnetization is small and in the molecular field approximation the difference ΔF between the free energy of the ferromagnetic and paramagnetic states can be expressed as a Landau expansion of the magnetization M:

$$\Delta F=\frac{A}{2}M^2+\frac{B}{4}M^4+\cdots-MH \tag{10.2.15}$$

As illustrated in Fig. 10.2.5, to be ferromagnetic (magnetization without applied field) A must be negative. Minimising ΔF as a function of M leads to:

$$M^2=-\frac{A}{B}+\frac{H}{BM} \tag{10.2.16}$$

This relation is identical to (10.2.12). The theory desciibed in the previous section allows the determination of the coefficients A and B:

$$A=\{(T/T_c)^2-1\}/2M(0,0)\chi_0 \tag{10.2.17}$$
$$B=[2M(0,0)^2\chi_0]^{-1} \tag{10.2.18}$$

We can notice that A is negative for $T<T_c$, becomes zero at $T=T_c$ and is positive at higher temperatures. It is worth noticing that near T_c:

$$A = -(T_c - T)(T_c + T)\frac{2M(0,0)\chi_0}{T_c^2} \simeq -(T_c - T)\frac{M(0,0)\chi_0}{T_c}$$

which is in agreement with relation (14.1.19) in the Landau expansion.

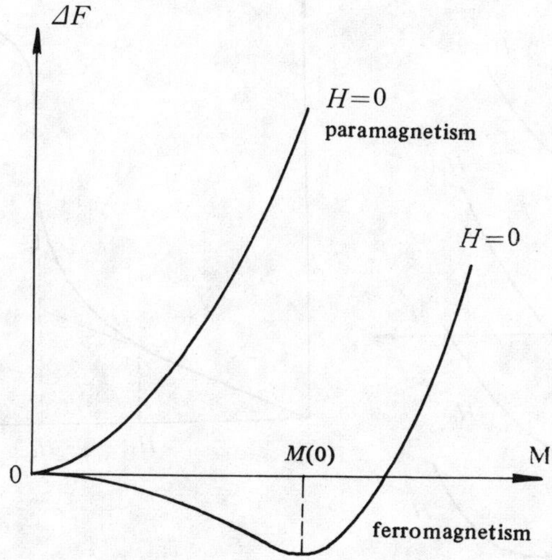

Fig. 10.2.5

10.3 COLLECTIVE ELECTRON METAMAGNETISM

The effect described here concerns the possibility of certain paramagnetic metals or alloys passing at a low temperature from a low to a high magnetization state by the application of a sufficiently strong threshold field. Substances to which these ideas are applicable are those which are described on the basis of the collective electron model.

Let us look at the Landau expansion of relation (10.2.15). When A is positive, the material is paramagnetic. The minimisation of ΔF is associated with a zero value of the magnetization when $H=0$. However, if $B<0$, a high magnetization state induced by the field can reach the same energy as the low magnetization state. (The increase of F with M for large values of M is due to the terms in M^6, $M^8, \cdots$ in the Landau expansion.) This transition theoretically reported by Wohlfarth and Rhodes is called collective electron metamagnetism. The variation of the free energy with the field and the associated variation of magnetization are schematized in Fig. 10.3.1.

The occurrence of the metamagnetic effect characterised by the curves in

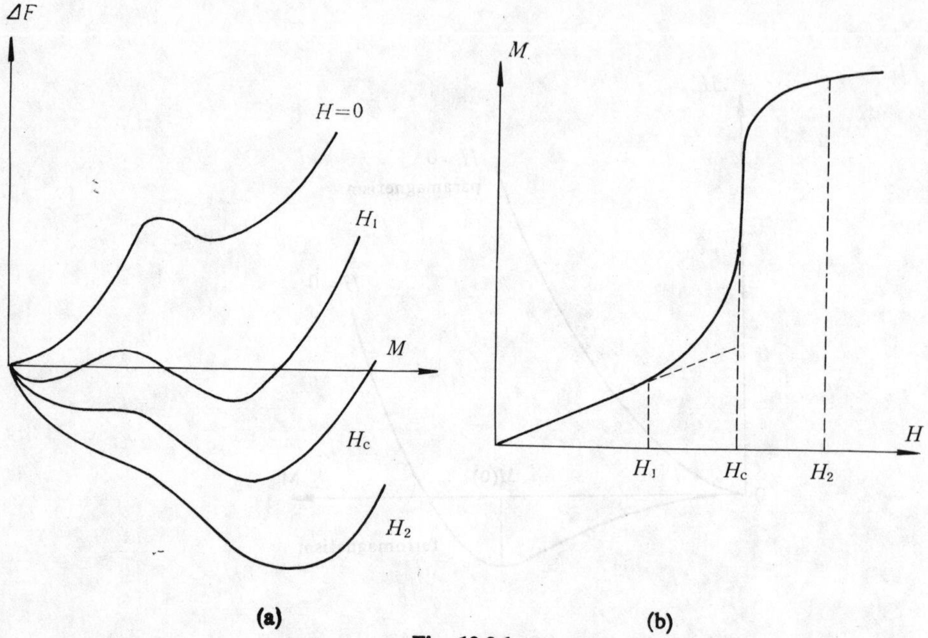

Fig. 10.3.1

Collective electron metamagnetism. (a) Variation of the difference between the free energy of the ferromagnetic and paramagnetic states as a function of magnetization at different fields; (b) variation of magnetization with the field.

Fig. 10.3.1 (a) depends critically on the form of $n(E)$, possibly over a wide range of E, and on the magnitude of the characteristic temperature θ'.

At $T=0$ we know that:

$$\frac{1}{2}n = \int_0^{E_F} n(E)dE \tag{10.3.1}$$

and that:

$$n_\uparrow = \frac{1}{2}n(1+m_0) = \int_0^{E_F^+} n(E)dE \tag{10.3.2}$$

and

$$n_\downarrow = \frac{1}{2}n(1-m_0) = \int_0^{E_F^-} n(E)dE \tag{10.3.3}$$

Using these three relations:

$$\frac{1}{2}nm_0 = \int_{E_F}^{E_F^+} n(E)dE = \int_{E_F^-}^{E_F} n(E)dE \tag{10.3.4}$$

In the Stoner model the energy between ferromagnetic and paramagnetic states in zero field can be written:

$$E = \int_{E_F}^{E_F^+} En(E)dE - \int_{E_F^-}^{E_F} En(E)dE - \frac{1}{2}nk\theta' m_0^2 \tag{10.3.5}$$

From relations (10.3.4) and (10.3.5) it follows that:

$$\frac{1}{n}\frac{dE(m_0)}{dm_0}=\frac{1}{2}(E_F^+-E_F^-)-k\theta' m_0 \tag{10.3.6}$$

and

$$\frac{1}{n}\frac{d^2E(m_0)}{dm_0^2}=\frac{1}{4}n\left[\frac{1}{n(E_F^+)}+\frac{1}{n(E_F^-)}\right]-k\theta' \tag{10.3.7}$$

$\left(\text{we use the fact that } \frac{dE}{dm_0}=\frac{dE}{dE_F^+}\times\frac{dE_F^+}{dm_0}=\frac{dE}{dE_F^-}\times\frac{dE_F^-}{dm_0}\right)$. Hence $E(m_0)$ has a minimum at $m_0=0$, where $E_F^+=E_F^-$ if

$$\frac{n}{2n(E_F)}-k\theta'>0 \tag{10.3.8}$$

i.e. the Stoner criterion is not satisfied. For a certain range of θ', depending on $n(E)$, $E(m_0)$ can have a second turning point in the significant range $0<m_0<1$; actually it is a maximum. It appears from these relations that the effect is most likely if (i) the left–hand side of (10.3.8) is not too large, i.e. the Stoner criterion for onset of ferromagnetism is nearly satisfied, (ii) the right–hand side of equation (10.3.7) decreases fairly rapidly as m_0 increases, thus giving a second zero of dE/dm_0 at a value of m_0 which is fairly low or at least less than 1. Condition (i) is satisfied if θ' is large and only just below the critical value $n/2kn(E_F)$, required for a maximum of $E(m_0)$ at $m_0=0$, i.e. for normal collective electron ferromagnetism. Condition (ii) is satisfied if either or both $n(E_F^+)$ and $n(E_F^-)$ are sufficiently large compared with $n(E_F)$. Both situations arise if $n(E)$ is relatively large and has a pronounced positive curvature in the energy range:

$$E_F^+\leqslant E\leqslant E_F^- \tag{10.3.9}$$

For special cases where $m_0\ll 1$ over the whole range of interest, so that the range specified by (10.3.9) is narrow, the above results are illustrated by expanding the right-hand side of (10.3.7) and assuming that $n(E)$ is differentiable at E_F. It is found that, in this limit and in terms of derivatives of $n(E)$ at E_F:

$$\frac{1}{n}\frac{d^2E(m)_0}{dm_0^2}=\frac{n}{2n(E_F)}\left[1-cm_0^2\right]-k\theta' \tag{10.3.10}$$

where:

$$c=\frac{1}{8}\left\{\frac{n}{n(E_F)}\right\}^2\left\{\frac{n''(E_F)}{n(E_F)}-3\left[\frac{n'(E_F)}{n(E_F)}\right]^2\right\}$$

The result that large values of $n(E_F)$ and θ' and a positive curvature of $n(E_F)$ are necessary, but not sufficient, for the effect to be realised, implies that collective electron magnetism is most likely to occur for substances with a large value of paramagnetic susceptibility χ and with a maximum in the temperature dependence of χ. These results follow from the relation (10.2.4) where we define the reciprocal susceptibility per atom as the limit of $\frac{dH}{n\mu_B dm}$ for $m\to 0$:

$$\frac{1}{\chi}=\frac{1}{2n^2(E_F)\mu_B^2}\left[1-aT^2+O(T^4)\right]-\frac{k\theta'}{2nn(E_F)\mu_B} \tag{10.3.11}$$

with:

$$a = \frac{1}{6}\pi^2 k^2 \left\{ \frac{n''(E_F)}{n(E_F)} - \left[\frac{n'(E_F)}{n(E_F)} \right]^2 \right\}$$

giving a large low temperature value of χ if the Stoner criterion is almost satisfied. Furthermore, relation (10.3.11) gives an increase of χ at low temperature (at high temperatures, $kT/E_F \gg 1$, χ decreases with increasing temperature whatever $n(E)$), if the positive curvature of $n(E)$ is sufficiently large at E_F. This is also the condition for $d^2E(m_0)/dm_0^2$, given by (10.3.7), to decrease rapidly with increasing m_0, at least for small values.

In conclusion, for compounds which almost fulfil the condition for the onset of ferromagnetism (Stoner criterion) and with a special shape of $n(E)$ near the Fermi level (pronounced positive curvature) a collective electron metamagnetism can be observed: the ferromagnetic state can be induced by the applied field. Associated with this behaviour, a maximum in the thermal variation of the susceptibility may be observed.

10.4 ONSET OF 3*d* Co MAGNETISM IN RCo_2 COMPOUNDS (R = rare earth)

The behaviour described in the previous section is particularly well illustrated in the compounds RCo_2.

The RCo_2 compounds crystallise in the cubic structure. YCo_2, as Y is not magnetic, is paramagnetic (Pauli type) at any temperature. In Figs. 10.4.1 and 10.4.2 we have reported respectively the thermal variation of the susceptibility $\chi(T)$ and the magnetization versus applied field at 4.2 K and in fields up to 400 kOe. In this compound Co is not magnetic but the maximum observed around 250 K for $\chi(T)$ and the beginning of a transition in the $M(H)$

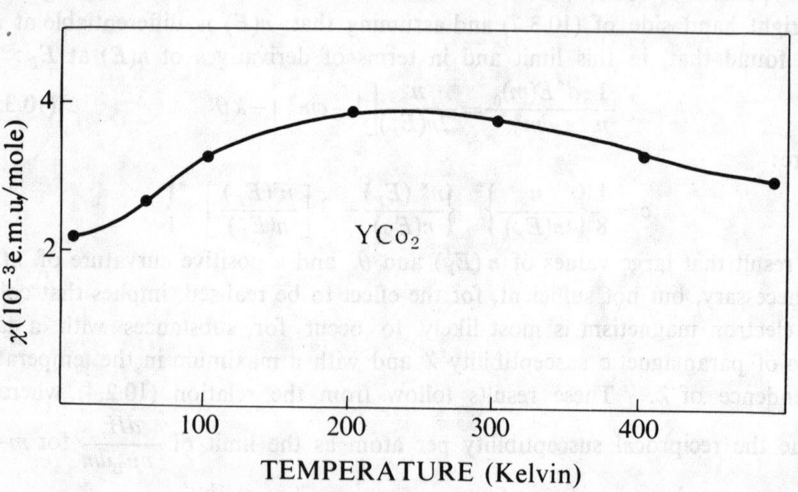

Fig. 10.4.1
Susceptibility versus temperature in YCo_2.

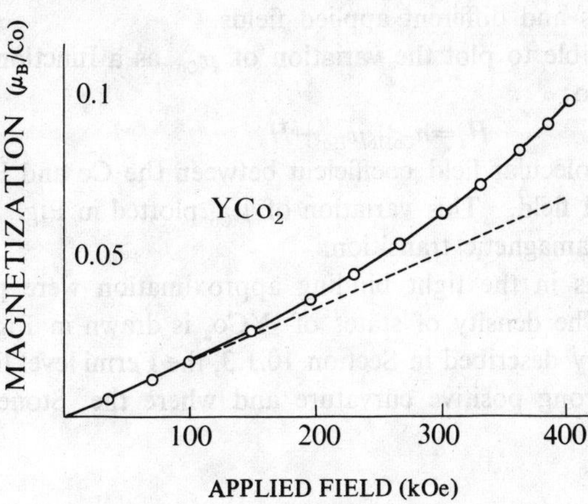

Fig. 10.4.2
Magnetization versus applied field in YCo_2.

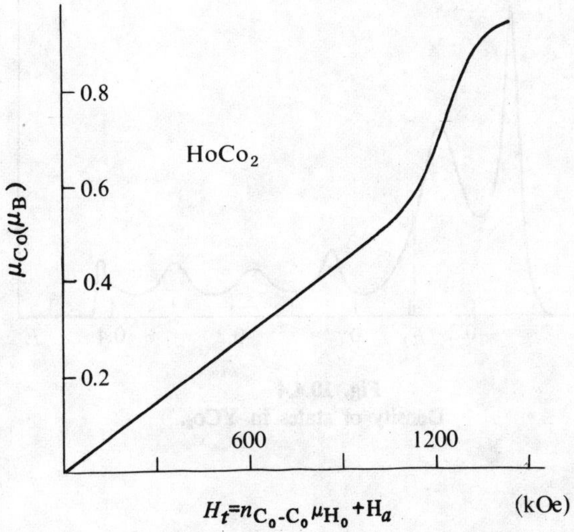

Fig. 10.4.3
Co moment versus H_t in $HoCo_2$.

variation shows that Co has a collective electron metamagnetism behaviour. The critical field necessary to reach the ferromagnetic state is larger than the magnetic field available in the laboratories. However, the transition can be provoked by the exchange field. When R is magnetic, the exchange field due to rare-earth atoms is large enough so that a moment of about 1 μ_B is observed on a Co atom. From studies using polarised neutrons, it has been possible to measure with a good accuracy the Co and Ho moments μ_{Co} and μ_{Ho} in $HoCo_2$ for different temperatures and different applied fields.

It was then possible to plot the variation of μ_{Co} as a function of the total field H_t acting on Co:

$$H_t = n_{CoHo}\mu_{Ho} + H_a$$

where n_{CoHo} is the molecular field coefficient between the Co and Ho sublattices and H_a is the applied field. This variation of μ_{Co} plotted in Fig. 10.4.3 is clear evidence for the metamagnetic transition.

Band calculations in the tight binding approximation were performed on these compounds. The density of states of YCo_2 is drawn in Fig. 10.4.4. As expected in the theory described in Section 10.1.3, the Fermi level lies in a region where $n(E)$ has a strong positive curvature and where the Stoner criterion is almost fulfilled.

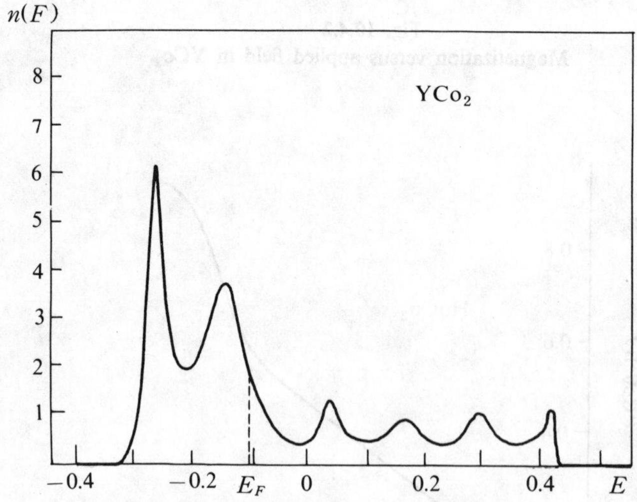

Fig. 10.4.4
Density of states in YCo_2.

REFERENCES

A. BLANDIN, in Magnetism: Selected Topics, Chap. 1, ed. by S. Foner, Gordon and Breach, New York (1976).

D.M. EDWARDS, E.P. WOHLFARTH, *Proc. R. Soc. London, Ser.* A **303,** 127 (1968).

N.F. MOTT, H. JONES, The Theory of the Properties of Metals and Alloys, Oxford University Press, Oxford.

E.P, WOHLFARTH, *J. Appl. Phys.*, **39,** 1061 (1968).

E.P. WOHLFARTH, in Magnetism: Selected Topics, Chap. 2, ed. by S. Foner, Gordon and Breach, New York (1976).

E.P, WOHLFARTH, P. RHODES, *Philos. Mag.*, **7,** 1817 (1962).

CHAPTER 11

MAGNETIC DOMAINS AND DOMAIN WALLS MAGNETIC BUBBLES

11.1 WEISS DOMAINS AND BLOCH WALLS

11.1.1 Exchange and dipolar energies. Spontaneous magnetization

In preceding chapters and especially in Chapter 3, the main kinds of magnetic interactions have been described. The two essential couplings between magnetic moments are the exchange coupling and the dipolar coupling. The exchange coupling, of quantum origin, $E_c = -J\mathbf{S}_i \cdot \mathbf{S}_j$ is sometimes written in classical magnetism:

$$E_c = -W\cos(\theta_i - \theta_j) \tag{11.1.1}$$

For ferromagnetics $W>0$. The exchange energy evaluated from the Curie temperature is of the order of 10^3 K in $3d$-based alloys and of the order of 10—10^2 K in $4f$-based alloys. This interaction is generally a short-range interaction (direct coupling) in concentrated $3d$ alloys and a long-range interaction in $4f$ alloys (RKKY indirect coupling). In both cases the consequent magnetic order concerns a very large number of magnetic moments; the interactions propagating from one atom to the others.

The dipolar energy:

$$U_{ij} = \frac{1}{4\pi\mu_0 r_{ij}^3}\left[\mathbf{M}_i \cdot \mathbf{M}_j - \frac{3}{r_{ij}^3}(\mathbf{M}_i \cdot \mathbf{r}_{ij})(\mathbf{M}_j \cdot \mathbf{r}_{ij})\right] \tag{11.1.2}$$

is not of quantum origin. It results from the Coulomb interactions between free magnetic poles in which the force F exerted on one pole by another is:

$$F = m_1 m_2 / 4\pi\mu_0 r^2 \tag{11.1.3}$$

This interaction is of very long range.

The order of magnitude of the dipolar energy is of 0.1 K, that is to say, about 10^{-4} times that of exchange in $3d$ metals. Thus the exchange energy is preponderant at short distances, or in small volumes, but for particles of size large enough the dipolar energy becomes preponderant. In such a case the spontaneous magnetization vanishes and magnetic domains are formed.

If the exchange energy is summed in a particle, it can be written $E_c = W \cos \Delta\theta$, where W is expressed in erg/cm³ (molecular field approximation).

In the presence of a single, $W>0$, exchange energy, the magnetic moments are parallel to each other. Free magnetic poles appearing at the surface of the sample give rise to a demagnetizing field $\mathbf{H}_d$ proportional to $-\mathbf{M}$. For a spherical sample $|\mathbf{H}_d|$ does not depend on the $\mathbf{M}$ direction and the proportionality coefficient is $N=4\pi/3$ in the e.m.u.–c.g.s. system. For a prolate ellipsoid $\mathbf{H}_d$ is larger when the magnetization $\mathbf{M}$ is forced to be perpendicular to the long axis, because the free magnetic poles of opposite sign are nearer to each other (Fig. 11.1.1). Two "demagnetizing factors" must be defined in this case: $N_{//}$ when $\mathbf{M}$ lies along the long axis and $N_{\perp}$ when $\mathbf{M}$ is perpendicular to this axis.

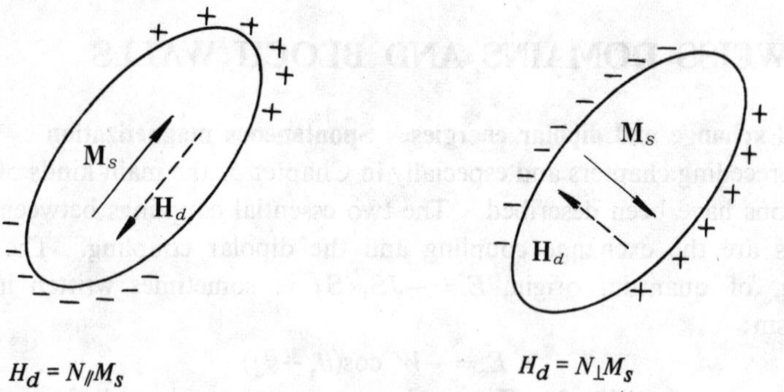

Fig. 11.1.1

The energy difference of these two configurations $K_f=(N_{\perp}-N_{//})\, M_s^2/2$ is called the shape anisotropy. The demagnetizing energy (as well as the shape anisotropy energy of elongated particles) is of the order of $E_d \simeq M_s^2 \simeq (10^3)^2 \simeq 10^6$ erg/cm^3. This energy is much smaller than the exchange energy (10^{10} erg/cm^3 in $3d$ elements and $\simeq 10^8$—10^9 in $4f$ elements). Nevertheless, the system of magnetic moments could increase its exchange energy slightly in order to decrease the demagnetizing field energy. The demagnetizing field energy associated with the spontaneous magnetization in Fig. 11.1.1 is

$$E_d = \frac{N_{//} M_s^2 V}{2} \tag{11.1.4}$$

where V is the ellipsoid volume. In this case the exchange energy $E_c = \frac{-WV}{2}$, is minimum. It is clear that the magnetostatic energy (demagnetizing field energy) would vanish if the moments situated near the sample surface became parallel to this surface (Fig. 11.1.2). As a consequence, the magnetic moments would rotate from 0 to π from each sample boundary to the opposite one (e.g. from A to B). Is such a configuration possible? This configuration leads to decrease in the magnetostatic energy of $\frac{1}{2} N_{//} M_s^2 V$. But the exchange energy increases, the magnetic moments being no longer parallel to each other.

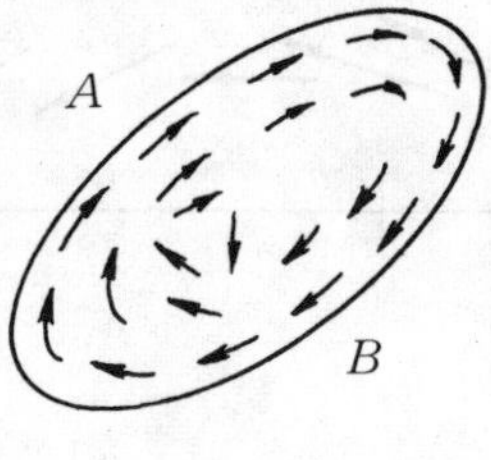

Fig. 11.1.2

The mean angle between two consecutive moments is $\Delta\theta = a\pi/D$ and where D is the mean particle size. Thus the increase of exchange energy is given roughly for a particle of volume $V \simeq D^3$ by:

$$E_c \simeq \frac{1}{2} W \left(\frac{\pi}{D} a \right)^2 D^3 = \pi^2 W D a^2 / 2 \tag{11.1.5}$$

The configuration of Fig. 11.1.2 is stable if the decrease of demagnetizing energy is larger than the increase of exchange energy, that is to say, if the smaller axis b of the ellipsoid is such that $b > D_c$, where

$$D_c = a\pi \sqrt{\frac{W}{N_{//} M_s^2}}. \tag{11.1.6}$$

Using the orders of magnitude given above, one gets $D_c \simeq$ some hundred angstrom If $b > D_c$ the particle is spontaneously magnetized and $M_s \neq 0$ but if $b < D_c$ the magnetic moments have an inhomogeneous distribution with $M_s = 0$.

11.1.2 Anisotropy energy. Weiss domains and Bloch walls

The shape anisotropy is a consequence of the shape of the sample and of the demagnetizing field energy. However, the main source of anisotropy is generally (particularly in $4f$ alloys) due to the spin–orbit coupling. The direction of the magnetization is fixed along particular directions of symmetry of the crystal. These directions are called easy directions of magnetization. The simplest form for the anisotropy energy of a crystal having a uniaxial symmetry is $E_A = K \sin^2\theta$ (if $K > 0$, $\theta = 0$; if $K < 0$, $\theta = \frac{\pi}{2}$ and in this case there is a plane of easy magnetization). What happens in the moment distribution of Fig. 11.1.2 if such an anisotropy is superimposed and becomes larger than the shape anisotropy?

In Fig. 11.1.3, we have schematized the progressive rotation of the magnetic moments from one boundary of the particle to the opposite one. This is a consequence of the dipolar energy. If we assume now that K increases slowly from zero, each magnetic moment rotates in order to come near to the easy direction of magnetization Δ.

Thus the magnetization reversals which took place for $K=0$, from one boundary of the sample to the opposite one are now localized in a much smaller volume, having the shape of a wall. This wall, where the magnetization reversal

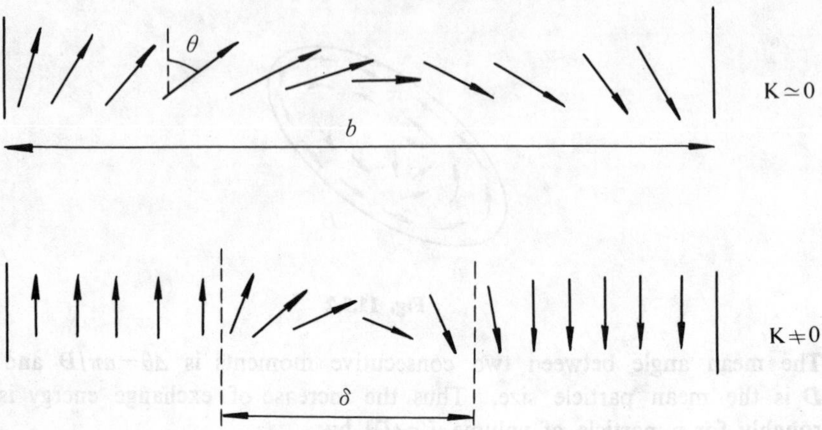

Fig. 11.1.3

is localized, is called a "Bloch wall". At each side the magnetization $+\mathbf{M}$ and $-\mathbf{M}$ is collinear to the easy direction of magnetization Δ. These two domains, spontaneously magnetized, are called "Weiss domains". However, the total magnetization of the particle is zero due to the demagnetizing field energy. As there is no reason to take Δ parallel to a principal axis of the ellipsoid the final configuration may be represented by Fig. 11.1.4. This example shows in particular that the spontaneous magnetization originates not only from the exchange, but also from the anisotropy. (If a small field is applied to move the Bloch wall, such a spontaneous magnetization can be measured.)

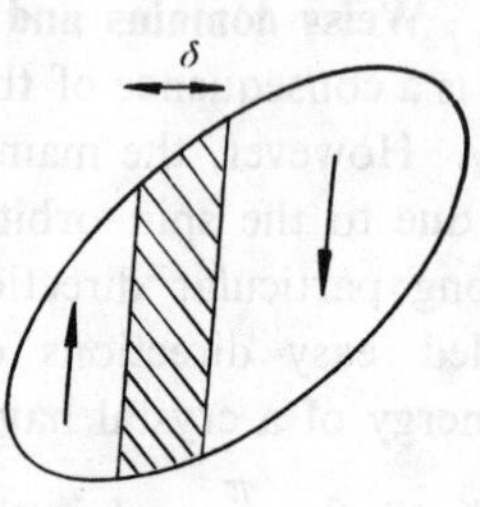

Fig. 11.1.4

The superficial energy γ_B of a Bloch wall results from the increase of exchange energy $2W(\Delta\theta)^2$ and also from the increase of the anisotropy energy $K\sin^2\theta$. It will be calculated exactly below; but roughly we have $\gamma_B \simeq \delta \times (2W\left(\frac{a}{\delta}\right)^2\pi + K)$. This energy is minimum for the thickness δ such that $d\gamma_B/d\delta = -\pi^2\frac{Wa^2}{\delta^2} + K = 0$. Thus: $\delta = \pi a\sqrt{\frac{W}{K}}$ and $\gamma_B = 2\pi a\sqrt{WK} \simeq 4a\sqrt{WK}$. The order of magnitude of δ is some 10^2 Å in $3d$ materials and less than 10^2 Å in rare-earth materials. The superficial wall energy is of the order of 0.1—2 erg/cm² in $4d$ materials and of some 10 erg/cm² in $4f$ materials.

The value δ of the wall thickness results from the balance between the exchange energy $-2W\cos(\theta_n-\theta_{n-1})$ (where θ_n and θ_{n-1} denote the angle of two consecutive magnetic moments with the easy axis of magnetization) and the anisotropy energy $K\sin^2\theta_n$. The former tends to give $\theta_n-\theta_{n-1}\to 0$ and thus to give $\delta\to\infty$ and the second tends to give $\theta_n\to 0$ and thus $\delta\to 0$ (Fig. 11.1.5). It is due to this necessary balance between exchange and anisotropy energy that a surface energy is stored.

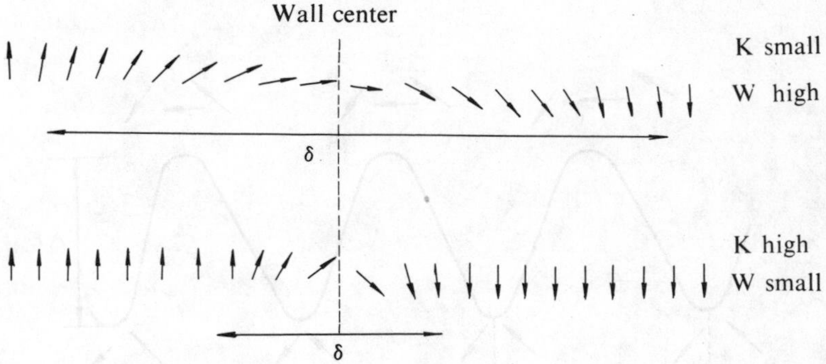

Fig. 11 1.5

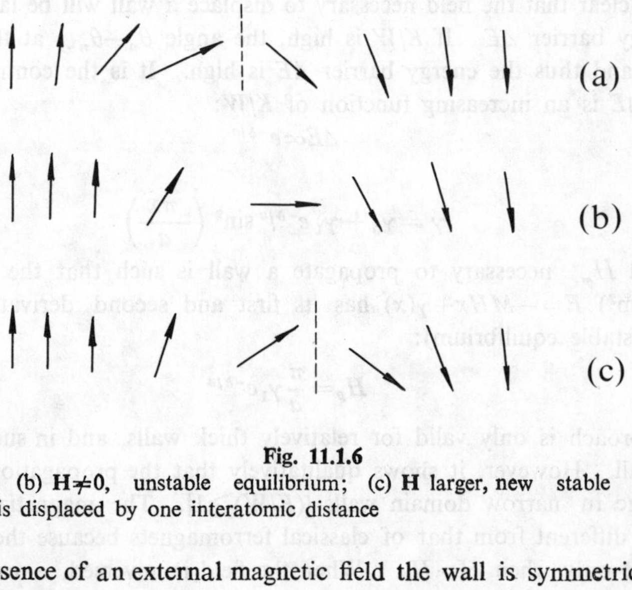

Fig. 11.1.6
(a) H=0; (b) H≠0, unstable equilibrium; (c) H larger, new stable equilibrium. The wall is displaced by one interatomic distance

In the absence of an external magnetic field the wall is symmetrical and its energy γ is minimum.

If a magnetic field is applied, the moments tend to rotate in the field direction and the Bloch wall becomes asymmetrical; its energy increases. The energy of the wall is maximum (when H increases) when it is again symmetrical (Fig. 11.1.6). If the equilibrium was stable in the former symmetrical configuration, it is unstable in this last symmetrical configuration.

When the wall moves by one interatomic distance, its energy passes through a maximum. In fact its energy varies sinusoidally with a period equal to the lattice periodicity in the direction of the wall propagation. Generally, the wall spreads over several interatomic distances, thus its energy varies generally with a period much smaller than its thickness.

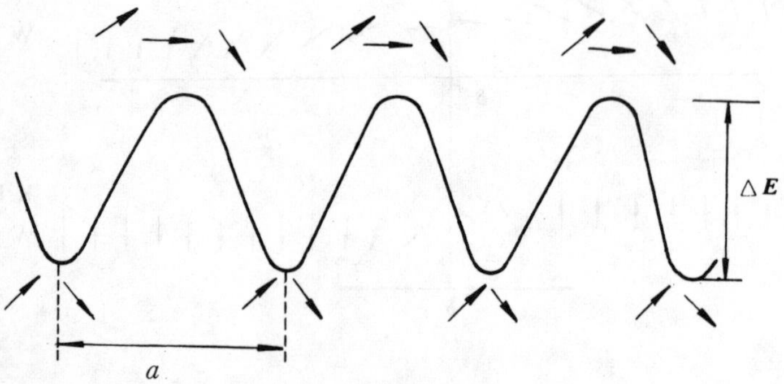

Fig. 11.1.7

It is clear that the field necessary to displace a wall will be larger the larger the energy barrier ΔE. If K/W is high, the angle $\theta_n - \theta_{n-1}$ at the wall center is large, and thus the energy barrier ΔE is high. It is the contrary if K/W is small. ΔE is an increasing function of K/W:

$$\Delta E \propto e^{-\delta/a}$$

and thus

$$\gamma = \gamma_0 + \gamma_1 e^{-\delta/a} \sin^2\left(\frac{\pi x}{a}\right) \tag{11.1.7}$$

The field H_p necessary to propagate a wall is such that the surface energy (for 1 cm²) $E = -MHx + \gamma(x)$ has its first and second derivatives equal to zero (unstable equilibrium):

$$H_p = \frac{\pi}{a} \gamma_1 e^{-\delta/a} \tag{11.1.8}$$

This approach is only valid for relatively thick walls, and in such a case H_p is very small. However, it shows qualitatively that the propagation field becomes very large in narrow domain walls [$(K/W) \gtrsim 1$]. The magnetization curve is therfore different from that of classical ferromagnets because the domain walls can move only when $H \geqslant H_p$. When the field is reversed, a coercive field of the same order of magnitude as H_p is foreseen. This particular process of magnetization has been obtained for the first time in Dy_3Al_2 showing the possible

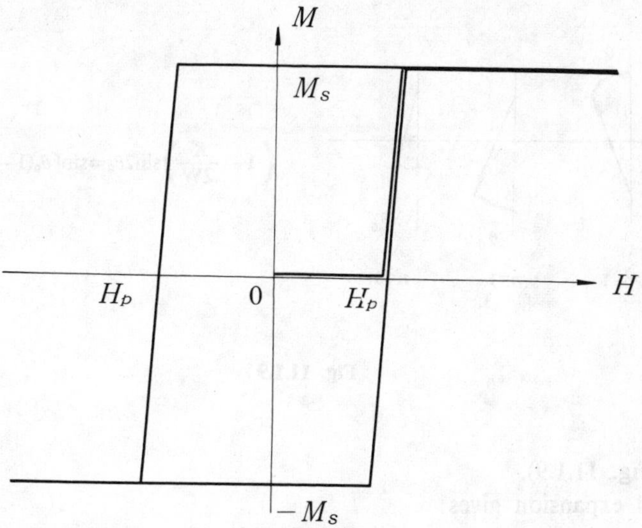

Fig. 11.1.8

existence of narrow domain walls.

In the calculation of a narrow domain wall it is necessary to take into account the discrete character of the matter, because the wall thickness is of the same order as the interatomic distance. The exchange and the anisotropy energy summed in the wall is:

$$E=\frac{1}{a^2}\sum_{n=-\infty}^{+\infty} K\sin^2\theta_n+2W\left[1-\frac{\cos(\theta_n-\theta_{n+1})+\cos(\theta_n-\theta_{n-1})}{2}\right] \quad (11.1.9)$$

The minimum (or maximum) energy symmetrical configuration is given by $dE/d\theta_n=0$. This gives an infinite set of non-linear equations:

$$\frac{K}{2W}\sin 2\theta_n=\sin(\theta_n-\theta_{n+1})+\sin(\theta_n-\theta_{n-1}) \quad (11.1.10)$$

where n varies from $-\infty$ to $+\infty$ in steps of 1.

In the case of narrow domain walls, $\frac{K}{W}\gtrsim 1$; these equations can be linearized:

$$\rho\theta_n=\theta_{n+1}+\theta_{n-1} \quad (11.1.11)$$

where

$$\rho=\frac{K}{W}+2$$

n varies from $-\infty$ to $+\infty$. The solution of this system of equations is

$$\theta_n=\theta_0 e^{-n\psi} \quad (11.1.12)$$

with

$$\psi=\text{arccosh}(\rho/2)$$

When n increases from the wall centre (the moment direction is defined by the angle θ_0), θ_n decreases as a geometrical progression of rate $x=e^{-\psi}$.

The value of θ_0 is obtained by writing the non-linearized equation for

$$\left(1-\frac{K}{2W}\right)\sin 2\theta_0 = \sin[\,\theta_0(1-x)]$$

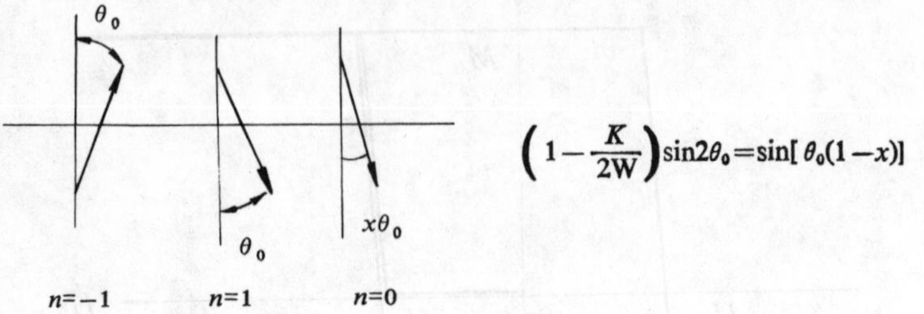

Fig. 11.1.9

$n=0$ (see Fig. 11.1.9).

A third expansion gives:

$$\theta_0^2 = \frac{6[(K/W)-1-x]}{4[(K/W)-2]+[1-x]^3} \qquad (11.1.13)$$

This equation shows that when K/W increases, θ_0 decreases rapidly and becomes zero for $K/W=4/3$. For $K/W>4/3$, the wall is of only one interatomic distance because $\theta_0=0$ is thus the only solution of the preceding equation. The coupling with a magnetic field leads to the supplementary term:

$$-M_s H \sum_{n=-\infty}^{+\infty} \frac{\theta_n^2}{2} \qquad (11.1.14)$$

Each linear equation is split into two equations (one for spin ↑ and the other for spin ↓). A third–order expansion leads to the value of H_p (see Fig. 11.1.10). In the region of small K/W, H_p increases slowly and then rapidly. When the applied field becomes equal to the local molecular field H_{mi} acting at the wall centre, the magnetic moments are spontaneously reversed and thus $H_p = H_{mi} \simeq WM_s$ remains constant (tunnelling effect).

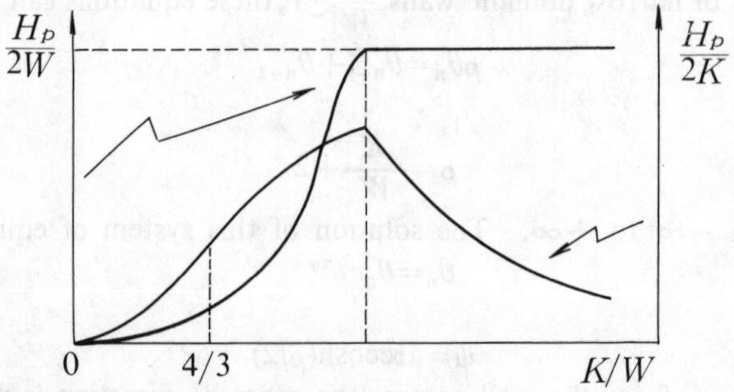

Fig. 11.1.10

The propagation field is equal to 21 kOe in Dy_3Al_2 at 4.2 K. Several other 4f materials have been observed with narrow domain walls. Their propagation fields range from some kOe to several tens of kOe.

This rapid description does not take into account the defects and particularly point defects, which play an important role in narrow domain walls (see Chapter 12).

11.2 MAGNETIC BUBBLES

11.2.1 Magnetic domains in a platelet

Let us consider a platelet of thickness L and of surface $S=ab$ (with $a \simeq b \gg L$) where the easy axis of magnetization is perpendicular to the surface (Fig. 11.2.1)

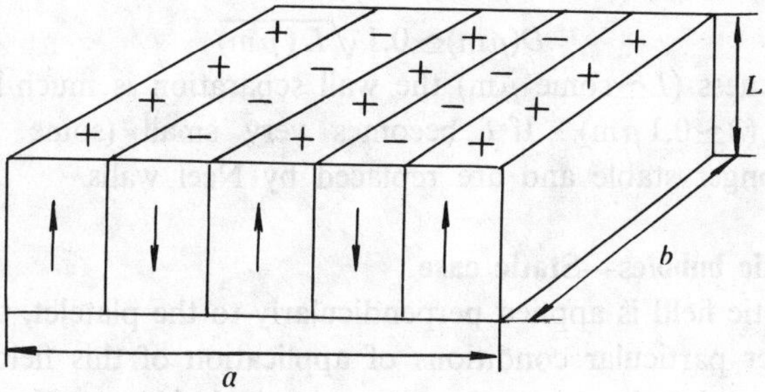

Fig 11.2.1

The magnetization is successively ↑ and ↓ in order to decrease the pole energy (which would be very important in the absence of domain walls, $E_d \simeq M_s^2 SL$). The number of Bloch walls appearing depends on the relative values of this energy and the wall energy. If the number of Bloch walls is large, the wall energy is large and the magnetostatic energy is small. Effectively, the dipolar interaction between the + and − magnetic charges at the platelet surface is smaller the smaller the separation between Bloch walls. This surface energy can be calculated if we expand in a Fourier series the spatial variation of the surface charges $\rho(x,y)$ [($\rho(x,y)$ is a square function)]:

$$\rho(x,y)=\frac{4M_s}{\pi}\left[\sin\left(\frac{\pi x}{D}\right)+\frac{1}{3}\sin\left(\frac{3\pi x}{D}\right)+\dots\right] \qquad (11.2.1)$$

D is the distance between two Bloch walls. We assume $D \ll L$ and thus the volume(bulk) dipolar energy is negligible compared to its surface contribution. There are only odd terms because $\rho(x,y)$ is real. Such a charge distribution creates in the vicinity of the boundary a field which is parallel to Oz (symmetry of the problem). Its expression is obtained from that of $\rho(x,y)$ using the Poisson equation:

$$H_z(x, y) = -2\pi M_s \frac{H}{\pi}\left[\sin\left(\frac{\pi x}{D}\right)\exp\left(\frac{\pi z}{D}\right)+\cdots\right] \tag{11.2.2}$$

Using only the first harmonic, the magnetic energy is per unity plateleted surface:

$$\gamma_m^{(1)} = -\frac{1}{2}\iint M_z H_z(x, y)dx\,dy = 4M_s^2\langle|\sin\frac{\pi x}{D}|\rangle\int_0^{-\infty}\exp\left(\frac{\pi z}{D}\right)dz$$

$$\gamma_m^{(1)} = 4M_s^2\times\frac{2}{\pi}\times\frac{D}{\pi} = \frac{8M_s^2 D}{\pi^2}$$

In the same conditions, the Bloch wall energy is equal to $(a/D)\gamma\times(Lb)$, where γ is the energy of unit surface. Thus the total energy is:

$$E = \frac{8M_s^2 Dab}{\pi^2} + \frac{abL\gamma}{D}$$

The stable configuration is given by:

$$\frac{dE}{dD} = 0 \longrightarrow D = \frac{\pi}{2M_s}\sqrt{\frac{\gamma L}{2}} \tag{11.2.3}$$

The Bloch wall separation varies as the square root of the platelet thickness. If $\gamma = 1$ erg/cm² and $M_s = 10^3$ e.m.u./cm³,

$$D(\mu m) \simeq 0.1\sqrt{L(\mu m)} \tag{11.2.4}$$

For usual thickness ($L \simeq$ some μm) the wall separation is much larger than the wall thickness ($\delta \simeq 0.1\,\mu$m). If L becomes very small (some 10^2 Å), Bloch walls are no longer stable and are replaced by Néel walls.

11.2.2 Magnetic bubbles—Static case

If a magnetic field is applied perpendicularly to the platelet, the Bloch walls move and under particular conditions of application of this field the magnetic domains become closed, giving rise to magnetic bubbles. The magnetization is antiparallel to **H** inside the bubble and parallel to **H** out of it.

The materials used for the platelets are generally garnets (YIG, GGG, subtituted garnets such as $(YSmLuCa)_3$ $(FeGe)_5O_{12}\cdots$). The different compositions allow modification of the main magnetic parameters: M_s the spontaneous magnetization, K the uniaxial anisotropy, W the exchange coupling. The equilibrium of a magnetic bubble (Fig. 11.2.2) results from the competition between three energy terms:

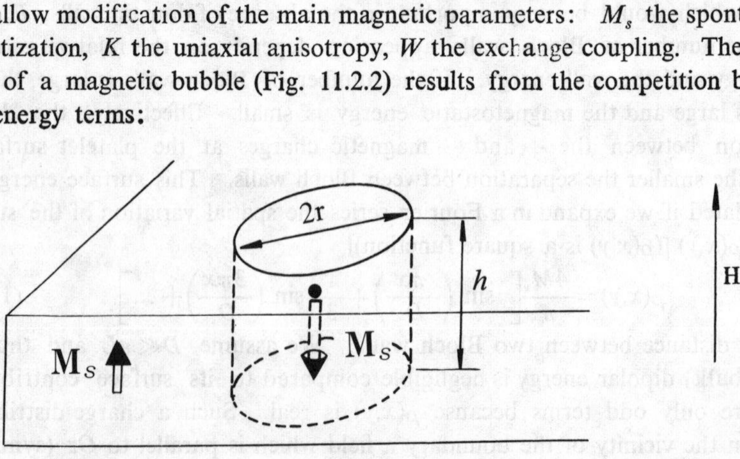

Fig. 11.2.2

— the total wall energy $E_W=2\pi rh\gamma$, where γ is the surface wall energy ($\gamma=4a\sqrt{WK}$).
— the interaction with the external field $\mathbf{H}_0$:

$$E_H=-2\mathbf{M}_s\mathbf{H}_0\pi r^2h=2M_sH_0\pi r^2h \tag{11.2.5}$$

— the third term is the demagnetizing energy $E_d=\int \mathbf{M}_s\mathbf{H}_d\,dv$ of a single cylindrical domain in an infinite platelet. This term, which is of the order of $4\pi M_s^2 \pi r^2h$, has been calculated firstly by Thiele, using elliptic integrals. We will give here a much simpler approximation:

It is convenient to use reduced variables: the dimensionless energy is:

$$\epsilon=E/16\pi^2M_s^2H_0^3 \tag{11.2.6}$$

the dimensionless field is:

$$H=H_0/4\pi M_s \tag{11.2.7}$$

and the dimensionless radius is:

$$x=r/h \tag{11.2.8}$$

We introduce also a dimensionless term λ characterising the ratio of the surface wall energy to the bulk demagnetizing field energy of a platelet:

$$\lambda=\frac{1}{h}\frac{\gamma}{4\pi M_s^2} \tag{11.2.9}$$

Returning to the bubble demagnetizing energy ϵ_d, Thiele's solution for the first derivative of this quantity is:

$$\frac{1}{x}\frac{dE_d}{dx}=\frac{4x}{\pi}\left[\left(\frac{4x^2}{1+4x^2}\right)^{-\frac{1}{2}}\cdot E\left(\frac{4x^2}{1+4x^2}\right)-1\right] \tag{11.2.10}$$

where $E(m)$ is the complete elliptic integral of the second kind. This quantity can be replaced by the simpler function:

$$\frac{1}{x}\frac{dE_d}{dx}=\frac{1}{1+3x/2} \tag{11.2.11}$$

For the entire range from $x=0.1$ to $x=10$, the deviation is always less than $\pm10^{-2}$. In particular, at the physically important value $x=1$, the difference is 1%. By differentiation of the total energy E_T one gets:

$$E_T=\left(\frac{\lambda}{2x}+H-\frac{1}{1+3x/2}\right)x\delta+\left[H-\left(1+\frac{3}{2}x\right)^{-2}\right](\delta x)^2+\cdots \tag{11.2.12}$$

the first-order term of this differentiation contains the three energy terms (wall energy, magnetic field coupling and magnetostatic energies) whereas the second-order term contains only the last two energy terms. Effectively, the wall energy term is a linear function of the bubble radius. The equilibrium radius is determined by the cancellation of the coefficient of δx. The stability of the bubble is determined by the sign of the coefficient of $(\delta x)^2$ (second derivative of the energy). Setting the first derivative term equal to zero, one obtains:

$$\frac{\lambda}{2}+Hx-\frac{x}{1+3x/2}=0 \tag{11.2.13}$$

The various terms appearing in this equation are shown in Fig. 11.2.3.
The values of x, solutions of this equation, are given by the intersections.

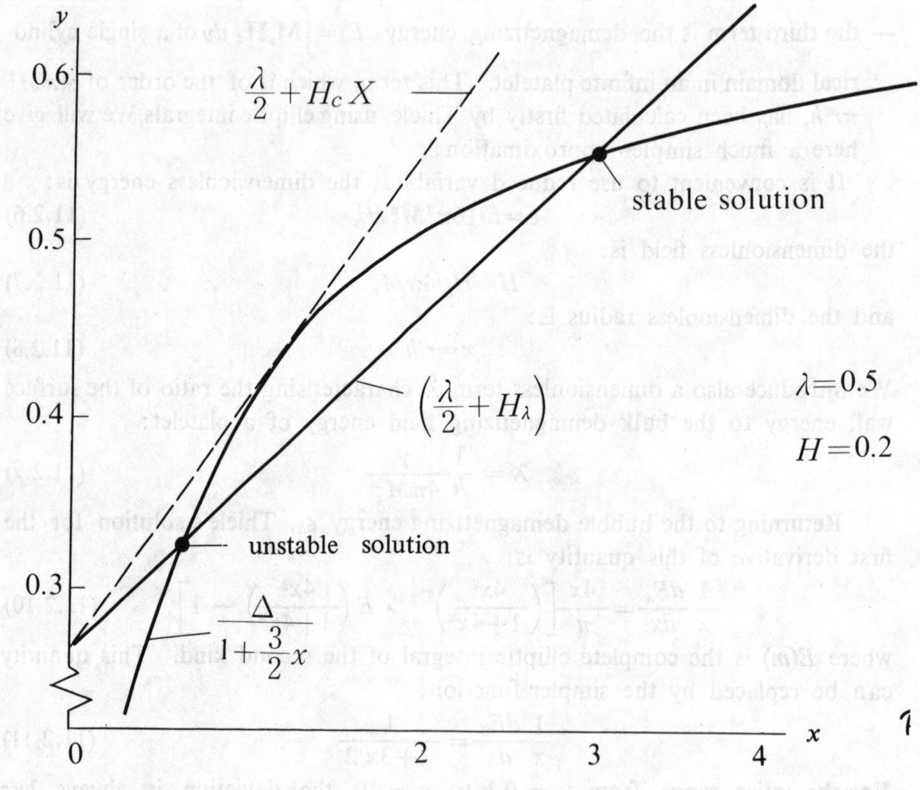

Fig. 11.2.3

The straight line intercepts the y-axis for $y=\lambda\propto\gamma$ the density of wall energy. If we assume that γ increases slightly, the bubble radius must decrease in order to minimise the energy.

Fig. 11.2.3 shows that if the straight line is slightly translated towards positive y the bubble radius decreases for the larger solution, which is the stable one. The smaller solution is unstable. The analytical expression of the stable solution is:

$$x=\frac{1-3\lambda/4+H}{3H}+\sqrt{\left(1-\frac{3\lambda}{4}-H\right)^2-3\lambda H} \tag{11.2.14}$$

These considerations of stability can be corroborated by inspection of the sign of the second derivative of the energy. There is a field H_0 above which bubbles are not stable. Graphically this is the field for which the straight line is tangent to the hyperbola. The two roots of (11.2.13) coalesce:

$$\left(1-\frac{3}{4}\lambda-H_c\right)^2=3\lambda H_c \tag{11.2.15}$$

Giving:

$$H_c=1+\frac{3\lambda}{4}-\sqrt{3\lambda} \tag{11.2.16}$$

(the second solution has no physical meaning). At this critical field the radius of the bubble is:

$$x_c=\frac{1}{\sqrt{3/\lambda-3/2}} \tag{11.2.17}$$

Thus, starting from a bubble radius x for a field H, if H increases, the bubble radius will decrease and for $H=H_c$, $X=x_c$. If $H>H_c$, $x\to 0$. H_c is the collapse field.

Physically, this variation results from the competition between the three energy terms. If H increases the bubble radius decreases ($\mathbf{M}_s$ in the bubble is antiparallel to $\mathbf{H}$) and when the field is large enough the magnetostatic energy is no longer sufficient to counterbalance the wall energy plus the field energy. One can see from Fig. 11.2.3 that if γ decreases (λ decreases) the collapse field increases.

The order of magnitude of this field is some tenths of an Oe. However, it can be much higher if the wall configuration is not entirely of Bloch wall type. Effectively the produced bubbles are often in a metastable state which is characterised

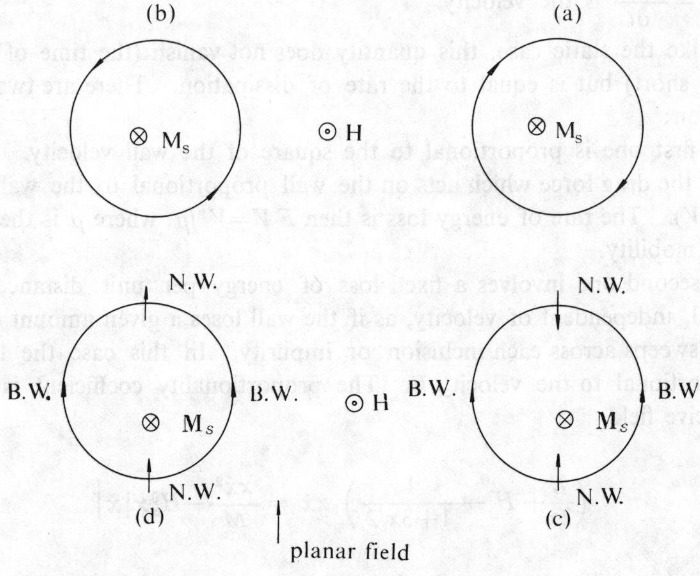

Fig. 11.2.4.

(a) and (b) Bloch walls of different chiralites (right and left); (c) and (d) bubble with two vertical Bloch lines.

by the presence of Bloch lines. A Bloch line corresponds to the region where two Bloch walls of different chiralities are in contact. The small transition wall portion between these two Bloch walls is such that the magnetization at its centre is perpendicular to the wall surface. It is a Néel wall portion. In Fig. 11.2.4, the arrows indicate the direction of the magnetization at the wall centre. In case (c) the two Bloch lines are characterised by a magnetization pointing to the bubble centre. Such configurations lead to a better closure of the magnetic flux. The collapse field is distributed (± 20 Oe); the number of Bloch lines being random. It has been shown that if the platelet contains a thin layer with planar magnetization, the number of Bloch lines decreases strongly, giving smaller and more homogeneous collapse fields. Effectively, if a small field is applied in order to saturate the planar magnetization, the Bloch lines are unstable except for two types of Bloch lines (Fig. 11.2.4, case (d)). If the field is not sufficient to saturate the planar layer, closure domains appear in place of the Bloch lines.

11.2.3 Magnetic bubbles—Dynamic case

In order to extend the previous analysis to the dynamic case, a supplementary term must in principle be added: the kinetic energy term. However, this term is very small and negligible. Thus we must take it into account only for the dissipation as the wall moves. From the equation giving δE_T we have to first order:

$$\frac{\delta E_T}{\delta t}=\left(\frac{\lambda}{2x}+H-\frac{1}{1+3x/2}\right)x\dot{x} \qquad (11.2.18)$$

where $\dot{x}=\dfrac{\delta x}{\delta t}$ is the velocity.

Unlike the static case, this quantity does not vanish (the time of variation must be short) but is equal to the rate of dissipation. There are two types of dissipation:

- The first one is proportional to the square of the wall velocity. It results from the drag force which acts on the wall proportional to the wall velocity ($F \propto V$). The rate of energy loss is then $F\,V=V^2/\mu$, where μ is the standard wall mobility.
- The second one involves a fixed loss of energy per unit distance of wall travel, independent of velocity, as if the wall loses a given amount of energy as it sweeps across each inclusion or impurity. In this case the losses are proportional to the velocity V. The proportionality coefficient is H_c^0 the coercive field.

Thus:

$$\left(\frac{\lambda}{2x}+H-\frac{1}{1+3x/2}\right)x\dot{x}=\frac{x\dot{x}^2}{M}-H_c^0 x|\dot{x}| \qquad (11.2.19)$$

giving:

$$\dot{x}=-\frac{1}{\mu}\left(\frac{\lambda}{2x}-\frac{1}{1+3x/2}+H\pm H_c\right) \qquad (11.2.20)$$

The sign + or − is related to $\dot{x}>0$ or $\dot{x}<0$.

If the field H is modified during a sufficiently short time so that the static equilibrium cannot be reached, the bubble radius changes with the radial velocity $\dot{x}$, the sign depending on whether H has been increased or decreased.

11.2.4 Bubble motion

The simplest way to displace bubbles is to apply a field gradient. It is however possible to displace bubbles by thickness gradients or temperature gradients. The resulting force **F** applied on a bubble and created by gradients can be calculated from the energy of a bubble E_T:

$$\mathbf{F}=-\frac{\partial E_T}{\partial h}\nabla h-\frac{\partial E_T}{\partial \gamma}\nabla\gamma-\frac{\partial E_T}{\partial M_s}\nabla M_s-\frac{\partial E_T}{\partial H_z}\nabla H_z \qquad (11.2.21)$$

H_z is the vertical component of the applied magnetic field.

We will now study the wall motion due to a gradient of vertical field. The field term is the only one contributing to

$$2M_s\pi r^2 h\,\Delta H_z = 2M_s\pi h\frac{\Delta Hr}{2} \qquad (11.2.22)$$

When the bubble is displaced it is also subjected to other forces:

— the coercivity force (see above) corresponding to a solid friction (each impurity takes the same amount of energy from the wall). It exerts on the wall a pressure $P_c = 2M_sH_c$ for a planar wall.

— the mobility force due to a viscous friction of the wall. It results from the damping of each magnetic moment during its precession. It can be obtained by the analysis of the moment precession responsible for the wall motion. The corresponding pressure is, for a planar wall, $\rho_\mu=2M_sV/\mu$.

Each small portion ds of the bubble surface can be considered as planar (Fig. 11.2.5). If **V** is the bubble velocity, its component perpendicular to ds is $V\cos\theta$, thus:

$$P_c=2M_sH_c$$
$$P_\mu=2M_sV\cos\theta/\mu \qquad (11.2.23)$$

The total forces exerted on the bubble are obtained by integrating on the bubble surface the component of the pressure parallel to **V**, that is to say, $P_\mu\cos\theta$ and $P_c\cos\theta$

$$F_\mu=2\int_{-\pi/2}^{\pi/2}\frac{2M_s}{\mu}V\cos\theta\cdot\cos\theta\cdot hrd\theta=2\pi rh\,M_sV/\mu$$
$$F_c=2\int_{-\pi/2}^{\pi/2}2M_s H_c\cos\theta\cdot hrd\theta=8rh\,M_sH_c \qquad (11.2.24)$$

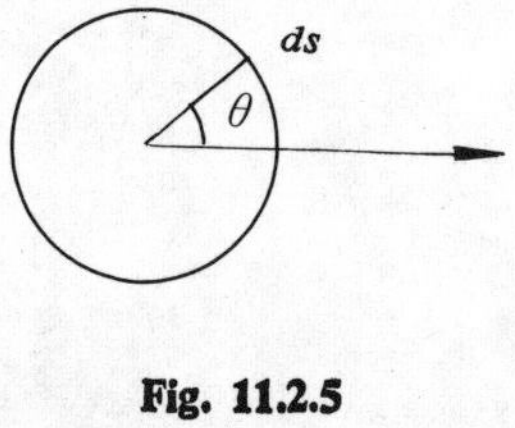

Fig. 11.2.5

Equating the sum F_c+F_H to the force F_H gives:

$$V=\frac{\mu}{2}\left(\Delta H-\frac{8}{\pi}H_c\right) \tag{11.2.25}$$

The bubble motion is along the field gradient.

The mobility μ is related to the λ coefficient of the Gilbert equation of motion by:

$$\frac{d\mathbf{m}}{dt}=-\gamma\mathbf{m}\times\left(\mathbf{H}-\frac{\alpha}{\gamma m}\frac{d\mathbf{m}}{dt}\right) \tag{11.2.26}$$

Its expression is:

$$\mu=\frac{\gamma}{\alpha}\frac{\delta}{\pi} \tag{11.2.27}$$

This result is easily obtained if one recalls that the wall motion results from moment precessions. The physical mechanism is the following. If the magnetic field is applied along the O_Z direction of the magnetic moments in a given domain, the moments of the wall $\mathbf{m}=-\gamma\mathbf{L}$ go round $\mathbf{H}_z$ (precession). Thus they come out of the yO_Z plane of the wall, producing a component M_x of the magnetization perpendicular to the plane of the wall. This results in a demagnetizing field $H_x=-4\pi M_x\cos\psi$ causing a new precession of the magnetic moments around Ox. This leads to the wall motion. In particular the wall velocity is maximum when the demagnetizing field $H_d=4\pi M_s$ is maximum. Such a velocity is called the Walker velocity V_W.

Recent experiments have shown that, in fact, the wall velocity depends on the time τ of application of the pulse of field gradient:

$$\frac{V-x_c/\tau}{1-\tau_c(\Delta H)/\tau}=\mu(\Delta H-\Delta H_\infty) \tag{11.2.28}$$

where x_c is a dimension of the order of the wall thickness and $\tau_c(\Delta H)$ a function of the field gradient which depends sensitively on the thermal activation mechanism.

REFERENCES

A. HERPIN, Théorie du Magnétisme, Presses Universitaires de France, Paris (1968).
H. KRONMULLER, *Phys. Status Solidi*(b), **59,** 71 (1973).
L. NÉEL, Oeuvres Scientifiques, Editions du C.N.R.S., Paris (1978).

CHAPTER 12

COERCIVITY

Ferromagnetic or ferrimagnetic materials generally present a "remanent magnetization" $\mathbf{M}_R$ after removal of an applied field **H**. The magnetization curve **M** (**H**) is irreversible, giving rise to a "hysteresis loop" (Fig. 12.0.1). The field H_c at which the sign of **M** changes is called the "coercive field". The metastable equilibrium of **M** is associated with energy barriers resulting from the magnetic anisotropy. Different types of anisotropies, as well as other terms of the magnetic energy, are defined in Section 12.1. The principal origins of the coercive field are discussed in Section 12.2. Section 12.3 is devoted to the influence of metallurgical transformations on the coercive field of the main classes of existing permanent magnets.

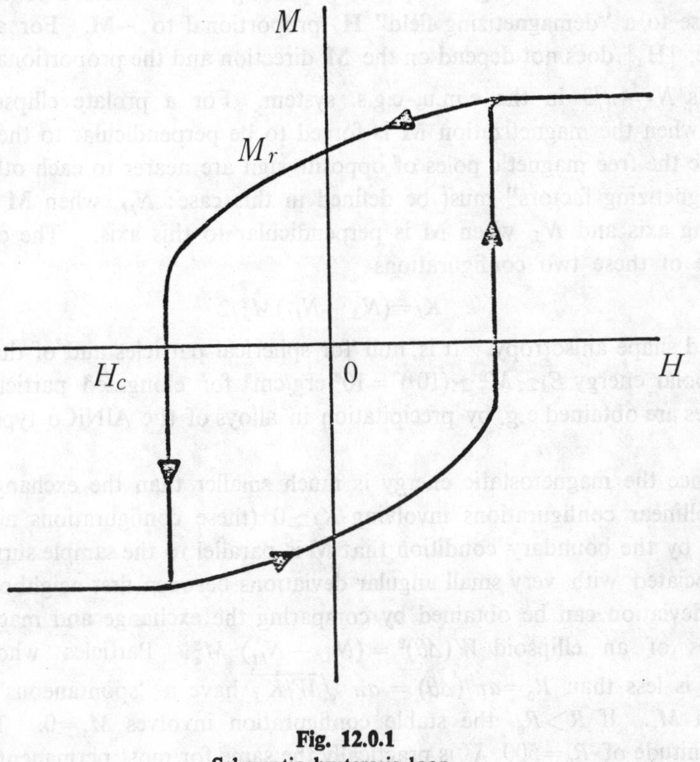

Fig. 12.0.1
Schematic hysteresis loop.

12.1 ENERGY OF A FERROMAGNETIC SYSTEM

There are several contributions to the energy of a ferromagnetic material, three of which are essential: the exchange, dipolar and magnetocrystalline energies.

12.1.1 Exchange energy

The preponderant term of the exchange interaction is generally $-J\mathbf{S}_m\mathbf{S}_n$, where $\mathbf{S}_m$ and $\mathbf{S}_n$ represent two first-neighbour spins. In classical magnetism it is convenent to write this energy per unit volume:

$$E_c = -W\cos(\theta_m - \theta_n) \qquad (12.1.1)$$

For ferromagnets, $W > 0$.

The exchange energy can be evaluated from the "Curie temperature" T_c, which is the temperature at which the thermal disorder destroys the long-range magnetic ordering. At $T > T_c$ the system is "paramagnetic". T_c is generally larger than 10^3K in $3d$-based alloys and smaller than 10^2K in $4f$-based alloys.

12.1.2 Magnetostatic energy. Shape anisotropy

In the presence of a single exchange energy, the magnetic moments are parallel to each other. Free magnetic poles, appearing at the surface of the sample, give rise to a "demagnetizing field" $\mathbf{H}_d$ proportional to $-\mathbf{M}$. For a spherical sample, $|\mathbf{H}_d|$ does not depend on the $\mathbf{M}$ direction and the proportionality coefficient is $N = 4\pi/3$ in the e.m.u.–c.g.s. system. For a prolate ellipsoid H_d is larger when the magnetization $\mathbf{M}$ is forced to be perpendicular to the long axis because the free magnetic poles of opposite sign are nearer to each other. Two "demagnetizing factors" must be defined in this case: $N_{//}$ when $\mathbf{M}$ lies along the long axis and $N_\perp$ when $\mathbf{M}$ is perpendicular to this axis. The energy difference of these two configurations

$$K_f = (N_\perp - N_{//})M_s^2/2 \qquad (12.1.2)$$

is called shape anisotropy. It is null for spherical particles and of the order of the dipolar energy $E_d \simeq M_s^2 \simeq (10^3)^2 = 10^6$ erg/cm³ for elongated particles. Such particles are obtained e.g. by precipitation in alloys of the AlNiCo type (Section 12.2).

Since the magnetostatic energy is much smaller than the exchange energy, non-collinear configurations involving $K_f \simeq 0$ (these configurations are characterised by the boundary condition that $\mathbf{M}$ is parallel to the sample surface) must be associated with very small angular deviations between first neighbours. The mean deviation can be obtained by comparing the exchange and magnetostatic energies of an ellipsoid $W(\Delta\theta)^2 = (N_\perp - N_{//})\, M_s^2$. Particles whose small axis R is less than $R_0 = a\pi/(\Delta\theta) = a\pi\sqrt{W/K_f}$ have a "spontaneous" magnetization M_s. If $R > R_0$, the stable configuration involves $M_s = 0$. The order of magnitude of $R_0 = 500$ Å is practically the same for most permanent magnets.

12.1.3 Magnetocrystalline anisotropy. Bloch walls (B. W.) and Weiss domains (W. D.)

Contrary to shape anisotropy, magnetocrystalline anisotropy is intrinsic. It is a direct consequence of the discrete, character of matter. The magnetization is fixed along an "easy direction of magnetization", Δ, associated with the local crystallographic symmetry. Competition between this direction and that associated with the shape of the sample are possible if the corresponding energies are comparable. The simplest expression for a uniaxial magnetocrystalline anisotropy is:

$$E_a = K \sin^2\theta \tag{12.1.3}$$

where θ is the angle between $\mathbf{M}_s$ and Δ. The easy direction of magnetization is unique if $K > 0$. K and K_f are generally of the same order in 3d-based alloys and $K/K_f \simeq 10^2$ in 4f-based alloys.

The moment distribution for $K \ll K_f$ (Fig. 12.1.1 (a)) is modified if a magne-

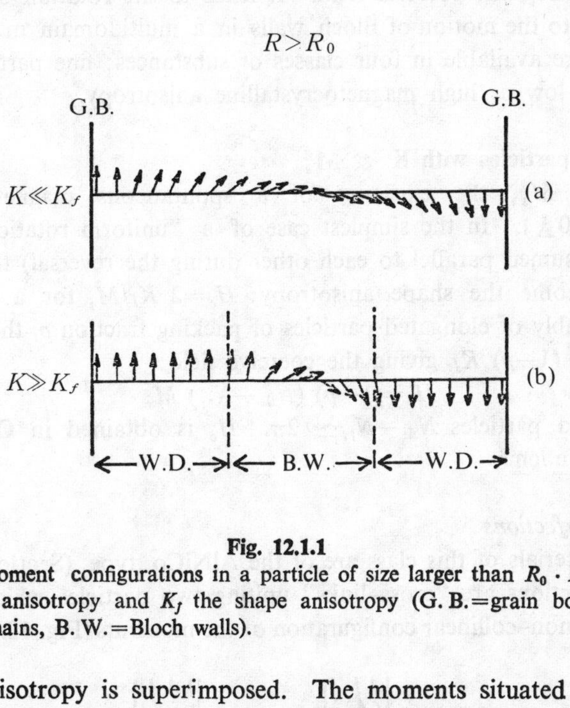

Fig. 12.1.1
Schematic moment configurations in a particle of size larger than R_0 · K is the magnetocrystalline anisotropy and K_f the shape anisotropy (G. B.=grain boundary, W. D. =Weiss domains, B. W.=Bloch walls).

tocrystalline anisotropy is superimposed. The moments situated on each side of the chain centre point along Δ. This leads to a narrowing of the transition region (Fig. 12.1.1 (b)), which no longer extends over the whole particle width. The rotation of magnetization is localized in space and is called a "Bloch wall". This wall divides the samples into two spontaneously magnetized "Weiss domains". The thickness of a Bloch wall is $\delta = a\pi\sqrt{W/K}$. The domain wall energy is $\gamma \simeq 2W(\Delta\theta)^2(\delta/a) \simeq 4a\sqrt{WK}$. δ and γ are of the order of 5×10^2 Å and 1 erg/cm² respectively in 3d-based alloys (W high, K low), 10—10² Å and 100 erg/cm² in 3d-4f alloys (W and K high), 2—10 Å and

1—10 erg/cm² in 4*f*–based alloys (*W* low and *K* high). The critical particle size R_K below which Bloch walls are unstable can be obtained by comparing the surface wall energy γR^2 and the bulk magnetostatic energy $NM_s^2 R^3$. $R_K = \gamma / NM_s^2$ is larger the larger the magnetocrystalline anisotropy *K*. Metastable states resulting from the presence of Bloch walls in magnetized particles are unlikely to occur in 3*d*–based particles where $\delta \gg R_K$. It is the contrary in certain conditions in 4*f*–based alloys where $R_K \gg \delta$. Such elements of domain walls delimit very small reversed domains which can play an important role as nucleation centres ($SmCo_5$, Section 12.1.3).

12.2 ORIGIN OF THE COERCIVE FIELD

The coupling of the magnetization with a magnetic field **H** introduces the supplementary term $E_H = -\mathbf{M} \cdot \mathbf{H}$. An instability of the moment configuration occurs at $H = H_c$, the coercive field. It leads to the rotation of **M** in a small particle, and to the motion of Bloch walls in a multidomain material. Highest coercivities are available in four classes of substances: fine particles or massive materials, of low or high magnetocrystalline anisotropy.

12.2.1 Fine particles with $K \ll M_s^2$

As $K \ll M_s^2$, the existence of a spontaneous magnetization implies $R < R_0$ ($\simeq 500$ Å). In the simplest case of a "uniform rotation" (all the moments are assumed parallel to each other during the reversal) the coercive field has to overcome the shape anisotropy: $H_c = 2\, K_f / M_s$ for a single particle. For an assembly of elongated particles of packing fraction *p*, the effective shape anisotropy is $(1-p)\, K_f$ giving the coercive field:

$$H_c = (1-p)\,(N_\perp - N_{//})\, M_s \qquad (12.2.1)$$

For elongated particles $N_\perp - N_{//} \simeq 2\pi$. H_c is obtained in Oersted if M_s is given in e.m.u./cm³.

Role of imperfections

Real materials of this class are of the AlNiCo type (Section 12.3.1). The main imperfections are "cross–links" uniting two particles which are no longer isolated. The non–collinear configuration of the moments (Fig. 12.2.1) favour non–

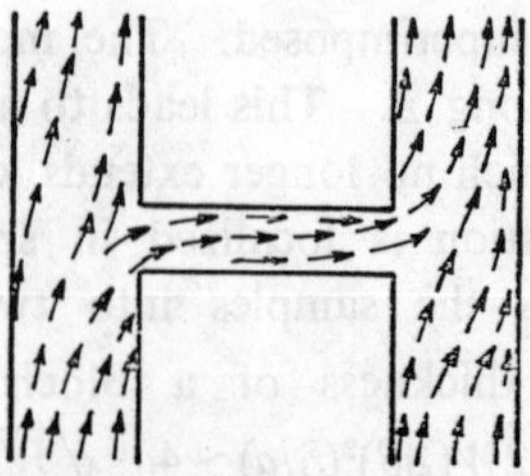

Fig. 12.2.1
Non–uniform magnetization in two particles connected by a cross–link.

uniform nucleations in fields smaller than the value H_c of (12.2.1)

12.2.2 Fine particles with $K \gg M_s^2$

When $K \gg M_s^2$ the magnetization M is, at equilibrium, different from zero only if $R < R_K$ (Section 12.1.3). In contrast to the previous case of low magnetocrystalline anisotropy, the instability associated with the reversal of $\mathbf{M}_s$ here does not extend over the whole particle. It is initially localized in a small region of the grain (of dimensions$=\delta$, the wall thickness; $\delta \ll R_K$, Section 12.1.3). At this scale of dimensions (50—100 Å) the thermal activation mechanism cannot be neglected. In non-perfect particles it will favour nucleations in small regions of the particles where the wall energy γ_D is smaller than that (γ) of the bulk value.

Role of imperfections

Under a magnetic field H the mean volume affected by thermal fluctuations is $V = kT \ln(t/\tau_0)/M_s H \simeq 20\, kT/M_s H$. Such fluctuations can activate a nucleation in a defect of mean size $R_D \simeq V^{1/3}$, that is to say, $R_D \simeq (20\, kT/M_s H)^{1/3}$. Otherwise the increase of surface energy $\gamma_D R_D^2$ must be compensated by the decrease of bulk energy $M_s H R_D^3$ and thus $\gamma_D = 20\, kT/R_D^2$. These two equations allow a characterisation of a nucleation defect (R_D, γ_D) at a given temperature T and quasi-static field H. As nucleated walls tend to extend through the whole particle they can be trapped by other kinds of defects (Section 12.2.4). The strongest pinning defects maintain small reverse domains in metastable equilibrium, even in high fields (Section 12.1.3). After reversal of the magnetic field these reversed domains constitute nucleation centres and hence reduce the coercive field ($SmCo_5$ particles, Section 12.3.2 (a)).

12.2.3 Massive materials with $\mathbf{K} \lesssim \mathbf{M}_s^2$

K is assumed smaller than or of the order of magnitude of M_s^2. The predominant term of the magnetic energy is essentially of dipolar origin ($\propto M_s^2$). This energy, stored in the vicinity of non-magnetic inclusions, is lowered by Bloch walls. These inclusions constitute wall-pinning centres. The strength of the pinning can be decreased by the formation of closure domains (which become unstable if the mean inclusion size is $R < R_K$ (Section 12.1.3).

The role of local deviations of $\mathbf{M}$ created by imperfections (such as non-magnetic inclusions) has been described in the theory of the coercive field, leading to an expression for H_c:

$$H_c = \frac{2K}{\pi M_s} v \left[0.386 + \frac{1}{2} \ln \frac{2\pi M_s^2}{K} \right] \qquad (12.2.2)$$

where v is the total volume of non-magnetic inclusions. This theory, whose basic ideas are fundamental in magnetism, can be applied to the case where K and M_s^2 are of the same order. With $3d$-based alloys such as steels, the maximum coercive field needs defects of size less than $R_K = 1/(10^3)^2 \simeq 100$ Å (Section 12.1.3). However, in order to prevent thermal activation effects, the optimum defect size must be larger than R_K and consequently closure domains may be present in these magnets.

12.2.4 Massive materials with $K \gg M_s^2$

The preponderant contributions to the magnetic energy stored in defects are of exchange and anisotropic origin. As in the previous section, closure domains are unstable if $R < R_K$. This can always be realized because R_K is of the order of 1 μm and such dimensions cannot be thermally activated at room temperature. Defects characterised by a wall energy γ_D lower than that of the bulk ($\gamma_D = 0$ for non-magnetic inclusions) constitute pinning centres. The field H_p necessary to extract a Bloch wall from a planar defect of width R_D has recently been calculated by different methods. It can be written:

$$H_p = \frac{\gamma}{8}\left(\frac{1}{W_D}\sqrt{\frac{W}{K}} + \frac{1}{K}\sqrt{\frac{K_D}{W_D}}\right)\frac{\Delta\gamma}{M_s}\frac{R_D}{\delta^2} \qquad (12.2.3)$$

For a given $\Delta\gamma = \gamma - \gamma_D$, H_p is larger the smaller the value of W_D, the exchange energy in the defect. If the defects are characterised by $\gamma_D > \gamma$ they do not trap the walls but they inhibit their motion. The field necessary to propagate a wall through such a planar defect is $H_p' = -H_p$.

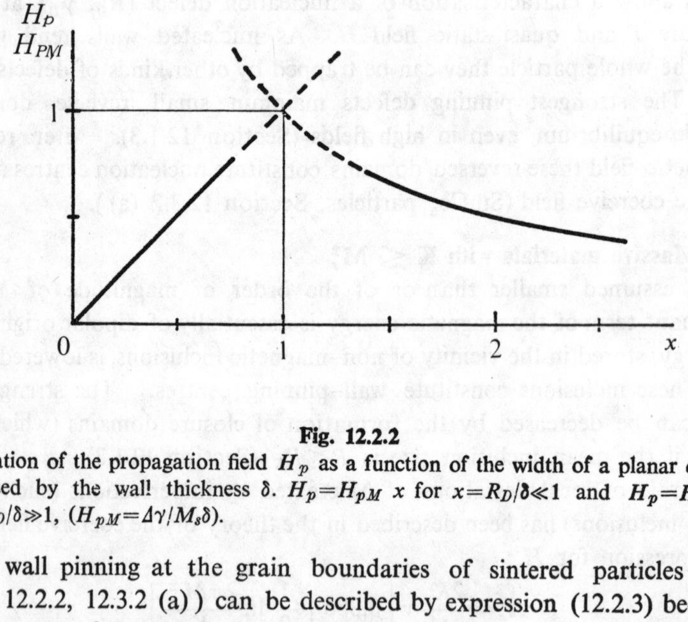

Fig. 12.2.2

Variation of the propagation field H_p as a function of the width of a planar defect normalised by the wall thickness δ. $H_p = H_{pM}\, x$ for $x = R_D/\delta \ll 1$ and $H_p = H_{pM}/x$ for $x = r_D/\delta \gg 1$, ($H_{pM} = \Delta\gamma / M_s \delta$).

The wall pinning at the grain boundaries of sintered particles ($SmCo_5$, Sections 12.2.2, 12.3.2 (a)) can be described by expression (12.2.3) because the wall curvatures, of the order of the reciprocal particle size R, are very small ($R = 5$ μm). However,in other materials such as the precipitation alloys ($Sm(CoCu)_5$, Section 12.3.2 (b)), the regions of low W_D are localized in small regions giving "pinning points". These points are generally very numerous. Under the simultaneous effects of an applied magnetic field and of thermal activation, strong wall curvatures between the trapping points are created. The corresponding propagation field is, at room temperature, much lower than that given in expression (12.2.3), where the Bloch wall is assumed rigid.

12.3 INFLUENCE OF METALLURGICAL TRANSFORMATIONS ON THE COERCIVE FIELD

The preceding discussion of the coercive field (Section 12.2) will be illustrated by different 3*d*– or 4*f*–based existing permanent magnets.

12.3.1 3*d*–based ferromagnetic materials ($K < M_s^2$)

Certain alloys (AlNiFe, AlNiCo, FeCoCr) have a miscibility gap in which two b.c.c. phases coexist (Fig. 12.3.1). One of them, α_1, rich in magnetic elements

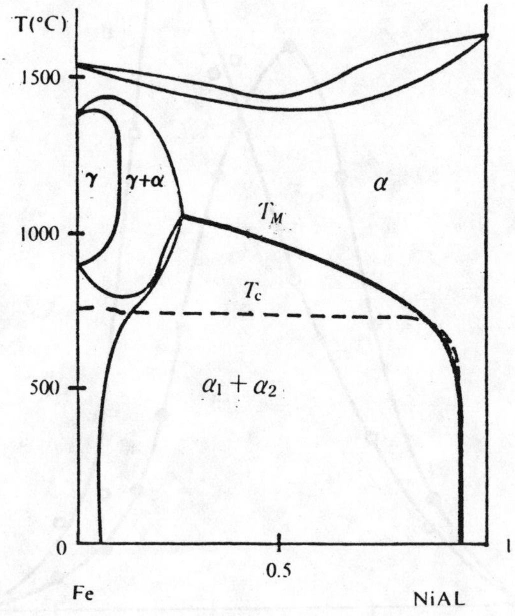

Fig. 12.3.1
Phase diagram of the system FeNiAl.
T_M=boundary of the miscibility gap;
T_c=Curie temperature.

(Fe or and Co) is formed by elongated particles, which are separated from each other by the second phase α_2, which is hardly or not at all magnetic. These materials have no significant magnetocrystalline anisotropy. They are a typical example of the case of a shape anisotropy coercive field (Sections 12.1.2, 12.2.1).

(a) *AlNiFe*

The coercive field of these alloys presents a maximum for about 50% atomic content of Fe (Fig. 12.3.2). Electron micrographs show that this maximum is associated with a particular microstructure: a regular alternation of the two phases with α_1 particles elongated along the fourfold axes. This structure is very sensitive to heat treatments. After slow cooling, the α_2 phase forms the continuous matrix while the α_1 phase is precipitated as relatively well isolated particles (Fig. 12.3.3 (a)). For quenched and tempered alloys it is the contrary (Fig. 12.3.3 (b)). The regions where $\mathbf{M}_s$//[100] are then coupled by exchange

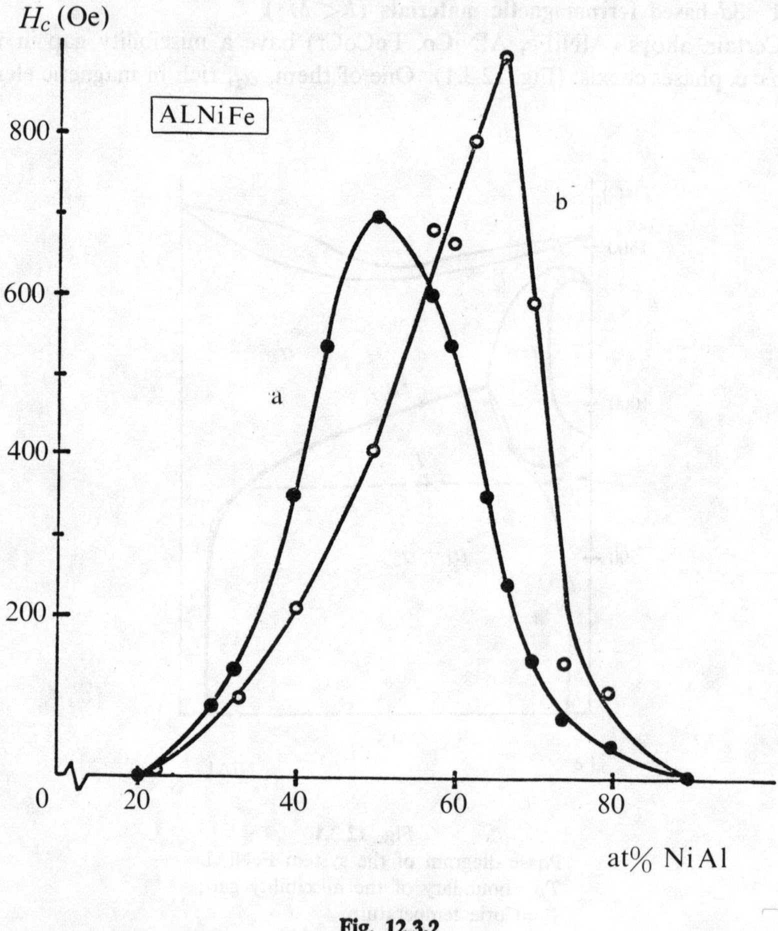

Fig. 12.3.2
Variation of the coercive field with composition in FeNiAl after continuous cooling (a) and quenching followed by tempering (b).

interactions, with regions where $\mathbf{M}_s$//[010] and $\mathbf{M}_s$//[001]. Their presence explains the lower value of H_c observed for the 50% alloy after tempering (Fig. 12.3.2 (b)). Otherwise, decreasing the Fe constant from 50% to 35% must favour the isolation of α_1 particles, leading to an increase of H_c. For smaller Fe contents, H_c tends to zero essentially by thermal activation, the size of α_1 particles becoming very small.

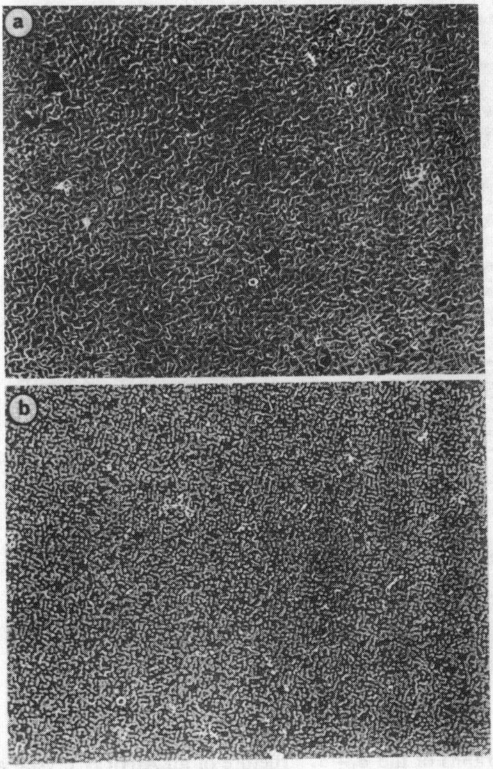

Fig. 12.3.3
Electron micrographs of the $\alpha_1 + \alpha_2$ structure in FeNiAl after continuous cooling (a), and quenching followed by tempering (b).

The maximum coercive field of AlNiFe is reached when ferromagnetic particles α_1 are small enough to be well separated and large enough to keep a strong spontaneous magnetization M_s (and hence shape anisotropy) at room temperature. This is obtained for 50% Fe after slow cooling or for 35% Fe after quenching and tempering. This influence of heat treatment will be discussed in the light of results obtained in AlNiCo.

(b) *AlNiCo*

In those alloys with sufficient Co content, the Curie temperature is raised into or above the 800—850°C temperature range in which the α_1 and α_2 phases separate. Alignment of the precipitates along a single direction by means of a thermomagnetic treatment becomes possible. This phenomenon, giving an elongation of the precipitates along those [100] axes lying near the field direction (Fig. 12.3.4), results essentially from minimisation of the particles' dipolar

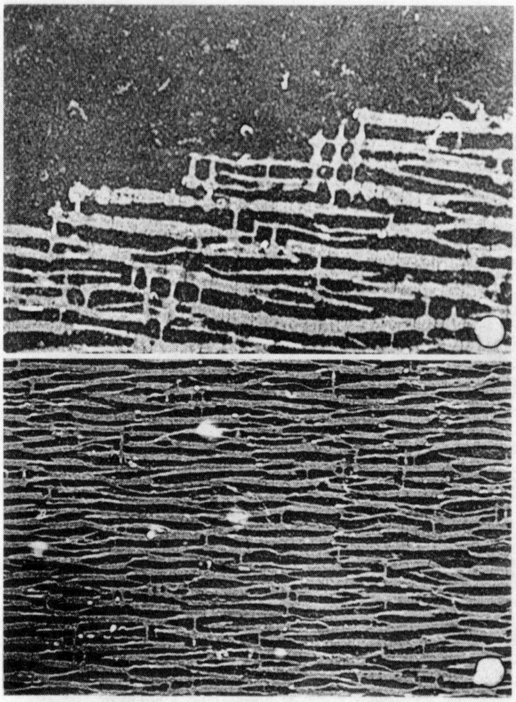

Fig. 12.3.4
Electron micrographs of the $\alpha_1+\alpha_2$ structure of an AlNiCo crystal after isothermal treatment in a magnetic field. Plane parallel to the field direction (a) $\times 5.10^4$ and (b) $\times 10^5$.

energy. The production of a main direction of elongation reduces the disadvantages of cross–links since it minimises their number and size. After quenching and subsequent annealing at 650°C, the coercive field is a maximum and the particles dimensions are 300×300×1200 Å. This coercive field ($H_c \simeq 1$ to 2 kOe) is reached at a temperature which depends on the reheating duration (Fig. 12.3.5). Such a behaviour cannot be understood from the simple idea, developed above, of either fully magnetized or unmagnetized phases. In fact, after quenching the two phases α_1 and α_2 are both ferromagnetic, but their spontaneous magnetizations at room temperature are different, because their Curie temperatures (defined for single phases, Section 12.1.1) are different. In the expression (12.2.1) for H_c, M_s must be replaced by $M_s(\alpha_1)-M_s(\alpha_2)$. When the sample corresponding to Fig. 12.3.5 is not annealed, H_c increases reversibly with temperature up to 450°C. This temperature being close to $T_c(\alpha_2)$, the maximum of H_c corresponds to the maximum value of $M_s(\alpha_1)-M_s(\alpha_2)$. Otherwise this maximum of H_c is shifted towards lower temperatures as the sample is heated (Fig. 12.3.5 (b), (c), (d)). This is due to a diffusion–induced change of composition between the two phases in which Fe (or Co) leaves the less magnetic α_2 phase. In con-

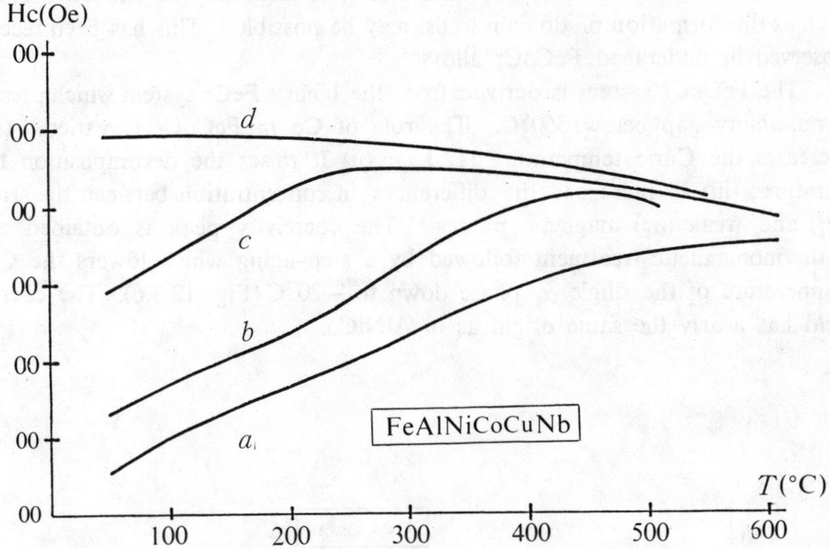

Fig. 12.3.5
Thermal variation of the coercive field in an FeAlNiCoCuNb alloy for different treatments. (a) Cooling from 1250°C; (b), (c) and (d) as (a) plus annealing at about 650°C for respectively 4 hours, 48 hours and 96 hours.

sequence, the Curie temperature of this phase decreases and becomes smaller than room temperature after an anneal of several days of the considered sample.

A similar diffusion process has been observed by Mössbauer spectrometry in Fe_2 NiAl. This enables one to understand the influence of heat treatment on the coercive field of AlNiFe (Section 12.3.1 (a)). In the tempered 50% Fe alloy (Fig.12.3.2 (b)) the Fe content of the α_1 phase is particularly high due to the diffusion induced process. As the gradient of Fe content between α_1 and α_2 particles cannot be infinite (as in a step function), the highest Fe contents in α_1 particles favour union of these particles to give a continuous α_1 matrix. Decreasing the total Fe amount, from 50% to 35%, leads to the isolation of α_1 particles and consequently to an increase of H_c. The maximum coercive field is larger from annealed samples (Fig. 12.3.2 (b)), where α_1 particles are more magnetic, than in the continuously cooled samples (Fig. 12.3.2 (a)).

At the peak coercivity, the magnetization of the α_2 phase is negligible. The expression (12.2.1) for the coercive field may be used. For AlNiCo, $H_c = 0.5 \times 2\pi \times 1800 \simeq 5.6$ kOe. This value is several times larger than the measured ones ($H_c \simeq 1$ to 2 kOe). The discrepancy essentially comes from the persistence of cross-links (12.2.1). It is probably not possible to avoid such defects because a better particle isolation needs the reduction of their size and this is necessarily limited by thermal effects.

In underaged conditions the matrix is ferromagnetic and collective effects, such as the formation of domain walls, may be possible. This has been recently observed in underaged FeCoCr alloys.

The FeCoCr system is derived from the binary FeCr system which presents a miscibility gap below 560°C. The role of Co in FeCoCr is varied. (i) It increases the Curie temperature (12.1.1); (ii) It raises the decomposition temperature; (iii) It increases the differences in concentration between the strong (α_1) and weak (α_2) magnetic phases. The coercivity peak is obtained after a thermomagnetic treatment followed by a step-aging which lowers the Curie temperature of the single α_2 phase down to −20°C (Fig. 12.3.6). The coercive field has nearly the same origin as in AlNiCo.

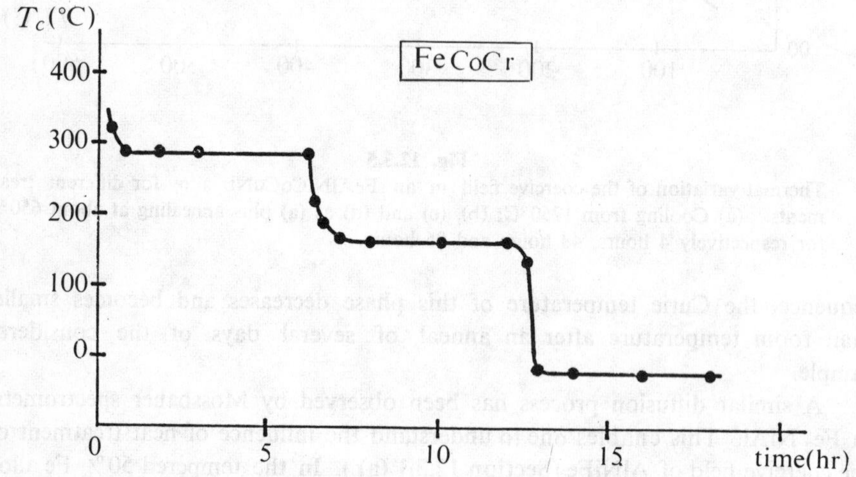

Fig. 12.3.6
Curie temperature of the single α_2 phase of an FeCoCr alloy aged at 640°C, 620°C and 600°C.

After a single aging at 650°C the α_2 phase is ferromagnetic at room temperature. In this case, Fresnel micrographs have revealed the existence of domain walls. The relative position of a wall and the α_1 particles have been determined by overaging at 650° for 50 hours. The size of the α_1 particles, which are about 150 Å at the peak coercivity, are here of the order of 900 Å. The domain wall lies within the α_2 Cr–rich phase (Fig. 12.3.7). In this case the coercive field is small. It results from the presence of FeCo α_1 rich particles which obstruct the motion of the wall, as discussed for Bloch walls in Section 12.2.4.

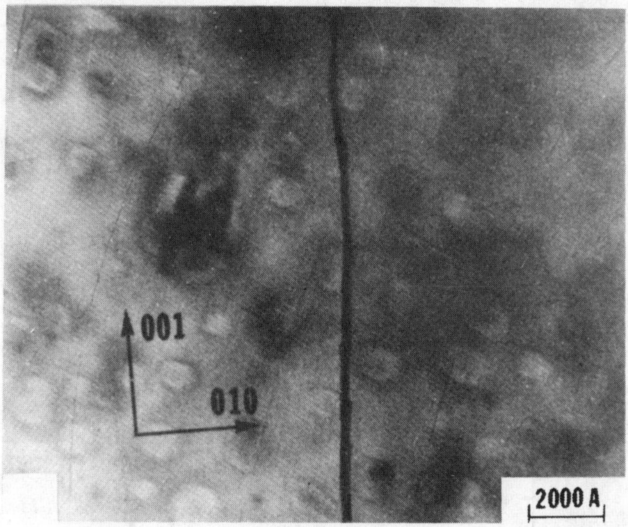

Fig. 12.3.7
Fresnel micrograph of the underaged alloy (650 °C) showing a domain wall, the motion of which is obstructed by the richer in Fe α_1 particles.

12.3.2 4f-based ferrimagnetic materials ($K \gg M_s^2$)

Introduction of copper into $SmCo_5$ and more generally into $SmCo_z$ leads to the formation of magnetically inhomogeneous phases. According to the value of z these alloys are constituted of either a single phase or a mixture of two phases. The single phases $Sm_2(CoCu)_{17}$ or $Sm(CoCu)_{15}$ are observed for z close to 8 or 5 respectively. In the first case the coercive field of a massive sample is very small. High coercivities are only produced after reduction to small single-domain particles. This method is especially used for $SmCo_5$ (Section 12.3.2 (a)). The problems of grinding do not come up in $Sm(CoCu)_z$ alloys with $z \lesssim 8$ where high coercivities are available in massive materials. This property is attributed to Co/Cu segregation in $Sm(CoCu)_5$ and to a mixing of two phases for $5.5 \lesssim z \lesssim 8$ (Section 12.3.2 (b)).

(a) *Sintered particles*

$SmCo_5$—This compound is characterised by a strong magnetocrystalline anisotropy energy ($\simeq 10^8$ erg cm, due to Sm) and important exchange interactions ($\simeq 5 \times 10^9$ erg/cm^3, due to Co). As very few defects are present, the attainment of significant coercive fields requires the reduction of the sample to small particles (Sections 12.1.3, 12.2.2). The hysteresis loops measured on a single particle of $SmCo_5$ show that the magnetization reversal results from Bloch wall nucleations (Section 12.2.2). The coercive field is a maximum (H_c=50 kOe) for powders ranging from 1—10 μm, if they are submitted to a heat treatment at 900 °C terminated by a rapid cooling to room temperature. However, if the particles are cooled slowly from 900°C a drastic lowering of H_c is observed (Fig. 12.3.8) which is accompanied by the formation of a secondary phase, Sm_2Co_{17}. Precipi-

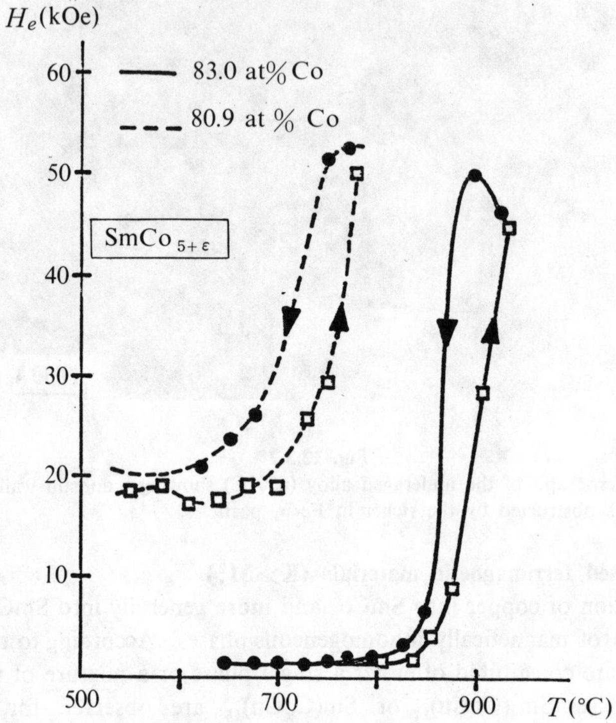

Fig. 12.3.8
Room temperature coercive field of $SmCo_5$ powder as a function of decreasing (O) and subsequently increasing (□) heat treatment temperature.

tates of Sm_2Co_{17} constitute nucleation centres in $SmCo_5$ particles. Such nucleations are effective if the nucleation field associated with a 2:17 defect is larger than its propagation field and hence $r_D/R_D > \Delta\gamma/\gamma_D$. This is always realised for large defects ($R_D \gtrsim 1000$ Å). Otherwise, the wall energy γ_D and the minimum size R_D of these defects, evaluated from the expressions given in Section 12.2.2, are respectively of about 1 erg/cm² and 100 Å in the low coercivity state ($H_N \simeq 1$ kOe) and 14 erg/cm² and 30 Å in the high coercivity state ($H_N \simeq 50$ kOe). Such values of wall energy are much smaller than $\gamma \simeq 100$ erg/cm², the wall energy of $SmCo_5$, excluding eventual nucleations in the pure $SmCo_5$ phase. However, the wall energy, $\gamma \simeq 40$ erg/cm², of the phase Sm_2Co_{17} constituting the nucleations centres is still too large. Sm_2Co_{17} precipitates in $SmCo_5$ are however probably less anisotropic than the compound Sm_2Co_{17} due to many lattice imperfections such as Sm vacancies or local atomic disorder.

The mechanism of formation of Sm_2Co_{17} is generally attributed to the eutectoid transformation of $SmCo_5$ at 800 °C (Fig. 12.3.9). However, a small excess of

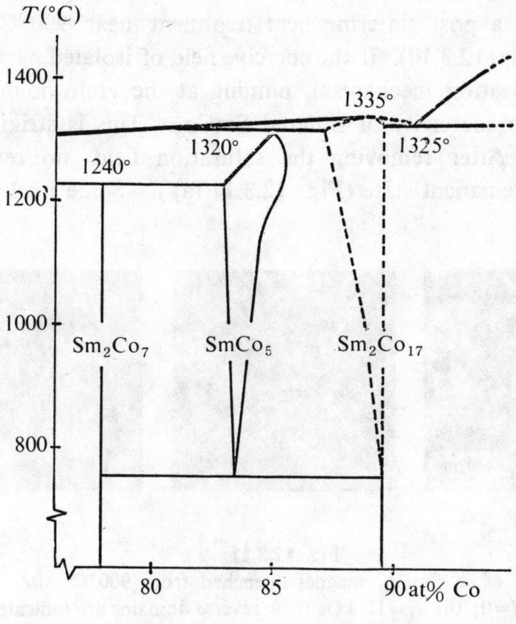

Fig. 12.3.9
Co-rich part of the phase diagram of the Sm–Co system.

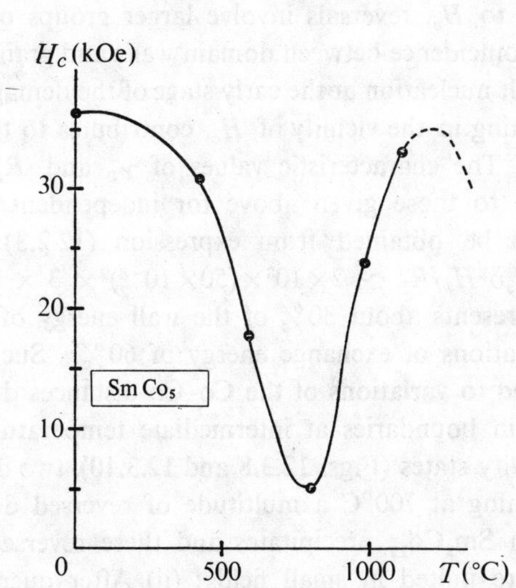

Fig. 12.3.10
Coercive field of $SmCo_5$ as a function of annealing temperature.

Sm shifts the fall of H_c towards lower temperatures suggesting that other mechanisms must be taken into account.

Permanent magnets of $SmCo_5$ can be produced from powders by magnetic aligning and subsequent densification (sintering at 1100 °C). Peak characteristics need a post-sintering heat treatment near 900 °C, followed by water quenching (Fig. 12.3.10). If the coercive field of isolated particles essentially results from a nucleation mechanism, pinning at the grain boundaries plays an essential role in the coercivity of sintered $SmCo_5$. This is strikingly shown by Kerr microscopy. After removing the saturation field, no reversed domains are formed in the remanent state (Fig. 12.3.11 (a)). Some nucleations occur in

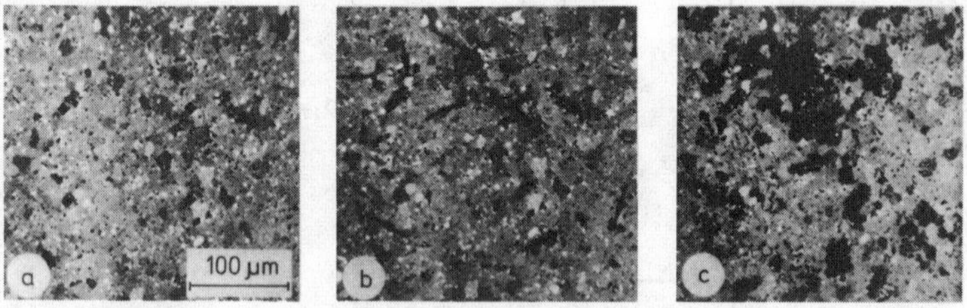

Fig. 12.3.11

Domain patterns of a $SmCo_5$ magnet quenched from 900 °C after application of a reverse field (a) $H=0$; (b) $H=15$ kOe (new reverse domains are indicated by the arrows); (c) $H=20$ kOe.

independent grains but these are limited to the grain boundaries (Fig. 12.3.11 (b)). In higher fields, close to H_c, reversals involve larger groups of adjacent grains and there is always a coincidence between domain walls and grain boundaries (Fig. 12.3.11(c)). The difficult nucleation at the early stage of the demagnetizing curve, as well as the strong pinning in the vicinity of H_c, contributes to the high coercivity of $SmCo_5$ magnets. The characteristic values of γ_D and R_D of the nucleation centres are close to those given above for independent particles. Those of pinning centres can be obtained from expression (12.2.3) To a first approximation, $\Delta\gamma = 2M_s\delta^2 H_p/R_D \simeq 2\times10^3\times(50\times10^{-8})^2\times 3\times10^4/(50\times10^{-8}) \simeq$ 30 erg/cm². This represents about 30% of the wall energy of $SmCo_5$ and corresponds to local variations of exchange energy of 60%. Such variations have been recently attributed to variations of the Co–Co distances due to oxygen segregations towards grain boundaries at intermediate temperatures.

In the low coercivity states (Figs. 12.3.8 and 12.3.10), two different situations exist: (i) After quenching at 700 °C a multitude of reversed domains are spontaneously nucleated in Sm_2Co_{17} precipitates and these reversed domains, which are very numerous, are united in small fields; (ii) After quenching at 1120 °C no reversed domains are formed in the remanent state, but after application of a relatively small field three large domains expending over many grains are immediately formed. In this case the loss of coercivity is due to a reduction of the pinning strength at the grain boundaries. This last can be associated with a dissolution of oxygen in the grains through the occupation of vacant Co sites.

$Sm_2(CoCu)_{17}$—The coercive field of the massive $z=8$ phases is, at room temperature, lower than 1 kOe. This is corroborated by the absence of pinning as shown by the important initial slope of the first magnetization curves. Otherwise, electron micrograph observations show a featureless microstructure. The origin of the coercive field in massive samples is not clear, since the low value of H_c allows several mechanisms to take place at the same time. As an example, the local demagnetizing field associated with surface imperfections cannot be neglected here. Intermediate coercivities (6—8 kOe) are provided from powders by sintering and subsequent heat treatment at 1100°C. The mechanism of coercivity is probably the same as that of sintered $SmCo_5$ (Section 12.3.2 (a)).

(b) *Precipitation alloys*

$Sm(CoCu)_5$—As for magnets of the AlNiCo type, these alloys are coercive in the single-crystal state. However, the origin of the coercive field is different since magnetization reversals here involve nucleation and propagation of Bloch walls (Sections 12.1.3, 12.2.2, 12.2.1). These mechanisms have been observed on a single crystal of $SmCo_{3.5}Cu_{1.5}$ by visualisation of the domain configurations by the Kerr effect. After saturation of the magnetization and reversal of the applied field H, the first reversed domains are nucleated for $H \simeq H_c/2$ (Fig. 12.3.12 (a)). The domains are not numerous suggesting (as for $SmCo_5$ quenched from $T \gtrsim 900$ °C, Section 12.3.2 (a)) a difficult nucleation. However, in $SmCo_{3.5}Cu_{1.5}$, the nuclei are not localized but elongated over several tenths of microns, showing a long-range coherency. In larger fields, domain walls grow slowly and irregularly (Fig. 12.3.12 (b), (c)) showing strikingly the effect of wall pinning. This pinning must be associated with Cu substitutions. The microstructure of the same single crystal of $SmCo_{3.5}Cu_{1.5}$, as that of other as-cast $Sm(CoCu)_5$ alloys, is a modulated single phase resulting from Co/Cu segregations (Fig. 12.3.13). The segregation range, $r_D \simeq 10 \mu m$, is of the same size as $SmCo_5$ particles of sintered magnets (Section 12.3.2). However, the transition regions in $Sm(CoCu)_5$, also of the order of 10 μm, are much larger than the grain boundaries of sintered $SmCo_5$ which are of about 50 Å. The resulting gradient of wall energy in the ternary alloys, $\Delta\gamma/r_D$ (Section 12.2.4), is too small to explain the observed coercive field ($H_c \simeq 15$ kOe). On the other hand, the mean wall energy in Cu-rich regions is much too high (12.2.2) to explain nucleation fields of the order of $H_c/2$. The coercivity of the $z=5$ alloys must be associated with larger variations of wall energy occurring at smaller distances (less or equal to 10^2 Å). This is provided by point defects of exchange resulting from the disordered substitution of Co by Cu. The propagation of exchange from site to site (through the short-range Co–Co interactions) can be either destroyed or only lowered according to the local concentration of Cu. This leads to a narrowing of Bloch walls whose thickness δ is of only one interatomic distance in the first case (Section 12.2.4). The associated propagation field H_p is of the order of some 10^2 kOe.

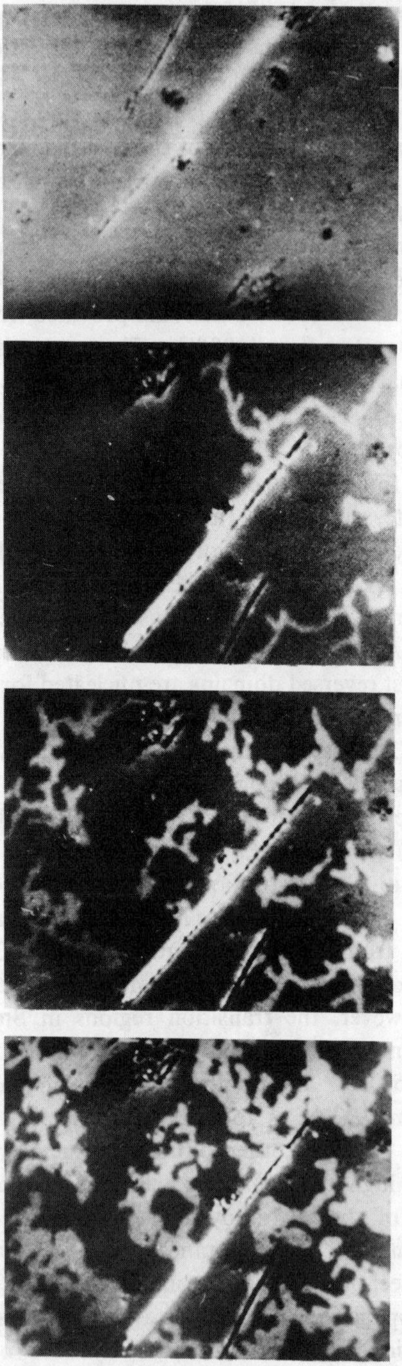

(a)

(b)

(c)

(d)

Fig. 12.3.12
Magnetic domains of a single crystal of $SmCo_{3.5}$ $Cu_{1.5}$ in the plane (100) for different reverse fields (a) $H=0$; (b) $H \simeq H_c/2$; (c) $H \simeq 3H_c/4$; (d) $H \simeq H_c$.

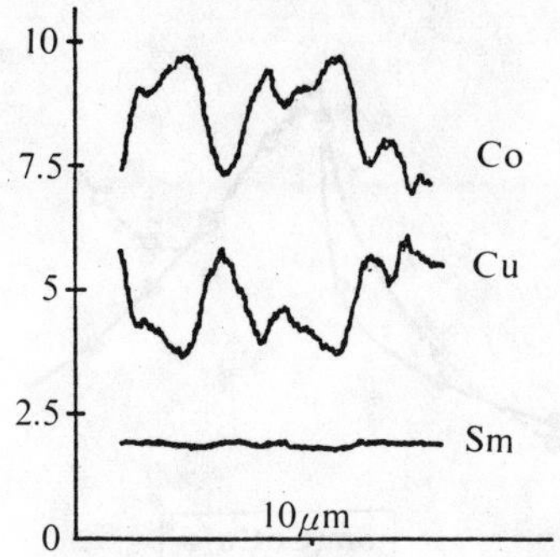

Fig. 12.3.13
Electron microprobe analyser scans across a 1:5 single phase showing constant Sm content and fluctuating Co/Cu ratio.

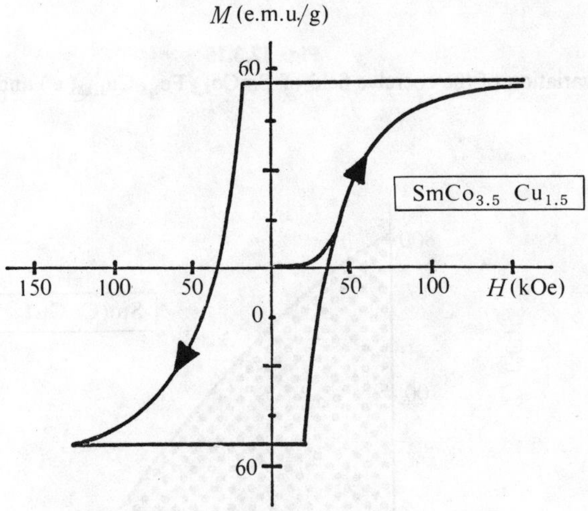

Fig. 12.3.14
Hysteresis loop of a single crystal of $SmCo_{3.5}Cu_{1.5}$. The field is applied along a [001] axis.

In the second case values of H_p of some tenths of kOe are obtained from (12.2.3) for $\Delta\gamma/\gamma \simeq 5$—20%. These propagation fields can be compared with magnetization measurements performed at 4.2 K of up to 150 kOe, on a single crystal of $SmCo_{3.5}Cu_{1.5}$. The scatter of the hysteresis loop shows that the strength of pinning centres is distributed over at least the range 20—150 kOe. At higher temperatures the hysteresis loop narrows, essentially because of the thermal activation (Section 12.2.4).

The influence of annealing on the coercive field of $Sm(CoCu)_5$ alloys is shown in Fig. 12.3.15. The increase of H_c at temperatures $T < 400$°C is generally

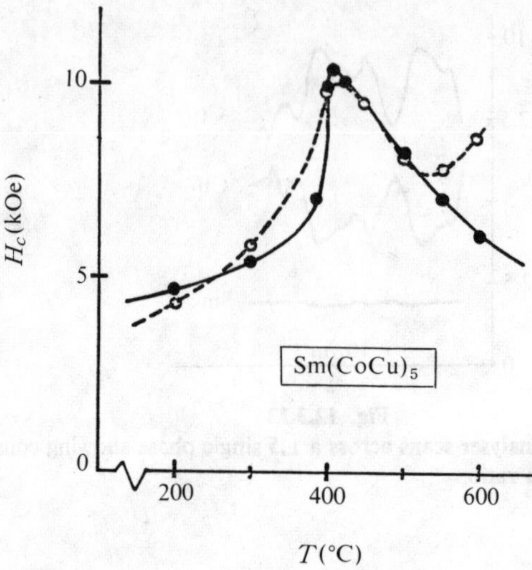

Fig. 12.3.15
Thermal variation of the coercive field of $SmCo_{3.5}Fe_{0.5}Cu_{1.35}$(●) and $SmCo_{3.6}Cu_2$(○).

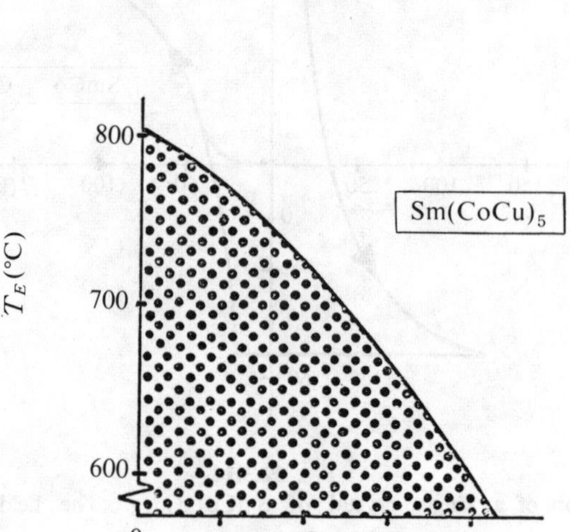

Fig. 12.3.16
Eutectoid transformation temperature sketched in to include the three phase regions in the Sm(CoCu)$_5$ system.

associated either with the growth of rich Cu regions in the 1:5 phase or with the precipitation of a new phase, namely $Sm_2(CoCu)_{17}$. Such precipitates have been effectively obtained after annealing at 400°C in samples of composition close to $SmCo_4Cu$. However, the same heat treatment leaves the Cu–rich alloy $SmCo_3Cu_2$ unchanged. This difference can be compared with the decrease of the upper limit of the eutectoid transformation temperature T_E of $Sm(CoCu)_5$ when the Cu content increases (For 1.2 Cu atom per formula unit, T_E passes from 800°C ($SmCo_5$, Fig. 12.3.9) to 600°C, Fig. 12.3.16. This decrease lowers the velocity of the transformation of the Cu–rich alloys at 400°C. If an anneal at this temperature is sufficient to precipitate the 2:17 and 2:7 phases after four hours, such precipitations may need a much longer time for Cu–rich alloys. This strongly suggests that the coercivity of the $Sm(CoCu)_5$ alloys usually originates from Cu/Co segregation in the 1:5 phase (nucleation and growth of rich Cu regions, eventually spinodal decomposition) for high Cu concentrations and from precipitation of the 2:17 phase for lower Cu concentrations. Overaging at $T >$ 400°C leads to a decrease of H_c (Fig. 12.3.15). This is attributed to too large a segregation range in the first case and to a dissolution of the 2:17 and 2:7 phases in the second case. These mechanisms are no longer valid for z slightly different from 5 because the homogeneity range of the 1:5 phase at $T > T_E$ is relatively narrow. For $6.5 \lesssim z \lesssim 7$, the 2:17 phase can precipitate at $T > T_E$, giving rise to a new maximum of H_c (see next section).

$Sm(CoCu)_z$ with $5.5 \lesssim z \lesssim 7$ — The precipitates of a 2:17 phase observed in a 1:5 matrix under particular conditions (Section 12.3.3 (a)) are extremely fine

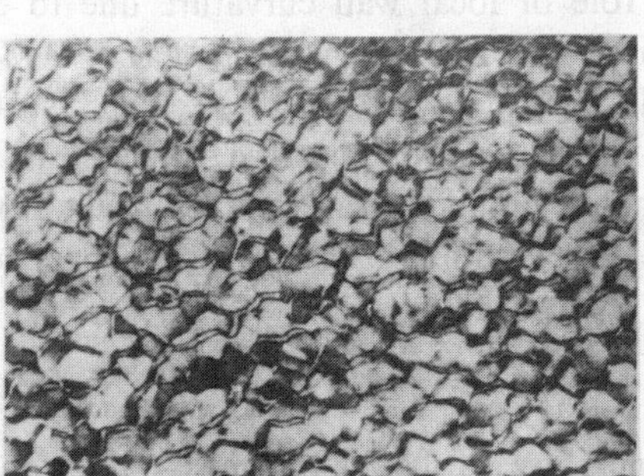

(a)

(b)

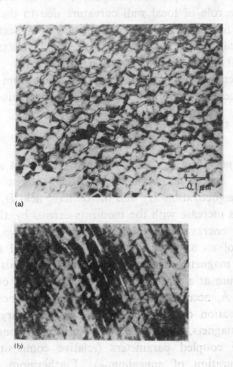

Fig. 12.3.17
Cellular microstructure of a $Sm(CoCuFe)_7$ magnet[69] at peak aged conditions. (a) section normal to [001]; (b) section parallel to [001].

and difficult to characterise. In contrast more recent experiments on sintered $Sm(CoCuFe)_7$ reveal a clearly solvable microstructure at the peak coercivity, H_c=7kOe, obtained after heat treatment at 850°C. Roughly equiaxed cells of about 500 Å (Fig. 12.3.17 (a)) are oblique to the basal plane (Fig. 12.3.17 (b)), i.e. lie along pyramidal planes. The cell interior has the 2:17 structure and the cell boundary the 1:5 one. After slight overaging the cell diameter increases up to about 800 Å and substantial overaging leads to particles of the 1:5 phase in a matrix of the 2:17 phase. At this stage the coercive field is very small and comparable to that of quenched or underaged samples. The microstructure observed after quenching from 1200°C is extremely fine and becomes more resolvable ($\simeq$100 Å) after annealing at 800°C.

These results strongly suggest that the coercivity of $Sm(CoCuFe)_7$ alloys results from the precipitation and growth of the 2:17 phase in a continuous matrix of the 1:5 phase, as seems to be the case for low Cu contents in $Sm(CoCu)_5$ (Section 12.3.2 (b)). However, the mechanism of coercivity is different: if very small precipitates of 2:17 can trap domain walls in $Sm(CoCu)_5$, in the case of $Sm(CoCuFe)_7$ domain walls lie in the 2:17 phase and their motion is obstructed by boundary layers of 1:5 phase in which the wall energy is higher. The value of the propagation field, calculated from $H'_p \propto \gamma_D - \gamma$ (Section 12.2.4, where γ_D is the wall energy in $SmCo_5$ and γ that in Sm_2Co_{17}), is of the order of the measured coercive field. The role of local wall curvature due to thermal fluctuations is not very important here since 500 Å$>[20\,kT/(M_s H_p)]^{1/3}$ (Sections 12.2.2, 12.2.3). However, local wall curvatures due to the cellular structure, i.e. to spatial fluctuations of wall energy, must affect the value of H_c. The low values of H_c observed in overaged or underaged samples result from the dissolution of the 1:5 phase in the first case and from "particle bypass" due to the wall rigidity in the second case.

CONCLUSION

Permanent magnets are probably the most important application of magnetism. The most important parameters that characterise permanent magnets are the remanent magnetization M_R and the coercive field H_c. For a given alloy these two quantities increase with the moments carried by the magnetic atoms and the anisotropy energy, respectively. When the relative composition of the different elements of an alloy changes, M_R is in general simply proportional to the content of magnetic atoms. However, H_c depends sensitively on the metallurgical structure at a fine scale of dimensions: that of the magnetization reversals (500 to 50 Å, according to the value of the magnetocrystalline anisotropy energy). The realisation of such microstructures, necessary for the production of new permanent magnets, is often difficult because their conditions of formation depend on several coupled parameters (relative composition of the alloys, temperature and duration of annealing…). Furthermore, any one type of microstructure does not necessarily give high coercivities, because microstructures mag play two opposing roles in the coercivity. On the one hand they can provide sites for heterogeneous magnetization reversal (AlNiCo, Section 12.3.1) or wall nucleation ($SmCo_5$, Section 12.3.2 (a)) and thereby decrease the coercive field. On the other hand, they can inhibit the wall motion and thereby increase the coercive field (sintered $SmCo_5$, Section 12.3.2 (a), SmCoCu, Section 12.3.2 (b)). Understanding of the exact role of microstructures on the magnetic properties needs a real identification of such microstructures. This is, in general, not easy, due to their small sizes. Larger sizes are obtained by overaging. However, this leads to an abrupt decrease of H_c and the observed microstructures are not necessarily similar to those associated with the peak coercivity cases. An example is the FeCoCr alloy aged at 650°C for 50 h (Section 12.3.1 (c)).

Although all which is given above is necessarily incomplete, it follows that metallurgical transformations play an essential role in the realisation of permanent magnets. However, it is generally difficult to understand in detail and to predict the mechanism of magnetic hardening. This is probably the reason why systematic studies still remain the most efficient method of investigation in this area of magnetism.

REFERENCES

B.D. CULLITY, Introduction to Magnetic Materials, Addison-Wesley, Reading, MA (1972).
A. HERPIN, Theórie du Magńetisme, Presses Universitaires de France, Paris (1968).
L. NEEL, Oeuvres Scientifiques, Editions du C. N. R. S., Paris (1978).
J.J. DE VOS, in Magnetism and Metallurgy, ed. by A.E. Berkowitz, F. Kneller, Academic Press, New York (1969).

CHAPTER 13

INTERMEDIATE VALENCY IN 4*f* SYSTEMS

In certain intermetallic rare–earth compounds, there exists an anomalous intermediate valence phase which is characterised by a variety of anomalies in transport properties, in Mössbauer, photoemission, X-ray and optical absorption spectra, in the neutron cross-section, etc. The common origin of these behaviours is the delocalization of 4*f* states at the Fermi level. However, these 4*f* states are much less delocalized than the transition 3*d* or 5*f* metals. This is the reason why the anomalies are larger in 4*f* alloys, and why they are of great interest.

The intermediate valency phase is separated from the normal phase by more or less sharp boundaries in the *P–T*, *P–V*, *T–H*,··· diagrams.

13.1 REVIEW OF THE PROPERTIES OF NORMAL RARE–EARTH METALS

13.1.1 The number of 4*f* electrons is integral

This leads to a well–defined magnetic moment. In particular, the effective paramagnetic moment:

$$\mu_{\text{eff}} = 2.83\sqrt{C_M} \tag{13.1.1}$$

corresponds to within a few percent with that predicted by Hund's rule:

$$\mu_{\text{eff}} = g_J \mu_{\text{B}} \sqrt{J(J+1)} \tag{13.1.2}$$

The molecular Curie constant is obtained experimentally from the slope of the reciprocal magnetic susceptibility versus temperature:

$$\frac{1}{\chi} = \frac{T+\theta}{C_M} \tag{13.1.3}$$

Such a Curie–Weiss law is observed at temperatures far above θ, the ordering temperature, and Δ, the crystal field splitting. In the expression (13.1.2) the value of J depends on the number n of 4*f* electrons. As an example, Hund's

L=	3	2	1	0	−1	−2	−3
spin ↑	↑	↑					
spin ↓							

rule gives for Pr^{3+}, $J=L-S=(3+2)-2\times\frac{1}{2}=4$. Similarly for Gd^{3+}, $J=L+S=(3+2+1+0-1-2-3)+\frac{7}{2}=\frac{7}{2}$. It is an S state. In Eu^{3+}, $J=(3+2+1+0-1-2)-6\times\frac{1}{2}=0$. The total angular momentum is zero. We must note, however, that a small moment is generally observed in Eu^{3+}, which is due to the mixing with the excited multiplets. In Sm^{3+} and Eu^{3+} the first excited multiplet is less than 2000 K above the ground state multiplet.

Rare earths such as Ce, Sm, Eu, Tm and Yb can take integral valencies different from 3: Ce^{4+} and Sm^{2+}, Eu^{2+}, Tm^{2+}, Yb^{2+}. The measurement of the Curie constant allows an unambiguous identification of n. As an example, for Eu^{2+}, $J=7/2$ and then $\mu_{eff}=7.94\mu_B$. This value is quite different from the almost zero one resulting from Van Vleck mixing in the case of Eu^{3+}. The $4f$ shell of Eu^{2+} may be compared with that of Gd^{3+}. They are both associated with the same value of J (and consequently several physical quantities must be almost equal). However, in Gd the 7 electrons are all well localized because Gd has a supplementary proton. This is not the case for Eu^{2+} and its $4f$ shell is consequently less localized.

In summary, in normal rare earths the occupation number n is integral. The eigenstates of the $4f$ system are then products of eigenstates of the local $4f$ shell. Strong mixing with the conduction band at the Fermi level, which would make n non-integral and introduce an energy width for the correlated $4f$ shell, is not observed. In dilute rare-earth systems, low-temperature susceptibility and EPR measurements put an upper limit of 10^{-3} meV ($\simeq 11\times 10^{-3}$ K$\simeq 0.01$ K) on the mixing width of integral n states of the $4f$ shell. Such rare-earth shells are called stable.

13.1.2 RKKY polarization

The conduction electrons of the metal do of course penetrate the $4f$ shell. Although the resulting interaction does not cause observable mixing (well-defined moment), it leads to a phase shift of the conduction electron waves, i.e. to charge and spin density oscillations (see Chapters 7, 11 and 12). The latter causes the well-known RKKY effects:

- small deviation of the effective $4f$ magnetic moment from the Hund's rule value.
- a several orders of magnitude increase of the $4f$ interaction temperatures compared with an insulator.
- a drastic depression of the transition temperature of superconductors with dilute rare-earth (R. E.) impurities.

The last two effects lead to an ordering temperature T_0 and to a depression of the superconducting temperature $x\, dT_c/dx$ (where x is the R. E. impurity concentration) both proportional, across the R. E. series, to the de Gennes factor $(g_J-1)^2J(J+1)$; g_J and J are the Landé factor and the total angular momentum which are associated with a given value of *n*.

13.1.3 The ionic radius

The third remarkable feature of normal R. E. metals is the apparent existence of a definite volume of the R. E. cell, which depends very strongly on the R. E. valence, but very little on the environment, e.g. on the partners in a compound. The valence is here defined by $V=Z-54-n$, where Z is the atomic number and 54 the number of electrons of the inner shells. n can be determined from the magnetic susceptibility as outlined above. In Fig. 13.1.1, the lattice constant

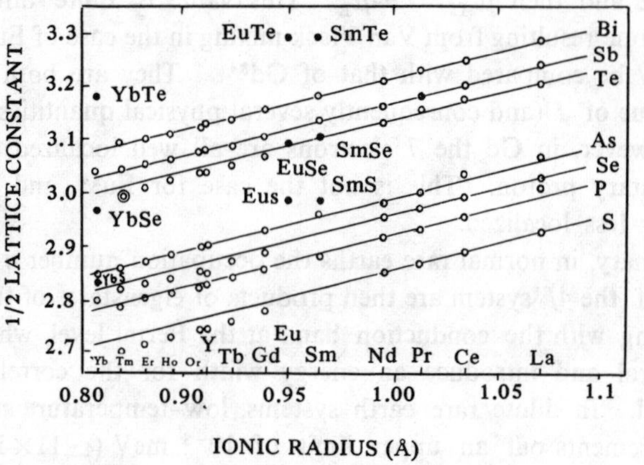

Fig. 13.1.1

of six series of R. E. compounds (the monochalcogenides and monopnictides) are plotted against the ionic radius. For $V=3$, one obtains six nearly straight lines with the same slope (open circles correspond to trivalent, solid dots to divalent configurations according to the magnetic data).

The strong dependence of the lattice constant on the R. E. valency can be understood as a simple atomic screening: the volume of a R. E. atom in the lattice is determined by the radius of the 6*s*–5*d* shell. The radius of the 6*s* and 5*d* shells is about the same and ten times larger than that of the 4*f* shell. Thus the nuclear charge Z' seen by the 6*s*–5*d* shell is in good approximation equal to the valency. A decrease of the 4*f* occupation number n by one (transition of a 4*f* electron to the 5*d* shell) will increase Z' by one. In consequence the 6*s*–5*d* shell will contract abruptly with a concomitant decrease of the average lattice constant of the host metal (cohesion energy). This effect persists (but is less pronounced) when the *s*–*d* electrons are partially delocalized and form bands. Table 13.1.1 gives the electronic configuration of ambivalent rare-earth elements in metals.

Table 13.1.1

R. E.	Configuration	Valency	C_M
Ce	$6s^2\,5d^1\,4f^1$	3	$\neq 0$
	$6s^2\,5d^2$	4	$=0$ ($L=S=0$ as in La)
Sm	$6s^2\quad 4f^6$	2	$=0$ ($L-S=0$)
	$6s^2\,5d^1\,4f^5$	3	$\neq 0$
Eu	$6s^2\quad 4f^7$	2	$\neq 0$
	$6s^2\,5d^1\,4f^6$	3	$=0$ ($L-S=0$)
Tm	$6s^2\quad 4f^{13}$	2	$\neq 0$
	$6s^2\,5d^1\,4f^{12}$	3	$\neq 0$
Yb	$6s^2\quad 4f^{14}$	2	$=0$ ($L=S=0$ as in Lu)
	$6s^2\,5d^1\,4f^{13}$	3	$\neq 0$

13.2 PHASE TRANSITIONS IN INTERMEDIATE VALENCY SYSTEMS

Let us call the configurational ground state energy associated with the number n of $4f$ occupation E_n. As one can see from Table 13.1, Sm can be observed in compounds with either 6 or 5 $4f$ electrons, Eu with either 7 or 6 electrons, etc. This means that for Sm either E_5 or E_6 can be the configurational ground state etc···, depending on the metallic environment. Thus for Sm, E_5 and E_6 cannot be very far from each other.

One way to go from one configuration to the other is by the application of hydrostatic pressure. Obviously, increasing pressure favours the state with smaller n since it is associated with a smaller volume. The intense interest in intermediate valency systems was triggered by resistivity measurements under hydrostatic pressure on the R. E. monochalcogenides (SmS, EuS): at a certain pressure, insulator→metal transitions were observed. These transitions were associated with a $4f$ valence transition, i.e. with delocalization of one electron of the $4f$ shell ($4f \rightarrow 5d$ transition where $5d$'s form a band).. This discovery put into a more general context the pressure–induced $\gamma \rightarrow \alpha$ transition in metallic cerium which had been known for a long time.

Table 13.2.1 lists some of the more important pressure–induced $4f$ valence transitions, their critical pressure, the order of the transition and whether the transition is of metal → metal type (m → m) or non–metal → metal type (nm → m).

Similar transitions can be induced by "lattice pressure" (or chemical pressure), i.e. by alloying the system into a ternary one. Thus any partner of a given compound (e.g. S in SmS) can be replaced by a chemically similar element (e.g. As) with smaller volume with slowly increasing concentration x ($SmS_{1-x}As_x$). The resultant reduction of the lattice constant reduces the volume available to the ambivalent element and leads eventually to a valence change at a critical composition x_c. One can also say that when x increases, the volume available for the 6*s*–5*d* electrons of the ambivalent element decreases, and then it becomes necessary for these electrons to come closer to the nucleus. For that, the effective >0 charge Z' must increase, and a 4*f* electron passes into the 5*d* band. The third possible way to induce valence transitions is by variation of temperature. The best known case is again the $\gamma \rightarrow \alpha$ transition in cerium.

Table 13.2.1

System	P_o (kbar)	Order	Character
Ce	7.5	I	$M \rightarrow M$
SmS	6.5	I	$NM \rightarrow M$
SmSe	30	II	$NM \rightarrow M$
SmTe	50	II	$NM \rightarrow M$
TmTe	20	II	$NM \rightarrow M$
YbTe	150	II	$NM \rightarrow M$
CeP	100	I	$M \rightarrow M$
EuO	300	I	$NM \rightarrow M$
$CeAl_2$	65	?	$M \rightarrow M$

These transitions, whether induced by hydrostatic pressure, lattice pressure or temperature, never went all the way from one state to the next state of integral valence. This is quite apparent from the susceptibility and the lattice constant, both of which are found to be intermediate between their expected values at the adjacent states *n* and *n*−1. Figs. 13.2.1 and 13.2.2 show as examples the susceptibility of

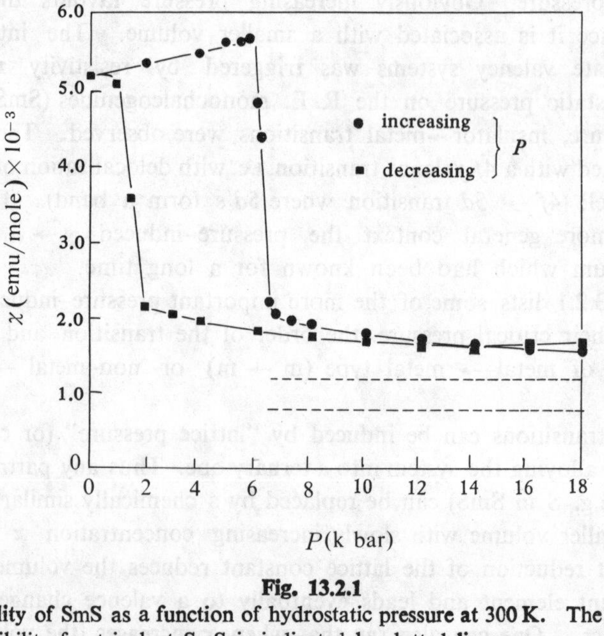

Fig. 13.2.1
Susceptibility of SmS as a function of hydrostatic pressure at 300 K. The expected range of susceptibility for trivalent SmS is indicated by dotted lines.

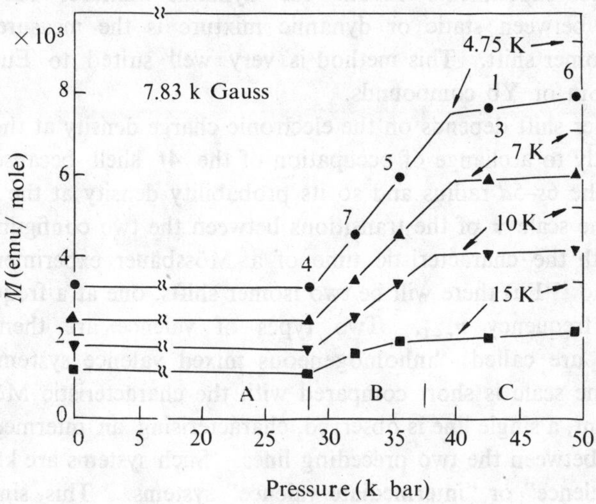

Fig. 13.2.2
Susceptibility of TmTe as a function of hydrostatic pressure at various temperatures. Pressure was varied in 8 steps, as indicated by numbers ($P=0$ at steps 2 and 8). Note reversibility. Susceptibility expected of trivalent TmTe is indicated on right hand ordinate for each temperature. Two *IV* phases (*B* and *C*) can be distinguished.

SmS and TmTe under hydrostatic pressure. The transitions start from Sm^{2+} and Tm^{2+}. In SmS it is of first order, and in TmTe of second order. The expected range of values for fully trivalent Sm^{3+} and Tm^{3+} is indicated in the high-pressure phase.

The existence of mixed valence phases is obvious in these two examples. In the first case the valence can be evaluated as 2.9 after the transition and in the second case there are two different regions of intermediate valence (*B* and *C*). The intermediate valence state cannot be avoided in a valence transition nor does any experiment so far indicate clearly a complete traversing of the intermediate valence phase from one integral to the next integral valence state (i.e. from a stable 4*f* shell with occupation number n to the next state with occupation number $n-1$).

13.3 STATIC AND DYNAMIC MIXTURES

The intermediate or mixed valence states can be visualised as a static or a dynamic mixture of the two configurations in question (n and $n-1$ electrons). In the static mixture the two configurations exist on different distinct sites for infinite time.

In the dynamic mixture each rare–earth site looks identical in time average, while the local state is best described by n at one time and $n-1$ at another. One must then associate a characteristic time scale τ with the temporal motion of the two configurations.

In general, experiments favour the dynamic mixture. An unequivocal tool to decide between static or dynamic mixture is the measurement of the Mössbauer isomer shift. This method is very well suited to Eu compounds, and also to Sm or Yb compounds.

The isomer shift depends on the electronic charge density at the nucleus and reacts distinctly to a change of occupation of the 4*f* shell because this causes a change of the 6*s*–5*d* radius and so its probability density at the nucleus.

If the time scale τ of the transitions between the two configurations is long compared with the characteristic time of a Mössbauer experiment (2×10^{-8} s with ^{149}Sm and ^{151}Eu) there will be two isomer shifts, one at a frequency ν_n and another at a frequency ν_{n-1}. Two types of valence are then identifiable. Such systems are called: "inhomogeneous mixed valence systems".

If the time scale is short compared with the characteristic Mössbauer time of measurement, a single line is observed, characterising an intermediate valence. This line lies between the two preceding lines. Such systems are known as "homogeneous valence" or "intermediate valence" systems. This single line has been observed by Mössbauer experiments performed in SmB_6, $EuCu_2Si_2$ and SmS. Its existence confirms the dynamic mixtures in these compounds and puts an upper limit of about 10^{-11} s for the lifetime of the individual configurations.

It should be emphasised that the physical origin of this single line is a fast charge fluctuation. It is not excluded that the alloyed elements do not play an important role in this mechanism of charge fluctuations of the 4*f* configuration. On the other hand, there are no appreciable differences between the single lines at 300 K or at 4.2 K. This shows that the dynamic mixture cannot be primarily driven by thermal excitations: it is a property of the ground state of these compounds.

For homogeneous or inhomogeneous valences in rare–earth compounds, with which we are concerned here, XPS experiments have clearly shown that there are only two unstable configurations n and $n-1$. The description of an intermediate valence state does not need more configurations. In Fig. 13.3.1, we have plotted the experimental and theoretical XPS spectra of SmB_6.

For a suitable range of energy of the exciting photons, the great majority of the photo–electrons which are emitted originate from the 4*f* shell. Each initial 4*f* configuration creates a unique spectrum of photoelectrons. In Fig. 13.3.1, there are two, and only two, such spectra characteristic of 4*f* photo–electrons from the initial $4f^5$ and $4f^6$ configurations. The calculated intensity assumes the average valence value $\bar{V}$ obtained by the intermediate lattice constant, by the position of the Mössbauer line and by the intermediate value of the susceptibility.

Note: XPS, is X–ray Photoemission spectroscopy. There is also a similar technique UPS, where X–rays are replaced by ultraviolet light.

The specimen (50 Å in depth) is irradiated with highly monochromatised X–rays or ultraviolet photons. The photon is absorbed with the emission

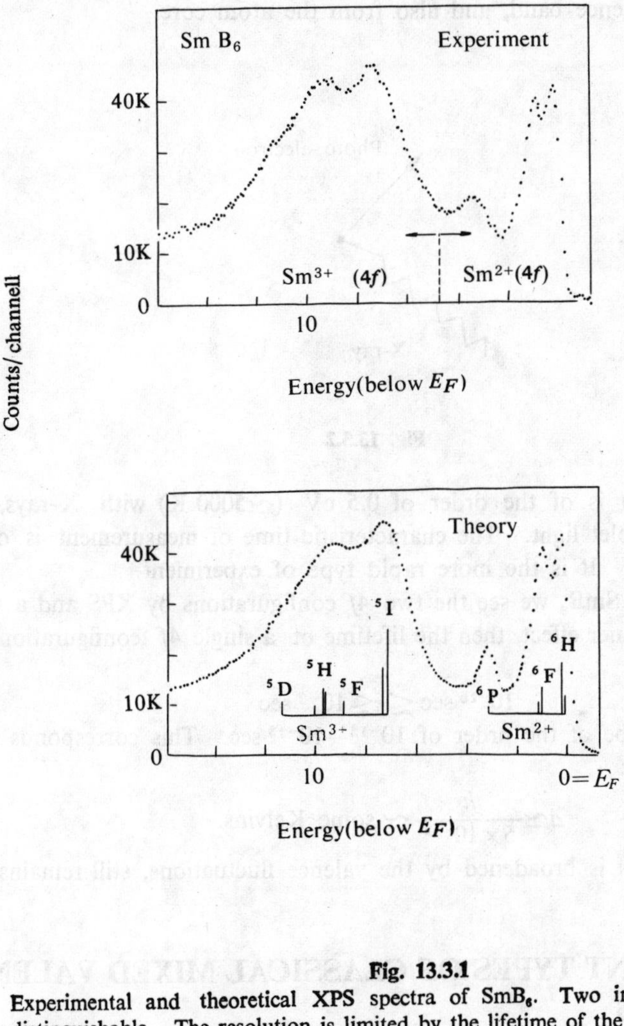

Fig. 13.3.1

Experimental and theoretical XPS spectra of SmB_6. Two initial configurations are distinguishable. The resolution is limited by the lifetime of the final XPS state. Ratio of initial Sm^{3+} to Sm^{2+} is 6:4.

of a photoelectron whose kinetic energy is equal to the energy of the incident photon minus the binding energy of the electron in the solid. These electrons come from the valence band, and also from the atom core.

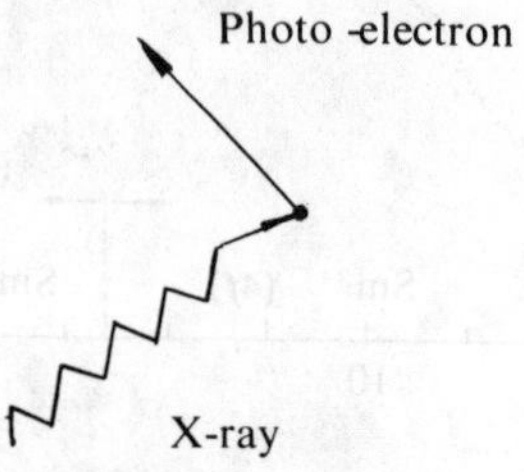

Fig. 13.3.2

The resolution is of the order of 0.5 eV ($\simeq$5000 K) with X-rays, and better with ultraviolet light. The characteristic time of measurement is of the order of 10^{-15} sec. It is the more rapid type of experiment.

In the case of SmB_6 we see the two $4f$ configurations by XPS and a single line by the Mössbauer effect, then the lifetime of a single $4f$ configuration τ is such that:

$$10^{-15}\ \text{sec} \lesssim \tau \lesssim 10^{-8}\ \text{sec}$$

They turn out to be of the order of 10^{-12}—10^{-13} sec. This corresponds to an energy uncertainty:

$$\Delta \simeq \frac{h}{5\times 10^{-12}} \simeq \text{some Kelvins.}$$

The $4f$ level, which is broadened by the valence fluctuations, still remains very narrow.

13.4 DIFFERENT TYPES OF CLASSICAL MIXED VALENCE SYSTEMS

13.4.1 SmS

This compound has been particularly studied. It displays a dramatic phase transition as we saw at P=6.5 kbar. At atmospheric pressure the compound has Sm^{2+} and S^{2-} ions in a NaCl lattice. The ground state multiplet of the $4f^6$ configuration is non-magnetic (Hund's rule). $Sm^{2+}S^{2-}$ presents then only a weak Van Vleck paramagnetism (the first excited multiplet being at only 420 K). The compound is black in colour and semiconducting due to a narrow energy gap ($\simeq$0.1 eV$\simeq$1000 K) between the $4f$ levels and the empty $5d$–$6s$ band of conduction. The band in the $4f$ level scheme as deduced from reflectivity experiments is shown in Fig. 13.4.1. On application of pressure, the gap changes at a rate of 10 meV/kbar due to an increase in the crystal field splitting of the e_g and t_{2g} peaks of the $5d$ conduction electrons. At 6.5 kbar there is a discontinuous collapse with a volume decrease of about 13%, a change from semiconductor to metal, and a colour change from black to gold, but no change in crystal structure. The obvious interpretation that one f electron per ion has been delocalized to give normal metallic $Sm^{3+}S^{2-}$ plus conduction electrons does not correspond to the observed behaviour in this new phase. As a matter

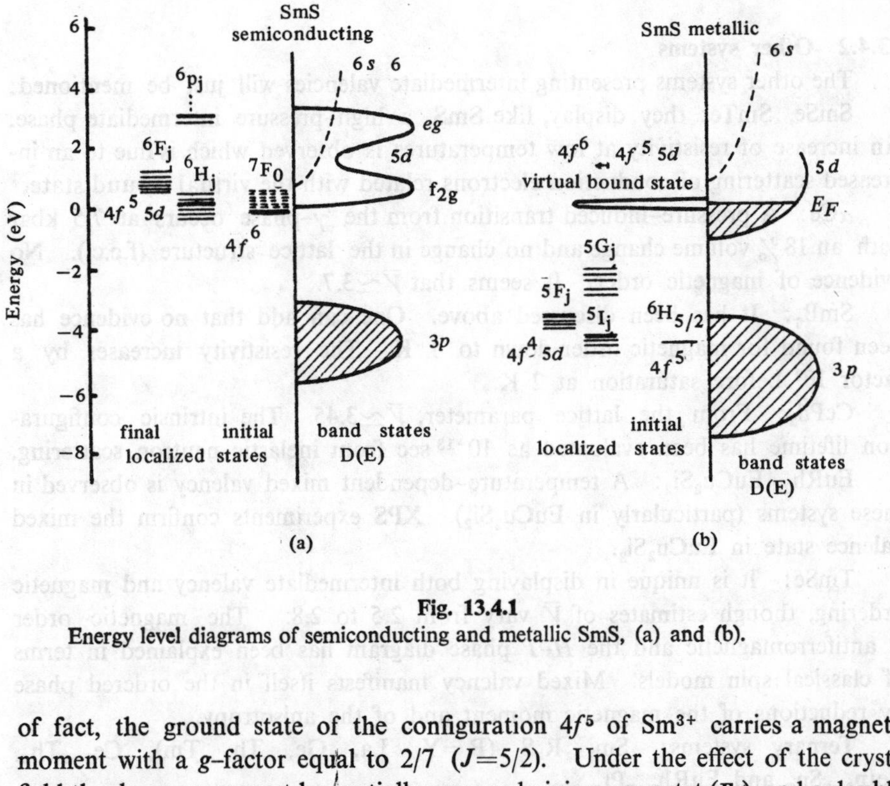

Fig. 13.4.1
Energy level diagrams of semiconducting and metallic SmS, (a) and (b).

of fact, the ground state of the configuration $4f^5$ of Sm^{3+} carries a magnetic moment with a g–factor equal to 2/7 ($J=5/2$). Under the effect of the crystal field the degeneracy must be partially removed giving a quartet (Γ_8) and a doublet (Γ_7). However, the gold phase of SmS is magnetically rather inert having a rather flat $\chi(T)$ curve and no evidence of magnetic order at low temperatures. We have seen in Section 13.2 that susceptibility experiments indicate an intermediate valence state for pressures larger than 6.5 kbar. This is confirmed by the large γ (electronic specific heat), $\gamma \simeq 145$ mJ/mole K^2 (about ten times the normal value in rare earths, indicating an increase of the density of states at the Fermi level), and particularly by XPS experiments on alloys of the type $Sm_{1-x}R_xS$ (where R=Y, Gd, Tb). Two peaks have been identified which are characteristic of the coexistence of Sm^{2+} and Sm^{3+}. The measured static lattice parameter has been found intermediate between that expected for these two valence states. From the areas under the XPS peaks the ratio of Sm^{3+} to Sm^{2+} is obtained. It is in the range 2.6—3.

Mössbauer measurements of the isomer shift reveal, as shown for SmB_6, a further aspect of the valency in the SmS type of compounds. In $Sm_{1-x}Y_xS$ a single line intermediate between that expected for Sm^{2+} and Sm^{3+} is observed. Thus the lifetime τ of a particular ionic state is shorter than the time scale of the Mössbauer effect and XPS experiments show that in SmS, $10^{-15} \leqslant \tau \leqslant 10^{-8}$ sec, as for SmB_6. The corresponding 4f broadened level width is of the order of some tenths of Kelvins. It forms a virtual bound state at the Fermi level (see Fig. 13.4.1).

13.4.2 Other systems

The other systems presenting intermediate valencies will just be mentioned:

SmSe, SmTe: they display, like SmS, a high–pressure intermediate phase. An increase of resistivity at low temperatures is observed which is due to an increased scattering of conduction electrons related with the virtual bound state.

αCe: A pressure–induced transition from the γ–phase occurs at 7.5 kbar with an 18% volume change and no change in the lattice structure (f.c.c.). No evidence of magnetic order. It seems that $\bar{V} \simeq 3.7$.

SmB_6: It has been discussed above. One can add that no evidence has been found for magnetic order down to 1 K. The resistivity increases by a factor 10^3 before saturation at 2 K.

$CePd_3$: From the lattice parameter, $\bar{V} \simeq 3.45$. The intrinsic configuration lifetime has been evaluated as 10^{-13} sec from inelastic neutron scattering.

$EuRh_2$, $EuCu_2Si_2$: A temperature–dependent mixed valency is observed in these systems (particularly in $EuCu_2Si_2$). XPS experiments confirm the mixed valence state in $EuCu_2Si_2$.

TmSe: It is unique in displaying both intermediate valency and magnetic ordering, though estimates of $\bar{V}$ vary from 2.5 to 2.8. The magnetic order is antiferromagnetic and the H–T phase diagram has been explained in terms of classical spin models. Mixed valency manifests itself in the ordered phase by reductions of the magnetic moment and of the anisotropy.

Ternary systems: $Sm_{1-x}R_xS$ (R=Y, La, Ge, Th, Tm), $Ce_{1-x}Th_x$, $CeIn_{3-x}Sn_x$ and $EuRh_{2-x}Pt_x$.

Compounds having integral valence (at the experimental uncertainties): $CeAl_3$ and $CeAl_2$. Their properties have been interpreted from the concept of a "Kondo lattice". $CeAl_3$ does not present any magnetic order, whereas $CeAl_2$ orders at a low temperature. The magnetic moments are reduced in the ordered phase due to the Kondo fluctuations. However, such properties are sometimes correlated with some valence fluctuations, although XPS indicates a 3+ state.

REFERENCES

A. C. HEWSON, *J. Mang. Mang. Mater.*, **12**, 83 (1979) and references therein.

CHAPTER 14
MAGNETIC PHASE TRANSITIONS

The concept of the molecular field has been introduced in Chapter 3, where its usefulness has been demonstrated. We will use this as an introduction to the Landau theory model of phase transitions, but it will be seen later on that such a model fails very close to the transition itself.

Let us consider a simple ferromagnet; the macroscopic magnetization is given by:

$$M = Nm_0\mathscr{B}_\infty\left(\mu_0\frac{KM}{kT}\right) \tag{14.0.1}$$

where $\mathscr{B}_\infty(x)$ is the Langevin function (Section 3.2.1) and $H_M = KM$ is the mole-onlar field, m_0 is the individual magnetic moment. It has been shown (see (3.2.8)) that below a critical temperature $T_c = \dfrac{KNm_0^2}{3k}$, (14.0.1) has a non-zero solution in addition to the trivial solution $M=0$; for $T>T_c$ only the trivial solution is found. Therefore we can distinguish two phases: for $T>T_c$, there is no magnetization, we are in the paramagnetic phase. At $T<T_c$ a finite magnetization M develops: we are in the ferromagnetic phase whose free energy is lower than the paramagnetic phase. When going close to T_c from below, M vanishes continuously as:

$$M \sim (T_c - T)^{1/2} \tag{14.0.2}$$

The two phases are not basically different, but at low temperatures ($T<T_c$) the existence of finite M breaks the symmetry of the high temperature paramagnetic phase: the ordered phase is not invariant under time reversal anymore. This change in symmetry is characterised by M, which is called the order parameter. In our case, the order parameter M goes continuously down to zero at $T=T_c$: the transition is said to be of second order. In general, phase transitions can be grouped into two main categories: first-order (discontinuous) transitions and second-order (continuous) transitions. In the first part of this chapter, we will discuss the order of phase transitions by using the Landau symmetry arguments, then it will be seen that Landau theory leads to incorrect results near T_c, because it neglects fluctuations and critical effects. Finally, we will briefly present some aspects of the renormalisation group symmetry arguments.

14.1 LANDAU THEORY OF SECOND-ORDER TRANSITIONS

The Landau theory of phase transitions imposes restrictions on the possible changes in symmetry that can occur at a second-order phase transition.

First of all, it must be pointed out that continuous transitions cannot take place between phases which have qualitatively different symmetries, such as a solid and a liquid phase; these transitions are discontinuous by nature. If the two phases have qualitatively similar symmetry, we must determine the order parameter, which is zero in the disordered phase and finite in the ordered phase, and which characterises the change in symmetry. The critical behaviour is derived by expanding the free energy in terms of the order parameter.

14.1.1 Order parameter

Let G_0 be the crystallographic space group of the crystal in the paramagnetic phase ($T > T_c$) and R the group which has E and time reversal as elements. The magnetic space of the paramagnetic phase is the direct product of the groups G_0 and R, ($G_0 \times R$). In the case of magnetic phase transitions, we are interested in the magnetization at a given point in the lattice, which can be expanded as a linear combination of the basis functions of the irreducible representations of $G_0 \times R$. In the case of a non-Bravais lattice of magnetic ions, we have:

$$\mathbf{M}(\mathbf{R}_l) = \sum_{q,j,\alpha} \boldsymbol{\varphi}_q(j, \alpha)\exp(i\mathbf{q}\cdot\mathbf{R}_l)$$

with

$$\boldsymbol{\varphi}_q(i,\alpha) = \sum_i \mathbf{m}_q^i(j, \alpha)\exp(i\mathbf{q}\cdot\mathbf{R}_l) \qquad (14.1.1)$$

The index i denotes the Bravais lattices; the Fourier components $\boldsymbol{\varphi}_q(j,\alpha)$ transform as irreducible representations $\Gamma^j_{\{q\}}$ of G_q, the group of the vector $\mathbf{q}$. Since $\mathbf{M}(\mathbf{R}_l)$ is real, $+\mathbf{q}$ and $-\mathbf{q}$ must be associated with $\mathbf{m}_{-q} = \mathbf{m}_q^*$. The identity representation is not included in (14.1.1), otherwise $\mathbf{M}(\mathbf{R}_l)$ would be non-zero in the paramagnetic phase (the two phases would have the same symmetry).

Since we are dealing with a second-order phase transition, $\mathbf{M}(\mathbf{R}_l)$ can be taken as vanishingly small near T_c and we assume that the thermodynamical potential ϕ can be expanded in terms of $\mathbf{M}$, i.e. in terms of the $\boldsymbol{\varphi}_q(j, \alpha)$. The potential ϕ is invariant under any symmetry operation of $G_0 \times R$. We can write:

$$\phi(\mathbf{H},T,\mathbf{M}) = \phi_0(\mathbf{H},T) + \phi_1(\mathbf{H},T,\mathbf{M}) + \phi_2(\mathbf{H},T,\mathbf{M}) + \cdots \qquad (14.1.2)$$

Where the ϕ_i are invariants of the i-th order in the $\boldsymbol{\varphi}_q(j,\alpha)$. The ϕ_i and $\boldsymbol{\varphi}_q(j,\alpha)$ are functions of the external fields such as magnetic field, temperature. The linear term ϕ_1 must be zero because the identity representation is not included in (14.1.1). There is only one second-order invaiiant for all representations; it is the quadratic from:

$$\sum_{\alpha=1}^{d_j} |\boldsymbol{\varphi}_q(j, \alpha)|^2 \qquad (14.1.3)$$

where d_j is the dimension of $\Gamma^j_{\{q\}}$. Thus ϕ_2 is written as:

$$\phi_2(\mathbf{H},T,\mathbf{M}) = \sum_{q,j} A_{qj}(\mathbf{H}, T) \sum_\alpha |\boldsymbol{\varphi}_q(j,\alpha)|^2 \qquad (14.1.4)$$

$$\phi = \phi_0 + \phi_2 + \cdots$$

At $T = T_c$, all the $\boldsymbol{\varphi}_q(j,\alpha)$ are zero. Now let us discuss the sign of the A_{qj}.

For $T>T_c$, ϕ has a minimum for all $|\varphi_q(j,\alpha)|=0$; this means that the A_{qj} are positive. However, if we had $A_{qj}>0$ at $T=T_c$, this would imply that, at a temperature slightly lower than T_c, the A_{qj} would still be strictly positive, and we would not have a phase transition. As a consequence, at least one coefficient A_{qj} $(\mathbf{H},T)$ must vanish at T_c. However, we must point out that only one A_{qj} $(\mathbf{H},T)$ vanishes at $T=T_c$; indeed two coefficients A_{qj} $(\mathbf{H},T)$ can vanish only at an isolated point in the (H,T) plane; at such a point, several second-order lines intersect (see Section 14.2.1).

Therefore, at a second-order phase transition, only one coefficient A_{qj} vanishes at T_c; below T_c, only the components $\varphi_q(j,\alpha)$, corresponding to the star $\{\mathbf{q}\}$ and the $\Gamma^j_{\{q\}}$, can develop. The change in symmetry is associated with only one irreducible representation of the paramagnetic space group. This is the first Landau condition for a second-order transition.

The coefficients $\varphi_q(j,\alpha)$ are the components of the order parameter. Above T_c, they are zero, below T_c, they take on finite values and they characterise the change in the symmetry. Knowledge of the $\varphi_q(j,\alpha)$ determines the magnetisation density:

$$\mathbf{M}(\mathbf{R}_l)=\sum_{\substack{\mathbf{q}\in\{\mathbf{q}\}\\ \alpha}} \varphi_q(j,\alpha)\exp(i\mathbf{q}\cdot\mathbf{R}_l) \tag{14.1.5}$$

The dimensionality s of the order parameter (i.e. number of components) is given by

$$s=d_q d_j$$

where d_q is the number of $\mathbf{q}$ vectors in the star $\{\mathbf{q}\}$ and d_j the dimension of $\Gamma^j_{\{q\}}$; s can be as high as 48.

Before going any further, we will see how to measure the order parameter.

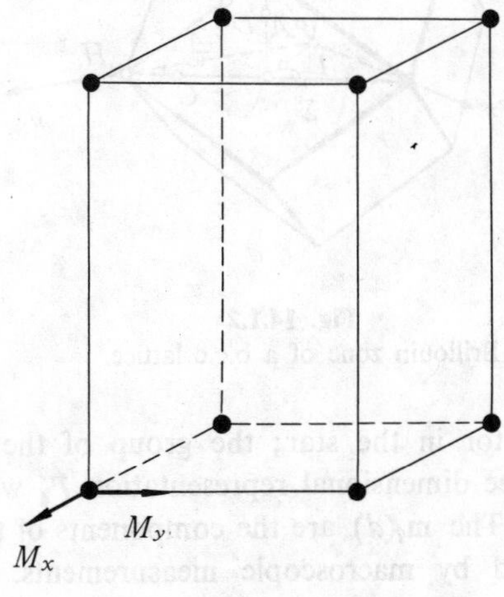

Fig. 14.1.1
Simple tetragonal ferromagnet.

First of all, the star $\{\mathbf{q}\}$, can be obtained from powder neutron diffraction; it characterises the symmetry in translation of the ordered phase. In the case of a Bravais lattice, the $\varphi_q(j,\alpha)$ reduce to the Fourier components of $\mathbf{M}(\mathbf{R})$ which are determined by neutron scattering experiments. In non-Bravais lattices, $\varphi_q(j,\alpha)$ are linear combinations of $\mathbf{M}_q^i$ (Section 14.1.1); the $\varphi_q(j,\alpha)$ can also be obtained from particular reflections in a neutron scattering experiment. If there are several non-equivalent ions, they are considered as different systems with their own order parameters which can order independently (ferrimagnetism).

14.1.2 Examples

We will consider three examples of the ideas that have been presented. First let us consider a simple tetragonal crystal with $G_0=D_{4h}$ (Fig. 14.1.1); below T_c, it orders ferromagnetically (the order parameter belongs to the $\mathbf{q}=0$ representation). In this case the order parameter can be measured by macroscopic measurements, which show that $\mathbf{M}$ lies in the basal plane; $\mathbf{M}$ belongs to the two-dimensional representation of the group of $\mathbf{q}=0$. The order parameter has two components, M_x and M_y.

Now let us consider a crystal with crystallographic space group $G_0=O_h^9$; the Bravais lattice is body centred cubic. We assume that the magnetic order is associated with the H point of the Brillouin zone (Fig. 14.1.2) $\mathbf{q}=(0,1,0)\,2\pi/a$.

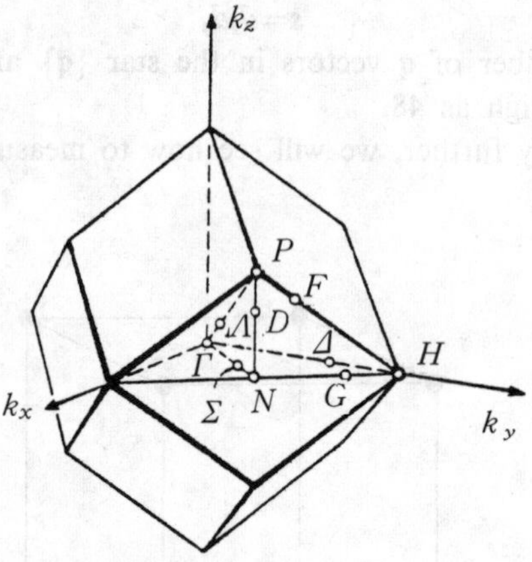

Fig. 14.1.2
Brillouin zone of a b.c.c lattice.

There is only one $\mathbf{q}$ vector in the star; the group of the vector $\mathbf{q}$ is $O_h\times R$. $\mathbf{M}$ transforms as the three dimensional representation Γ_4 whose basis functions are $\mathbf{m}_q(x)$, $\mathbf{m}_q(y)$, $\mathbf{m}_q(z)$. The $\mathbf{m}_q(d)$ are the components of the order parameter, they cannot be measured by macroscopic measurements. The magnetization density $\mathbf{M}(\mathbf{r})$ is given by:

$$\mathbf{M}(\mathbf{r})=(\mathbf{m}_q(x)+\mathbf{m}_q(y)+\mathbf{m}_q(z))\exp(i\,\mathbf{q}\cdot\mathbf{r}) \tag{14.1.6}$$

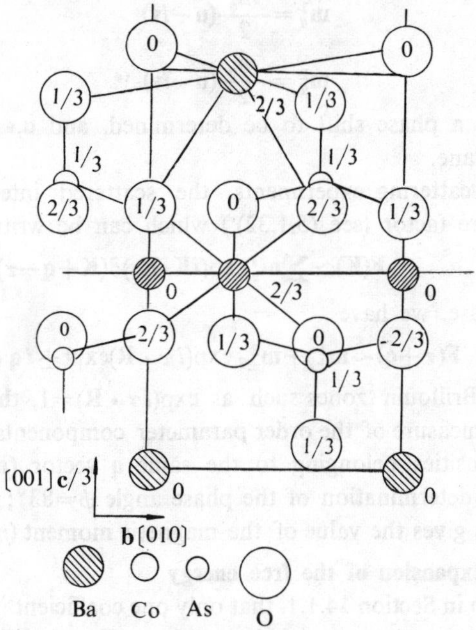

Fig. 14.1.3
Crystallographic structure of $BaCo_2(AsO_4)_2$.

The two sites, A and B, of the b.c.c. lattice have an opposite magnetization:

$$\mathbf{M}_A = \mathbf{M}(0,0,0) = \mathbf{m}_q(x) + \mathbf{m}_q(y) + \mathbf{m}_q(z)$$

$$\mathbf{M}_B = \mathbf{M}(1/2,1/2,1/2) = -[\mathbf{m}_q(x) + \mathbf{m}_q(y) + \mathbf{m}_q(z)] \qquad (14.1.7)$$

Macroscopic measurements yield $\mathbf{M}_A + \mathbf{M}_B = 0$ only; the order parameter is the staggered magnetisation $(\mathbf{M}_A - \mathbf{M}_B)/2$.

As a third example, we describe a non-Bravais lattice: a quasi two-dimensional system $BaCo_2(AsO_4)_2$ (L. P. Regnault, P. Burlet, J. Rossat-Mignod, *Physica*, **86—88 B**, 660 (1977)). The crystallographic space group G_0 of the paramagnetic phase is $R\bar{3}$ $(S_6^2 = C_{3i}^2)$. The structure is shown in Fig. 14.1.3. The Co atoms occupy the $\pm(0, 0, Z/2)$ positions, with $Z \simeq 1/3$. An ordered magnetic phase appears with a propagation vector $(k_x, 0, -4/3)$ with $k_x \simeq 0.26$; this has been observed by neutron scattering experiments. In order to study this phase transition, and also to determine the magnetic structure, we would like to investigate the nature of the order parameter as well as any eventual relationship between the Fourier components of the two Bravais lattices, $\mathbf{m}_q^1$ and $\mathbf{m}_q^2$. The star of $\mathbf{q}$ vectors contains 6 $\mathbf{q}$ vectors. The group of the $\mathbf{q}$ vector is reduced to one element, E; thus the order parameter has 6 components of the form

$$\mathbf{m}_q^1 + \mathbf{m}_q^2 \exp(i\mathbf{q} \cdot \mathbf{R}) \qquad (14.1.8)$$

where $\mathbf{R} = (0, 0, z)$ and $\mathbf{q}$ is one of the 6 $\mathbf{q}$ vectors of $\{\mathbf{q}\}$. From magnetization measurements, it is known that the magnetic moments lie in the basal plane; assuming that the two cobalts have the same magnetic moment, we can write

$$\mathbf{m}_q^1=\frac{m_0}{2}(\mathbf{u}-i\mathbf{v})$$
$$\mathbf{m}_q^2=\frac{m_0}{2}(\mathbf{u}-i\mathbf{v})e^{i\phi} \tag{14.1.9}$$

where ϕ denotes a phase shift to be determined, and $\mathbf{u},\mathbf{v}$ are two orthogonal vectors in the plane.

In neutron scattering experiments, the scattered intensity is given by a magnetic structure factor (see (5.1.32)) which can be written as:

$$\mathbf{F}(\mathbf{K})\simeq\sum\mathbf{m}_q^i\exp(i\mathbf{K}\cdot\mathbf{R}_i)\delta(\mathbf{K}+\mathbf{q}-\boldsymbol{\tau}) \tag{14.1.10}$$

In the present case, we have:

$$\mathbf{F}(\boldsymbol{\tau}\pm\mathbf{q})\sim\mathbf{m}_{\pm q}^1+\mathbf{m}_{\pm q}^2\exp(i\boldsymbol{\tau}\cdot\mathbf{R})\exp(\pm i\mathbf{q}\cdot\mathbf{R}) \tag{14.1.11}$$

Thus, in some Brillouin zones such as $\exp(i\boldsymbol{\tau}\cdot\mathbf{R})=1$, the scattered magnetic intensity gives a measure of the order parameter components $\boldsymbol{\varphi}_q$. Measurements of different intensities belonging to the same $\mathbf{q}$ vector (in fact $\pm\mathbf{q}$ with $\mathbf{m}_{-q}=\mathbf{m}_q$) provide a determination of the phase angle $\phi=83°$; the sum of intensities from all domains gives the value of the magnetic moment ($m=2.9\mu_B$ at $T=0$ K).

14.1.3 Landau expansion of the free energy

We have seen in Section 14.1.1. that only one coefficient A_{qj} $(H,T\cdots)$ vanishes at T_c, while the others remain strictly positive. For simplicity, we will omit, in the following, the indexes q and j. The symmetry group G of the crystal is a subgroup of $G_0\times R$ consisting of those elements which do not change $\mathbf{M}(\mathbf{R})$ in (14.1.5). In order to find the group G, we must know the coefficients $\varphi_{\{q\}}$. However, these coefficients cannot take on any values, since they must minimise the potential ϕ. Let us consider this question. First we will assume that we can normalise the $\varphi_{\{q\}}$:

$$\eta^2=\sum_{\{\mathbf{q}\},\alpha}|\varphi_{\{q\}}(\alpha)|^2,\ \varphi_{\{q\}}(\alpha)=\eta\psi(\alpha) \tag{14.1.12}$$

Landau has assumed that ϕ could be expanded as:

$$\phi=\phi_0+\eta^2A(\mathbf{q},H,T)+\eta^3\sum_a B_a(\mathbf{q},H,T)f_a^{(3)}(\psi(\alpha))$$
$$+\eta^4\sum_a C_a(\mathbf{q},H,T)f_a^{(4)}(\psi(\alpha))+\cdots \tag{14.1.13}$$

At $T=T_c$, $A(\mathbf{q},H,T)$ vanishes, and below T_c, $A(\mathbf{q},H,T)$ is negative, which ensures that ϕ has a minimum for a finite value of η (Fig. 14.1.4). However, this minimum must be stable: the fourth-order coefficient must be positive and no third order should appear; this is the second Landau condition for a second-order transition.

Assuming a positive fourth-order term, let us consider the third-order term. There are two possible cases:

(a) the third-order term does not appear in (14.1.13) by symmetry, this can be formulated as follows:
The symmetric cube $[\Gamma_{\{q\}}^j]_s^3$ does not contain the identity representation of G_0. If $[\Gamma_{\{q\}}^j]_s^3$ contains the identity representation of G_0, then the transition is of first order.

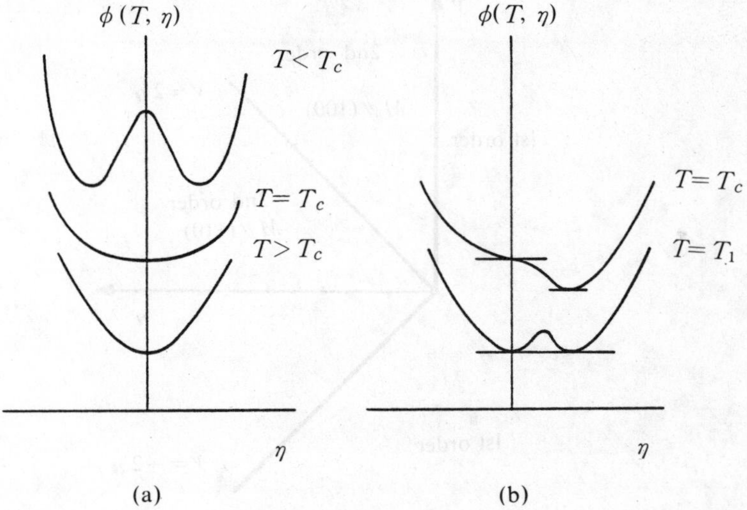

Fig. 14.1.4
The thermodynamical potential ϕ as a function of η at different temperatures.
(a) No third-order term and $C>0$: second-order phase transition;
(b) Existence of a third-order term: first order transition at $T=T_1$.

However, in the case of a magnetic phase transition, with no applied magnetic field, no odd-order term in η (i.e. M) can appear in ϕ because odd-order terms are not invariant under time reversal. This Landau condition does not restrict the number of the possible representations $\Gamma_{\{q\}}^{j}$ for a magnetic phase transition.

(b) There is a third-order term in (14.1.13) but it vanishes at T_c. Again this mean that T_c is special point in the (H,T) plane given by the set of the two equations:

$$A(\mathbf{q},H,T)=0$$
$$\sum_a B_a(\mathbf{q},H,T)f_a^{(3)}(\psi_{\{q\}}(\alpha))=0 \qquad (14.1.14)$$

Such special points are not studied here.

The minimum of ϕ must also be stable with respect to a small change in **q**, if **q** has a special value; by special value, we mean that **q** occupies a special position in the Brillouin zone. If **q** is not in a special position, then it can vary along the critical line $T_c(H_c)$; thus moving **q** is equivalent to changing H, for example. When **q** occupies a special position, the stability around $(\mathbf{q}+\mathbf{k})$ requires that there is no linear term in **k** in the expansion of ϕ; in other words, the anti-symmetric product $\{\Gamma_{\{q\}}^{j}\}^2$ must not contain the vector representation of G_0. This is the Lifshitz condition. From now on, we assume that the $\Gamma_{\{q\}}^{j}$ that we are interested in meet all the necessary but not suffi-

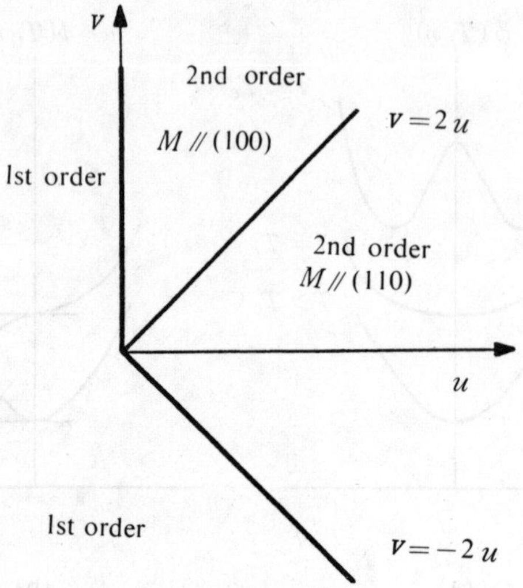

Fig. 14.1.5
Phase diagram for a simple tetragonal ferromagnet (Eq. (14.1.16)).

cient conditions for a second-order transition. Finally we write:

$$\phi=\phi_0+\eta^2 A(\mathbf{q},H,T)+\eta^4\sum_a C_a(\mathbf{q},H,T)f_a{}^{(4)}(\psi(\alpha))+\cdots \tag{14.1.15}$$

The critical behaviour in this model is obtained from (14.1.15); it will be the subject of Section 14.1.4.

The exact symmetry of the ordered phase is given by the set of $\psi(\alpha)$ which minimizes the fourth-order term in (14.1.15). We consider the example of a simple tetragonal ferromagnet (Fig. 14.1.1). The order parameter has 2 components, M_x and M_y; we find that there are 2 fourth-order invariants, $(M_x^4+M_y^4)$ and $M_x^2M_y^2$. The thermodynamical potential is written as:

$$\phi=\phi_0+rM_0^2+uM_0^4(\gamma_x^4+\gamma_y^4)+vM_0^4\gamma_x^2\gamma_y^2 \tag{14.1.16}$$

where

$$M_0^2=M_x^2+M_y^2,\ M_x=M_0\gamma_x,\ M_y=M_0\gamma_y$$

For the transition to be second order, the fourth-order term F_4 must be positive

$$F_4=u+(v-2u)\gamma_x^2\gamma_y^2>0 \tag{14.1.17}$$

with $\gamma_x^2+\gamma_y^2=1$ and ϕ minimum.

If $v-2u>0$, then the minimum of ϕ is obtained for $\gamma_x=0$ (or $\gamma_y=0$) and $M_y\neq 0$ (or $M_x\neq 0$). The magnetic moment is along a (010) direction. But the positiveness of F_4 imposes $u>0$.

If $v-2u<0$, the minimum value of ϕ is $\dfrac{2u+v}{4}$; it is obtained for $\gamma_x^2=\gamma_y^2=1/2$. The order parameter components are coupled together $|M_x|=|M_y|$ and the net moment is along a (110) direction. Again the positiveness of F_4 requires $2u+v>0$. We then arrive at the phase diagram (Fig 14.1.5) in the (u,v) plane.

14.1.4 Critical behaviour in the Landau theory

For the sake of simplicity, we will consider a one-dimensional parameter η. This does not modify the results of the Landau phenomenological theory, which does not take into account the dimensionality of the order parameter explicitly. We rewrite ϕ:

$$\phi=\phi_0+A(\mathbf{q},H,T)\eta^2+C(\mathbf{q},H,T)\eta^4+\cdots \tag{14.1.18}$$

The coefficients, A and C, are assumed to be analytic functions of $T,H\cdots$ Therefore, in the vicinity of T_c, we can put $A(H,T)=a(T-T_c)$ if we consider a constant field transition ——$C(H,T)$ is supposed to be constant. The thermal variation of η near T_c is obtained by minimising (14.1.18) with respect to η. We obtain $\eta(A+2C\eta^2)=0$; hence

$$\eta^2=-\frac{A}{2C}=\frac{a}{2C}(T_c-T) \tag{14.1.19}$$

The solution $\eta=0$ corresponds to a maximum of ϕ (a is positive). Below T_c, we have two solutions $\eta=\pm\sqrt{\frac{a}{2C}}\,|T_c-T|^{1/2}$; these two solutions are identical; they correspond to opposite directions of the magnetization (time-reversal operation). In the theories of critical phenomena, the critical exponent β is defined as:

$$\eta\sim(T_c-T)^\beta$$

In the Landau theory, β takes the classical value $\beta=1/2$.

Let us determine the entropy S in the vicinity of T_c; S is given by $S=-\frac{\partial\phi}{\partial T}=S_0-\frac{\partial A}{\partial T}\eta^2$. In the disordered phase $(T=T_c+\varepsilon)$, $\eta=0$ and $S=S_0$; but in the ordered phase $(T=T_c-\varepsilon)$, $\eta^2=-\frac{A}{2C}$ and

$$S=S_0+\frac{A}{2C}\frac{\partial A}{\partial T}=S_0+\frac{a^2}{2C}(T-T_c) \tag{14.1.20}$$

At $T=T_c$, $S=S_0$, the entropy is a continuous function of T (second-order phase transition).

Now let us turn to the specific heat $C_H=T\left(\frac{\partial S}{\partial T}\right)_H$. In the symmetric phase $(T=T_c+\varepsilon)$, $S=S_0$, thus $C_H=C_{H_0}$. But in the non-symmetric phase $(T=T_c-\varepsilon)$, from (14.1.20) we get $C_H=C_{H_0}+\frac{a^2T_c}{2C}$. At T_c, the specific heat is discontinuous with $C_H>C_{H_0}$: the specific heat increases when going from the disordered to the ordered phase.

Let us consider the isothermal susceptibility χ_T. We introduce an ordering field h which is conjugate to the order parameter η: $h=-\frac{\partial F}{\partial\eta}$. If η is the magnetization of a ferromagnet, then h is the applied magnetic field; if η is the staggered magnetization $\frac{1}{2}(\mathbf{M}_A-\mathbf{M}_B)$ of an antiferromagnet (see Section 14.1.2), then h is a staggered field, pointing upwards at the A sites and downwards at the B sites. In the presence of such a field the potential (14.1.18) becomes:

$$\phi=\phi_0+a(T-T_c)\eta^2+C\eta^4-h\eta \tag{14.1.21}$$

Minimising ϕ leads to the condition

$$2a(T-T_c)\eta+4C\eta^3-h=0 \tag{14.1.22}$$

The isothermal susceptibility is defined as $\chi_T=\left.\frac{\partial\eta}{\partial h}\right|_T$, which gives

$$2a(T-T_c)\chi_T+12C\eta^2\chi_T-1=0 \tag{14.1.23}$$

In the symmetric phase $(T>T_c)$, $\eta=0$; thus

$$\chi_T(T>T_c)=\frac{1}{2a(T-T_c)} \tag{14.1.24}$$

This is the well-known Curie–Weiss law (3.2.9). In the ordered phase, η^2 is given by (14.1.19) which yields

$$\chi_T(T<T_c)=\frac{1}{4a(T_c-T)} \tag{14.1.25}$$

It is seen that χ_T diverges on both sides of T_c with critical exponents $\gamma=\gamma'=1$.

Furthermore, at $T=T_c$, the order parameter varies as:

$$4C\eta^3-h=0 \tag{14.1.26}$$

or $\eta\sim h^{1/3}$ at $T=T_c$, which gives the value for the critical exponent $\delta=3$.

Table 14.1.1

Values of some critical exponents in the Landau theory. The α,γ,ν indices have the same value on both sides of the transition. Experimental values represent some averaged experimental results for magnetic phase transitions

Physical Quantity	Critical Exponent	Definition	Landau Theory	Experimental Values
Specific Heat	α	$C_h\sim\|T-T_c\|^{\alpha}$ $h=0$	$\alpha=0$	$\alpha<0.12,\ T>T_c$ $\alpha<0.16,\ T<T_c$
Order Parameter	β δ	$\eta\sim(T_c-T)^{\beta}$ $\eta\sim h^{1/\delta}, T=T_c$	$\beta=0.5$ $\delta=3$	$\beta\simeq0.34$ $\delta\simeq4.5$
Isothermal Susceptibility	γ	$\chi_T\sim\|T-T_c\|^{-\gamma}$	$\gamma=1$	$\gamma\simeq1.35$
Correlation Length	ν	$R_c\sim\|T-T_c\|^{-\nu}$	$\nu=0.5$	$\nu=0.67$

We have summarised, in Table 14.1.1, the values of some critical exponents predicted by the Landau theory of second-order transitions. If these values are compared with those obtained from experimental results, very little agreement is found except perhaps, when the range of actual interactions is very large. This is because the Landau theory, as has been shown, neglects any fluctuations of the order parameter. Before going into this problem, it is worth summarising the main features of the Landau theory of second-order phase transitions.

First of all, it emphasises the important role of symmetry breaking at T_c, then it selects from among the possible changes in symmetry those which are compatible with a continuous phase transition; in turn if a transition is known to be of second order the Landau theory may help in determining the symmetry (structure) of the thermodynamical potential that has the right symmetry and can be used as a starting point for further developments. This last point is illustrated in the next section.

14.2 MULTICRITICAL POINTS

There are several kinds of multicritical points corresponding to all the special cases that we have encountered when discussing the Landau theory.

14.2.1 Two irreducible representations of G_0 become critical

This is the first isolated point that was mentioned. When applying an external field such as pressure, it may happen that two different A_{qj} coefficients in (14.1.4) become critical at the same temperature.

14.2.2 The fourth-order coefficient vanishes

From (14.1.15) it is clear that the coefficient of η^4 must be positive. A tricritical point (TCP) appears in the (H,T) plane if

$$\begin{aligned} &A(\mathbf{q},H_t,T_t)=0 \\ &C(\mathbf{q},H_t,T_t)=\sum_a C_a(\mathbf{q},H_t,T_t) f_a^{(4)}(\psi(\alpha))=0 \end{aligned} \qquad (14.2.1)$$

At this point, T_t, the Landau expansion must be carried on a step further:

$$\phi=\phi_0+A\eta^2+D\eta^6-h\eta+\cdots \qquad (14.2.2)$$

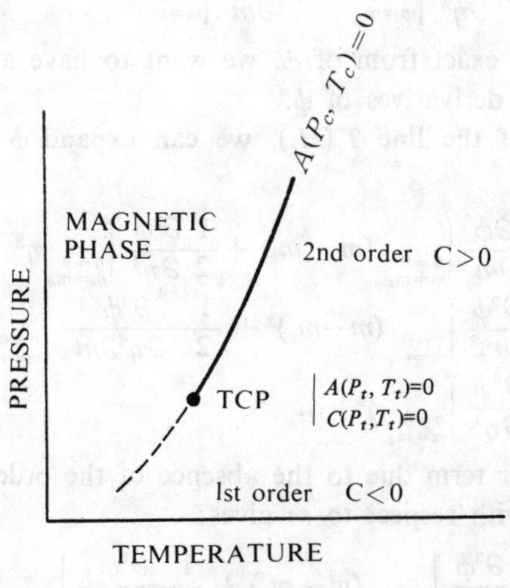

Fig. 14.2.1
Pressure dependence of the order of a phase transition.

New values for the critical exponents are found. In particular, minimising (14.2.2) with $h=0$ leads to:

$$2A\eta+6D\eta^5=0 \tag{14.2.3}$$

Assuming an analytic form $A=a\,(T-T_t)$ we get for η

$$\eta^4=\frac{A}{3D}(T_t-T) \tag{14.2.4}$$

which corresponds to a tricritical exponent $\beta_t=1/4$ instead of 1/2 for a second-order transition.

A classical example of one type of TCP is given by the magneto elastic coupling; when taking into account the distance dependence of the exchange constants and the elastic energy of the crystal [D. Bloch, D. Herrmann-Ronzaud, C. Vettier, W. B. Yelon and R. Alben, *Phys. Rev. Lett.*, **35**, 963 (1975) and C. P. Bean, D. S. Rodbell, *Phys. Rev.*, **126**, 104 (1962)] such a tricritical point can be induced, leading to the phase diagram in Fig. 14.2.1. Another example is provided by the metamagnetic compounds such as $FeCl_2$. In metamagnets there is competition between two order parameters, the antiferromagnetic order parameter η, which couples to the staggered field h and a secondary ferromagnetic order parameter M, which couples to the internal magnetic field H ($H=H_{app}-NM$ due to the demagnetizing effects). Let us consider such a system in more detail.

The antiferromagnetic phase is stable at low temperature and low fieldds H. In the absence of any staggered field h, we minimise ϕ:

$$\frac{\partial\phi}{\partial\eta}=0,\ \frac{\partial\phi}{\partial m}=0 \tag{14.2.5}$$

Along the transition line $T_c(H_c)$, $\eta=0$; thus the equation of this line is given by:

$$\left.\frac{\partial^2\phi}{\partial\eta^2}\right|_{\substack{\eta=0\\ m=m_c}}=0,\ \left.\frac{\partial\phi}{\partial m}\right|_{\substack{\eta=0\\ m=m_c}}=0 \tag{14.2.6}$$

Without knowing the exact from of ϕ, we want to have an expression for C (q,H_t,T_t) in terms of derivatives of ϕ.

In the vicinity of the line $T_c(H_c)$, we can expand ϕ in terms of η and $(m-m_c)$.

$$\begin{aligned}\phi=\phi_0&+\left.\frac{\partial\phi}{\partial m}\right|_{\substack{\eta=0\\ m=m_c}}(m-m_c)+\frac{1}{2}\left.\frac{\partial^2\phi}{\partial\eta^2}\right|_{\substack{\eta=0\\ m=m_c}}\eta^2\\&+\frac{1}{2}\left.\frac{\partial^2\phi}{\partial m^2}\right|_{\substack{\eta=0\\ m=m_c}}(m-m_c)^2+\frac{1}{2}\left.\frac{\partial^3\phi}{\partial\eta^2\partial m}\right|_{\substack{\eta=0\\ m=m_c}}\eta^2(m-m_c)\\&+\frac{1}{4!}\left.\frac{\partial^4\phi}{\partial\eta^4}\right|_{\substack{\eta=0\\ m=m_c}}\eta^4+\dots\end{aligned} \tag{14.2.7}$$

There is no odd-order term due to the absence of the ordering field h. Minimisation of (14.2.7) with respect to m gives:

$$\left.\frac{\partial\phi}{\partial m}\right|_{\substack{\eta=0\\ m=m_c}}+\left.\frac{\partial^2\phi}{\partial m^2}\right|_{\substack{\eta=0\\ m=m_c}}(m-m_c)+\frac{1}{2}\left.\frac{\partial^3\phi}{\partial\eta^2\partial m}\right|_{\substack{\eta=0\\ m=m_c}}\eta^2=0 \tag{14.2.8}$$

At $H=H_c$, from (14.2.6), we have:

$$m-m_c=-\frac{1}{2}\frac{\left.\dfrac{\partial^3\phi}{\partial\eta^2\partial m}\right|_{\substack{\eta=0\\m=m_c}}}{\left.\dfrac{\partial^2\phi}{\partial m^2}\right|_{\substack{\eta=0\\m=m_c}}}\cdot\eta^2 \tag{14.2.9}$$

which leads a fourth-order coefficient in (14.2.7):

$$C(H_t,\ T_t)=\frac{1}{4!}\frac{\partial^4\phi}{\partial\eta^4}\bigg|_{\substack{\eta=0\\m=m_c}}-\frac{1}{8}\frac{\left(\left.\dfrac{\partial^3\phi}{\partial\eta^2\partial m}\right|_{\substack{\eta=0\\m=m_c}}\right)^2}{\left.\dfrac{\partial^2\phi}{\partial m^2}\right|_{\substack{\eta=0\\m=m_c}}} \tag{14.2.10}$$

The TCP occurs when the coefficient $C(H_t,T_t)$ in (14.2.10) vanishes.

Now, we consider a physical system, such as $FeCl_2$ which is known to exhibit a TCP. We assume a two-sublattice system with spin 1/2, alternatively up and down along the z-axis. In the presence of the internal field H, the Hamiltonian of the system is written as:

$$\begin{aligned}\hat{H}=&-g\mu_B H\Big(\sum_\alpha\hat{S}^z_{\alpha u}+\sum_\beta\hat{S}^z_{\beta u}\Big)\\&-g^2\sum_{\alpha,\beta}I\{\hat{S}_{\alpha u}\hat{S}_{\beta u}+\hat{S}_{\alpha d}\hat{S}_{\beta d}\}\\&-g^2\sum_{\alpha,\beta}J\{\hat{S}_{\alpha u}\hat{S}_{\beta d}+\hat{S}_{\alpha d}\hat{S}_{\beta u}\}\end{aligned} \tag{14.2.11}$$

where I (J) is the nearest neighbour intra (inter-) sublattice exchange constant. I is ferromagnetic ($I>0$) while J is antiferromagnetic ($J<0$). An expression for the thermodynamic potential ϕ is obtained from an approximate density operator $\hat{\rho}$.

$$\phi=\mathrm{S_P}\{\hat{\rho}\hat{H}\}+k_B\mathrm{S_P}\{\hat{\rho}\ln\hat{\rho}\} \tag{14.2.12}$$

We assume that all the sites are statistically independent; the average values of $\hat{S}^z$ on the two sublattices (u and d) are taken as variational parameters; in this case we have

$$\begin{aligned}&\mathrm{S_p}\{\hat{\rho}\}=1\\&\mathrm{S_p}\{\hat{\rho}\hat{S}^x\}=\mathrm{S_p}\{\hat{\rho}\hat{S}^y\}=0\\&\mathrm{S_p}\{\hat{\rho}\hat{S}^z_u\}=\langle\hat{S}^z_u\rangle,\qquad \mathrm{S_p}\{\hat{\rho}\hat{S}^z_d\}=\langle\hat{S}^z_d\rangle\end{aligned} \tag{14.2.13}$$

The operator $\hat{\rho}$ is written as a 4×4 diagonal matrix:

$$\frac{1}{2}\times\begin{bmatrix}\frac{1}{2}+\langle\hat{S}^z_u\rangle & 0 & 0 & 0\\ 0 & \frac{1}{2}-\langle\hat{S}^z_u\rangle & 0 & 0\\ 0 & 0 & \frac{1}{2}+\langle\hat{S}^z_d\rangle & 0\\ 0 & 0 & 0 & \frac{1}{2}-\langle\hat{S}^z_d\rangle\end{bmatrix} \tag{14.2.14}$$

Thus the thermodynamical potential ϕ per site is obtained from (14.2.12):

$$\begin{aligned}\phi=&-\frac{g\mu_B H}{2}(\langle S_u^z\rangle+\langle S_d^z\rangle)\\&-\frac{g^2Z_1I}{4}\{(\langle S_u^z\rangle)^2+(\langle S_d^z\rangle)^2\}-\frac{g^2Z_2J}{2}\langle S_u^z\rangle\langle S_d^z\rangle\\&+\frac{kT}{2}\left\{\left(\frac{1}{2}+\langle S_u^z\rangle\right)\ln\left(\frac{1}{2}+\langle S_u^z\rangle\right)+\left(\frac{1}{2}-\langle S_u^z\rangle\right)\ln\left(\frac{1}{2}-\langle S_u^z\rangle\right)\right.\\&\left.+\left(\frac{1}{2}+\langle S_d^z\rangle\right)\ln\left(\frac{1}{2}+\langle S_d^z\rangle\right)+\left(\frac{1}{2}-\langle S_d^z\rangle\right)\ln\left(\frac{1}{2}-\langle S_d^z\rangle\right)\right\}\end{aligned} \tag{14.2.15}$$

We introduce the antiferromagnetic order parameter $n=1/2\,(\langle S_u^z\rangle-\langle S_d^z\rangle)$, and the ferromagnetic quantity $m=1/2\ (\langle S_u^z\rangle+\langle S_d^z\rangle)$. For convenience, we use the following notations:

$$\begin{aligned}&kT_N=\frac{g^2Z_1I-g^2Z_2J}{4}\\&kT_F=\frac{g^2Z_1I+g^2Z_2J}{4}\\&H=\frac{g\mu_B H}{kT_N},\quad t=\frac{T}{T_N},\quad t_F=\frac{T_F}{T_N}\\&-1<t_F<+1\end{aligned} \tag{14.2.16}$$

where Z_1 (Z_2) denotes the number of first neighbours in the same (other) sublattice.

Using (14.2.16), the potential ϕ takes the form:

$$\begin{aligned}\frac{\phi}{kT_N}=&-Hm-2t_Fm^2-2n^2+\frac{t}{2}\left\{\left(\frac{1}{2}+m+n\right)\ln\left(\frac{1}{2}+m+n\right)\right.\\&+\left(\frac{1}{2}-m-n\right)\ln\left(\frac{1}{2}-m-n\right)+\left(\frac{1}{2}-m+n\right)\ln\left(\frac{1}{2}-m+n\right)\\&\left.+\left(\frac{1}{2}+m-n\right)\ln\left(\frac{1}{2}+m-n\right)\right\}\end{aligned} \tag{14.2.17}$$

The second-order transition line is defined by (14.2.6), which gives:

$$\begin{aligned}&t_c=1-4m_c^2\\&H_c=-4t_Fm_c+t_c\ln\left(\frac{1+2m_c}{1-2m_c}\right)\end{aligned} \tag{14.2.18}$$

It is displayed in Fig. 14.2.2.

In zero applied field ($H_c=0$, $m_c=0$), the transition occurs at $T=T_N$. Using (14.2.10) we find that the fourth-order term goes to zero at a TCP defined by

$$4m_t^2=\frac{1-t_F}{3(1+t_F)} \tag{14.2.19}$$

or

$$t_t=\frac{2\,(1+2t_F)}{3\,(1+t_F)} \tag{14.2.20}$$

From (14.2.20) it is evident that a TCP can only exist if $-1/2<t_F<1$ (t_t must be positive and m_t is less than 1/2).

At a temperature lower than T_t, there is a first-order transition ($C\,(H_c, T)$ is negative) between the antiferromagnetic phase ($n\neq 0, m\neq 0$) and the saturated

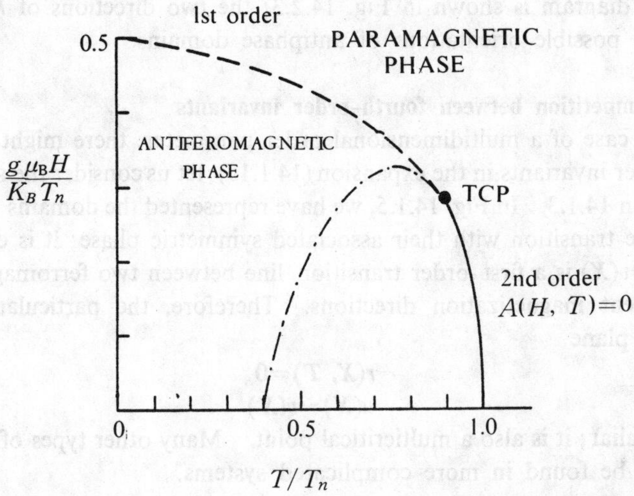

Fig. 14.2.2

Phase diagram in the (H_{int}, T) plane of an Ising metamagnet, intrasublattice to inter-sublattice coupling ratio is chosen to be $I/J=-3$ ($t_F=1/2$).

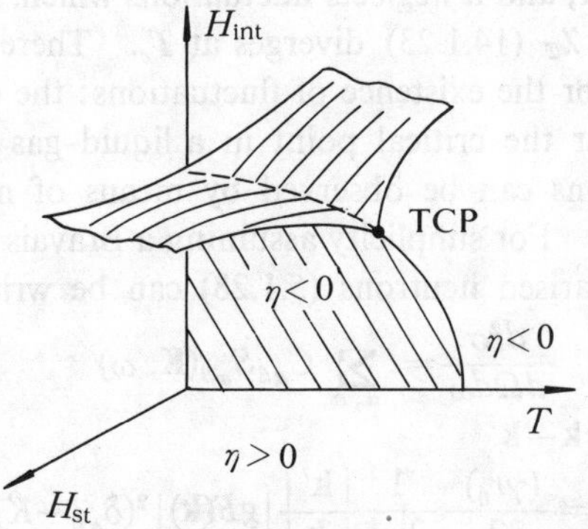

Fig. 14.2.3

Phase diagram of a metamagnet exhibiting a tricritical point T_t.

paramagnetic phase ($n=0$, $m\neq 0$). At $T=0$ K, the threshold field is given by:

$$g\mu_B H_c = 2(1-t_F)kT_N = -g^2 Z_2 J \tag{14.2.21}$$

The phase diagram is shown in Fig. 14.2.2.

A more detailed study of the phase diagram in the presence of the ordering field h would show that three critical lines (second-order transition lines) merge at $T=T_t$ (this is why T_t is called a tricritical point). The thermodynamical potential would be written as:

$$\phi(T,H,n,m)-hn \qquad (14.2.22)$$

The phase diagram is shown in Fig. 14.2.3; the two directions of h correspond to the two possible orientations of antiphase domains.

14.2.3 Competition between fourth-order invariants

In the case of a multidimensional order parameter, there might exist several fourth-order invariants in the expansion (14.1.15); let us consider the same example as in Section 14.1.3. In Fig. 14.1.5, we have represented the domains of a second-order phase transition with their associated symmetric phase; it is clear that the line $u(X)=v(X)$ is a first-order transition line between two ferromagnetic phases with different magnetization directions. Therefore, the particular point D in the (X, T) plane

$$r(X, T)=0$$
$$u(X)=v(X)$$

is very peculiar; it is also a multicritical point. Many other types of multicritical points can be found in more complicated systems.

14.3 CRITICAL EFFECTS

As can be seen from Table 14.1.1, the Landau theory fails near T_c; this can be accounted for by noting that the Landau expansion assumes a homogeneous order parameter, and it neglects fluctuations which, in fact, are important, since the susceptibility χ_T (14.1.23) diverges at T_c. There are several pieces of experimental evidence for the existence of fluctuations: the classic example is the critical opalescence near the critical point in a liquid-gas system. In magnetic systems, such fluctuations can be observed by means of neutron scattering, as can be shown quickly. For simplicity assuming a Bravais lattice, the magnetic cross-section for unpolarised neutrons (5.1.28) can be written as:

$$\frac{d^2\sigma}{d\Omega d\omega}=\sum_{\alpha,\beta} C_{\alpha\beta}S_{\alpha\beta}(\mathbf{K},\omega) \qquad (14.3.1)$$

where $\mathbf{K}=\mathbf{k}-\mathbf{k}'$

$$C_{\alpha\beta}=\frac{(\gamma r_0)^2}{2}\frac{1}{2\pi\hbar}\frac{|\mathbf{k}'|}{|\mathbf{k}|}|gF(\mathbf{k})|^2(\delta_{\alpha\beta}-\hat{K}_\alpha\hat{K}_\beta) \qquad (14.3.2)$$

$$S_{\alpha\beta}(\mathbf{K},\omega)=\int_{-\infty}^{+\infty}\langle\hat{S}^+_\alpha(K,0)\hat{S}^-_\beta(K,t)\rangle_T e^{-i\omega t}dt \qquad (14.3.3)$$

Assuming forward scattering (**k** is almost equal to **k**′, we can integrate (14.3.1) over ω while keeping $C_{\alpha\beta}$ constant. In this static approximation, we arrive at:

$$\left.\frac{d\sigma}{d\Omega}\right|_{s\,a}=\sum_{\alpha,\beta}C_{\alpha\beta}\langle\hat{S}^+_\alpha(K,0)\hat{S}_\beta(K,0)\rangle_T \qquad (14.3.4)$$

The function $I(K,0)=\langle\hat{S}^+_\alpha(K,0)\,\hat{S}_\beta(K,0)\rangle_T$ is the Fourier transform of the static pair correlation. Expressing $\hat{S}^+_\alpha(K,0)$ as

$$\hat{S}_\alpha(K,0)=\langle\hat{S}_\alpha(K)\rangle_T+\delta\hat{S}_\alpha(K,0) \qquad (14.3.5)$$

the cross-section (14.3.4) splits into two parts:

$$\left.\frac{d\sigma}{d\Omega}\right|_{s\,s} = \sum_{\alpha,\beta} C_{\alpha\beta} \langle \hat{S}_\alpha(K) \rangle_T \langle \hat{S}_\beta(K) \rangle_T + \sum_{\alpha,\beta} C_{\alpha\beta} \langle \delta\hat{S}^+_\alpha(K,0)\delta\hat{S}_\beta(K,0) \rangle_T \tag{14.3.6}$$

The first part represents the elastic Bragg scattering from the ordered magnetic system (it is zero if $T > T_c$); the second part is proportional to the space Fourier transform of the correlation function:

$$\langle \delta\hat{S}^\alpha_i \delta\hat{S}^\beta_j \rangle_T \tag{14.3.7}$$

An example of critical scattering in the forward direction in nickel is shown in Fig. 14.3.1.

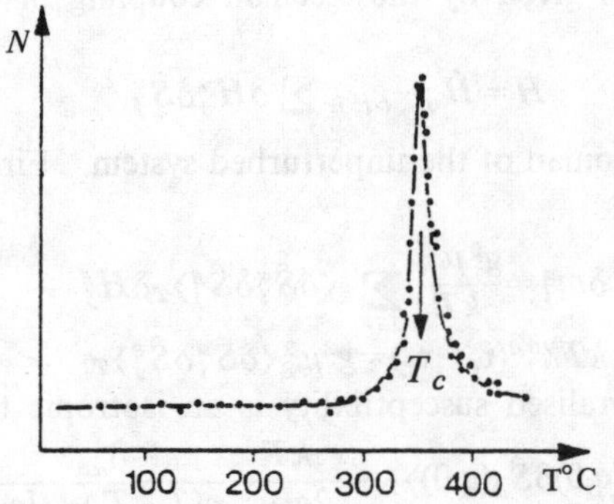

Fig. 14.3.1
Critical scattering in nickel.

14.3.1 Theory of Ornstein and Zernike

Using a theory as simple as the Landau theory, we would like to evaluate the pair correlation (14.3.7) near T_c. Assuming a order parameter $\mathbf{m}_q$ we rewrite (14.1.18) as:

$$\phi = \phi_0 + A(\mathbf{q},H,T)\,|\mathbf{m}_q|^2 + \sum_a C_a(\mathbf{q},H,T) f^{(4)}_a |\mathbf{m}_q|^4 - \mathbf{h}_{-q}\cdot\mathbf{m}_q \tag{14.3.8}$$

where $\mathbf{h}_q$ is the Fourier component of $\mathbf{h}(\mathbf{r})$ which couples to $\mathbf{m}(\mathbf{r})$. The order occurs for a given $\mathbf{q}_0$; $A(\mathbf{q}, H, T)$ can be expanded analytically around $T = T_c$ and $\mathbf{q} = \mathbf{q}_0$ (Landau assumption). Neglecting the fourth-order and the field dependence, we get for $T > T_c$:

$$\phi = \phi_0 + \sum_q \{a(T - T_c) + J(\mathbf{q}_0 - \mathbf{q})^2\}\,|\mathbf{m}_{q_0-q}|^2 - \mathbf{h}_{q-q_0}\cdot\mathbf{m}_{q_0-q} \tag{14.3.9}$$

For simplicity, we will assume $\mathbf{q}_0 = 0$. We minimise (14.3.9) with respect to $\mathbf{m}_q$, which leads to:

$$2\{a(T - T_c) + Jq^2\}\mathbf{m}_q = \mathbf{h}_q \tag{14.3.10}$$

The generalised susceptibility is defined as

$$\mathbf{m}(\mathbf{r}_i) = \int d\mathbf{r}'\,\overline{\overline{\chi}}(\mathbf{r}_i - \mathbf{r}')\mathbf{h}(\mathbf{r}') \tag{14.3.11}$$

Thus, in terms of Fourier transforms:

$$\mathbf{m}_q = \overline{\overline{\chi}}(\mathbf{q})\mathbf{h}_q \tag{14.3.12}$$

and

$$\overline{\overline{\chi}}(\mathbf{q}) = \frac{1}{2a(T-T_c)+2Jq^2} \tag{14.3.13}$$

Let us express $\overline{\overline{\chi}}(\mathbf{r}_i - \mathbf{r}_j)$ in terms of the correlation function $\langle \delta\hat{S}_i^\alpha \delta\hat{S}_j^\beta \rangle_T$. Let us consider a magnetic moment $\delta\mathbf{m}_i$ in the presence of a small change of the magnetic field δH_j^β at sites j, which induces a local modification:

$$\delta m_i^\alpha = \sum_{\beta, j} \chi^{\alpha\beta}(\mathbf{r}_i - \mathbf{r}_j)\delta H_j^\beta \tag{14.3.14}$$

which is the equivalent to (14.3.11). But

$$\delta m_i^\alpha = g\mu_B \langle \delta\hat{S}_i^\alpha \rangle_T = g\mu_B \frac{\mathrm{Sp}(\delta\hat{S}_i^\alpha \exp(-\beta\hat{H}))}{\mathrm{Sp}(\exp(-\beta\hat{H}))} \tag{14.3.15}$$

The Hamiltonian, $\hat{H}$, is given by the Zeeman coupling of the local field $\delta\mathbf{H}_j$ with $\delta\hat{S}_j$

$$\hat{H} = \hat{H}_0 - g\mu_B \sum_{j,\gamma} \delta H_j^\gamma \delta\hat{S}_j^\gamma \tag{14.3.16}$$

where $\hat{H}_0$ is the Hamiltonian of the unperturbed system. First-order expansions in (14.3.15) yield:

$$\delta m_i^\alpha = \frac{g^2\mu_B^2}{kT} \sum_{j,\beta} \langle \delta\hat{S}_i^\alpha \delta\hat{S}_j^\beta \rangle_T \delta H_j^\beta \tag{14.3.17}$$

$$kT\chi^{\alpha\beta}(\mathbf{r}_i - \mathbf{r}_j) = g^2\mu_B^2 \langle \delta\hat{S}_i^\alpha \delta\hat{S}_j^\beta \rangle_T \tag{14.3.18}$$

In our model, the generalised susceptibility is an isotropic tensor, we arrive at

$$\langle \delta\hat{S}_\alpha(\mathbf{q},0)\delta\hat{S}_\beta(\mathbf{q},0)\rangle_T \sim \frac{kT}{2g^2\mu_B^2} \frac{\delta_{\alpha\beta}}{a(T-T_c)+Jq^2} \tag{14.3.19}$$

Thus near $\mathbf{q}=0$, the scattered neutron intensity varies as:

$$\frac{kT}{a(T-T_c)+Jq^2} \tag{14.3.20}$$

This Lorentzian function can be rewritten in the following way:

$$\frac{kT}{J\left(\frac{1}{R_c^{+2}} + q^2\right)} \tag{14.3.21}$$

with

$$R_c^+ = \sqrt{\frac{J}{a}}\,|T-T_c|^{-1/2} \tag{14.3.22}$$

By inverting the Fourier transform we obtain:

$$\langle \delta\hat{S}_i^\alpha\, \delta\hat{S}_j^\beta \rangle_T = \frac{kT}{4\pi J} \frac{1}{2g^2\mu_B^2} \frac{\exp(-|\mathbf{r}_i - \mathbf{r}_j|/R_c^+)}{|\mathbf{r}_i - \mathbf{r}_j|} \tag{14.3.23}$$

The length R_c^+ characterises the range of the fluctuations in real space, it is called the correlation length; (14.3.22) shows that R_c^+ diverges at $T=T_c$ with the critical exponent $\nu=1/2$ (Table 14.1.1). But this is not observed experimentally ($\nu_{\mathrm{exp}} \simeq 0.67$).

14.3.2 Ginzburg criterion

Many experimental results have shown that Landau theory fails near a second-order phase transition. The reason for this failure is that near T_c the fluctuations $\langle|\delta\eta|^2\rangle$ in the order parameter are large compared to the order parameter η itself. Ginzburg has estimated the temperature range where the Landau theory is bound to fail.

Starting from (14.3.8) with a one-dimensional order parameter η_q:

$$\phi=\phi_0+A(\mathbf{q},T)|\eta_q|^2+C|\eta_q|^4-h_{-q}\eta_q \tag{14.3.24}$$

From (14.3.18) we have:

$$\langle|\delta\eta|^2\rangle=kT\chi(0) \tag{14.3.25}$$

Minimising (14.3.24) for $T<T_c$ leads to:

$$2A(\mathbf{q},T)\eta_q+4C|\eta_q|^2\eta_q=h_q \tag{14.3.26}$$

By differentiating, we get:

$$2A(\mathbf{q},T)\chi_q+12C|\eta_q|^2\chi_q=1 \tag{14.3.27}$$

Expanding $A(\mathbf{q},T)$ as:

$$A(\mathbf{q},T)=a(T-T_c)+J(\mathbf{q}-\mathbf{q}_0)^2 \tag{14.3.28}$$

and using (14.3.19), we obtain:

$$\chi_q=\frac{1}{4a(T_c-T)+2J(\mathbf{q}-\mathbf{q}_0)^2} \tag{14.3.29}$$

which is similar to (14.3.13). The fluctuations (14.3.25) are thus given by inverting (14.3.29) in a d-dimensional space:

$$\langle|\delta\eta|^2\rangle\sim\frac{kT}{2\pi^d J}\int\frac{d_{\mathbf{q}}^d}{\frac{1}{R_c^{-2}}+q^2} \tag{14.3.30}$$

with

$$R_c=\sqrt{\frac{J}{2a}}(T_c-T)^{-1/2}$$

We can neglect the fluctuations if $|\mathbf{r}|\gg R_c$, see (14.3.23); thus we will limit the integration in (14.3.30)

$$\langle|\delta\eta|^2\rangle\sim\frac{kT}{2\pi^d J}\int_0^{\frac{1}{R_c}}dq\,\frac{1}{R_c^{-2}+q^2}S_d(\mathbf{q})$$

where $S_d(\mathbf{q})$ is the surface of a n-dimensional sphere of radius $|\mathbf{q}|$:

$$S_d(\mathbf{q})=\frac{d\pi^{d/2}}{(d/2)!}q^{d-1}$$

This leads to:

$$\langle|\delta\eta|^2\rangle\sim\frac{T}{JR_c^{d-2}}\sim\frac{1}{a}\left(\frac{aT_c}{J}\right)^{\frac{d}{2}}\left(\frac{T_c-T}{T_c}\right)^{\frac{d-2}{2}} \tag{14.3.31}$$

From (14.3.31), (14.3.30) and (14.1.19) we arrive at:

$$\frac{\langle|\delta\eta|^2\rangle}{\langle\eta\rangle^2}\sim\frac{C}{a^2T_c}\left(\frac{aT_c}{J}\right)^{\frac{d}{2}}\left(\frac{T_c-T}{T_c}\right)^{\frac{d-4}{2}} \tag{14.3.32}$$

Therefore the fluctuations $\langle|\delta\eta|^2\rangle$ become much larger than $\langle\eta^2\rangle$ near T_c if the space dimensionality is less than a critical unphysical value $d_c=4$. For $d>4$, the Landau theory would give exact results. However, for the physical situation $d=3$, we can write

$$\frac{\langle|\delta\eta|^2\rangle}{\langle\eta\rangle^2}\sim\frac{C}{a^2T_c}\left(\frac{aT_c}{J}\right)^{3/2}\left(\frac{T_c-T}{T_c}\right)^{-1/2} \tag{14.3.33}$$

For the Landau theory to be valid, this ratio must remain small near T_c, which gives the condition

$$\frac{C}{a^2T_c}\left(\frac{aT_c}{J}\right)^{3/2}\sim\left(\frac{T_c-T^*}{T_c}\right)^{1/2}\ll 1$$

Introducing the zero-temperature correlation length, $R_0^2=\frac{J}{2aT_c}$ (cf. (14.3.30)) and the jump $\Delta C_p=\frac{a^2T_c}{2C}$ of specific heat at T_c (cf. (14.1.20)) we have the condition:

$$\frac{T_c-T}{T_c}>\frac{T_c-T^*}{T_c}\sim\frac{R_0^{-6}}{\Delta C_p} \tag{14.3.34}$$

which explains why the Landau theory leads to correct results in the case of very long range interactions (i.e. very large R_0) such as in the case of superconductivity. However in the case of magnetic systems, the range of interaction is rather short, except in the case of dipolar coupling which is small compared to other exchange mechanisms. Thus, in general, more elaborate models are required near T_c. Without getting into a discussion of these theories (see the books edited by Domb and Green), it is worthwhile presenting briefly the renormalisation group theory as a conclusion.

14.3.3 Recent developments——Renormalisation group theory

We have already mentioned that the Landau theory provides all information about the symmetry changes at $T=T_c$. The symmetry of the disordered phase is reflected by the expression of the thermodynamical potential ϕ which contains all invariants of the order parameter invariants. Since the fluctuations are important, the natural generalisation of (14.1.15) consists in including invariants of gradients. The starting point is the Ginzburg–Landau–Wilson (GLW) Hamiltonian defined as follows: from the Landau free energy expansion (14.1.15) we construct a Hamiltonian including gradient terms:

$$\hat{H}_{\text{GLW}}=\sum_{k_c}\eta^2A(\mathbf{q},T)+\eta^4\sum_{a}C_a(\mathbf{q},T)f_a^{(4)}+\sum_{i,j}\alpha_i\alpha_jq_iq_j\eta^2 \tag{14.3.35}$$

In the case of an isotropic system, when there is only one fourth-order invariant, H_{GLW} reduces to:

$$\hat{H}_{\text{GLW}}=\sum_{q<k_c}[a(T-T_c)+Jq^2]\eta^2+\frac{C}{N}\sum_{q_1+q_2+q_3+q_4<k_c}\eta_{q_1}\eta_{q_2}\eta_{q_3}\eta_{q_4} \tag{14.3.36}$$

We have assumed a transition at $\mathbf{q}_0=0$. The idea is to renormalise $\hat{H}_{\text{GLW}}$ by changing the length scale: near T_c, the correlation length diverges which means that all the information about the critical properties are contained in a d-dimensional sphere of radius k_c with $k_c\to 0$. We renormalise $\hat{H}_{\text{GLW}}$ by going from k_c to $k_c'<k_c$; terms with $k_c'<q<k_c$ are integrated and renormalise the coefficients $a(T-T_c)$, J and C. If the iteration of this process leads to a stable fixed point in the phase diagram $(a(T-T_c), J, C)$ then the transition is second order; critical exponents can be determined. If not, the transition is of first order.

This theory is more restrictive than the Landau theory as far as the conditions for a continuous transition are concerned, because it takes into account the order parameter dimensionality (i.e. number of fourth-order invariants). Furthermore, it emphasises the importance of symmetry: modifications of the symmetry G_0 of the disordered phase (by applying uniaxial stress or magnetic field…) may induce a cross over from a first-order to a second-order transition.

REFERENCES

P. BAK, in Modern Trends in the Theory of Condensed Matter, Lecture Notes in Physics, Vol. 115, ed. by A. Pekalski, J. Przystawa, Springer, Berlin, Heidelberg, New York (1980).

N. BOCCARA, Symétries Brisées, Hermann, Paris (1976).

C. DOMB, M.S. GREEN, Phase Transitions and Critical Phenomena, Academic Press, New York.

L. D. LANDAU, E.M. LIFSHITZ, Statistical Physics, Pergamon Press, Oxford (1959).

G. Yu. LYUBARSKII, The Application of Group Theory in Physics, Pergamon Press, New York (1960).

D. MUKAMEL, S. KRINSKY, *Phys. Rev.*, **B13,** 5065 (1976).

G. TOULOUSE, P., PFEUTY, Introduction du Groupe de Renormalisation et à ses Applica tions, Presses Universitaires de Grenoble (1975).